Glencoe Science
Features and Benefits

		Pages
Dynamic Instructional Strategies	**... present clear and comprehensive coverage of middle school science.**	
	■ Each engaging chapter opener includes a *Launch Lab* and *Foldables*™.	7, 35
	■ *National Geographic Visualizing* features illustrate important concepts in middle school science.	16, 41
A Strong Reading Strand	**... encourages active reading and learning for students of all reading levels. In the *Student Edition*:**	
	■ **as you read** gives students a preview of learning objectives and vocabulary for each section;	8, 36
	■ *Reading Checks* help students check their reading comprehension; and	10, 39
	■ *Caption questions* ask students to interpret visuals.	10, 38
	■ *Reading Essentials, An Interactive Student Textbook* is designed to help struggling readers comprehend core content. It is written at a reading level of about two to three grades below the *Student Edition*.	
Meeting the Needs of All Students	**... facilitates understanding of science concepts for students of all learning levels. In the *Teacher Wraparound Edition*:**	
	■ *Differentiated Instruction* strategies help meet the needs of students with learning disabilities and physical challenges, or create opportunities to enrich and extend students' learning;	9, 38
	■ *Daily Intervention* provides intervention strategies for struggling students; and	13, 53
	■ *Identifying Misconceptions* helps uncover and address common science misconceptions.	34F
	■ The *English/Spanish Glossary*, also in the *Student Edition*, helps English-language learners comprehend science terms.	248–256
Extensive Standardized Test Practice	**... gives students the opportunity to practice for state and national exams.**	
	■ Each chapter ends with a variety of standardized test practice questions, including *Multiple Choice, Short Response/Grid In*, and *Open Ended*.	142–143
A Variety of Labs	**... gets students excited about being involved in science. The *Student Edition* provides:**	
	■ *MiniLABs*, traditional labs, and *Design Your Own, Model and Invent*, and *Use the Internet* labs; and	18, 22, 54
	■ *Extra Try at Home Labs* provide opportunities for students to practice their science skills at home with adult supervision using materials from the kitchen, junk drawer, or backyard.	218–221
	■ *Virtual Labs* CD-ROM contains an interactive virtual lab for each chapter.	8
	■ *Video Labs* (VHS) reinforce lab techniques and safety skills, offer troubleshooting tips, and give expected outcomes.	25
	■ The *Science Lab Manual, Probeware Lab Manual*, and *Science Inquiry Lab Manual* provide additional opportunities to practice laboratory techniques.	
Multi-Level Review	**... presents multiple opportunities for all students to review and master content.**	
	■ Each section ends with a review that contains a *Summary* of the section's major concepts and a *Self Check* that has questions to assess student learning and practice math or science skills.	13, 45
	■ The *Study Guide* at the end of each chapter can preview, review, summarize, and visualize the chapter's main ideas.	29, 57
	■ *Study Guide* and *Reinforcement* help students grasp core content.	
Teacher Resources	**... provide innovative strategies to help new and experienced teachers.**	
	■ *Chapter Resources Fast File* ™ contains important reproducible masters.	62B
	■ Section Focus, Assessment, and Teaching transparencies accompany each chapter.	90C
	■ *Performance Assessment in the Science Classroom* has assessment guidelines, strategies, sample rubrics, and more.	
Online Resources	**... enrich the learning experience with the click of a mouse.**	
	■ For prescreened Web links, standardized test practice, self-check quizzes, chapter tests, *Vocabulary PuzzleMaker*, extra math practice, science career information, current science news, and *WebQuest* interactive projects, visit **bookd.msscience.com**.	
	■ The complete interactive *Student Edition* is available at The McGraw-Hill Learning Network Web site, **mhln.com**.	
Technology	**... provides timesaving products to help teachers creatively engage their students.**	
	■ *MindJogger Videoquizzes* (VHS & DVD) provide a game-show style interactive quiz for each chapter.	
	■ Easy to edit *Interactive Chalkboard* Microsoft® PowerPoint® presentations include step-by-step lessons, an image bank, chapter and section review questions, standardized test practice, and transparencies.	
	■ *ExamView® Pro Testmaker* CD-ROM in English or Spanish allows you to customize assessments.	
	■ *TeacherWorks* CD-ROM is your all-in-one resource center that helps you plan and organize lessons.	
	■ *StudentWorks* CD-ROM solves the heavy backpack problem.	

SAFETY SYMBOLS

SAFETY SYMBOLS	HAZARD	EXAMPLES	PRECAUTION	REMEDY
DISPOSAL	Special disposal procedures need to be followed.	certain chemicals, living organisms	Do not dispose of these materials in the sink or trash can.	Dispose of wastes as directed by your teacher.
BIOLOGICAL	Organisms or other biological materials that might be harmful to humans	bacteria, fungi, blood, unpreserved tissues, plant materials	Avoid skin contact with these materials. Wear mask or gloves.	Notify your teacher if you suspect contact with material. Wash hands thoroughly.
EXTREME TEMPERATURE	Objects that can burn skin by being too cold or too hot	boiling liquids, hot plates, dry ice, liquid nitrogen	Use proper protection when handling.	Go to your teacher for first aid.
SHARP OBJECT	Use of tools or glassware that can easily puncture or slice skin	razor blades, pins, scalpels, pointed tools, dissecting probes, broken glass	Practice common-sense behavior and follow guidelines for use of the tool.	Go to your teacher for first aid.
FUME	Possible danger to respiratory tract from fumes	ammonia, acetone, nail polish remover, heated sulfur, moth balls	Make sure there is good ventilation. Never smell fumes directly. Wear a mask.	Leave foul area and notify your teacher immediately.
ELECTRICAL	Possible danger from electrical shock or burn	improper grounding, liquid spills, short circuits, exposed wires	Double-check setup with teacher. Check condition of wires and apparatus.	Do not attempt to fix electrical problems. Notify your teacher immediately.
IRRITANT	Substances that can irritate the skin or mucous membranes of the respiratory tract	pollen, moth balls, steel wool, fiberglass, potassium permanganate	Wear dust mask and gloves. Practice extra care when handling these materials.	Go to your teacher for first aid.
CHEMICAL	Chemicals can react with and destroy tissue and other materials	bleaches such as hydrogen peroxide; acids such as sulfuric acid, hydrochloric acid; bases such as ammonia, sodium hydroxide	Wear goggles, gloves, and an apron.	Immediately flush the affected area with water and notify your teacher.
TOXIC	Substance may be poisonous if touched, inhaled, or swallowed.	mercury, many metal compounds, iodine, poinsettia plant parts	Follow your teacher's instructions.	Always wash hands thoroughly after use. Go to your teacher for first aid.
FLAMMABLE	Flammable chemicals may be ignited by open flame, spark, or exposed heat.	alcohol, kerosene, potassium permanganate	Avoid open flames and heat when using flammable chemicals.	Notify your teacher immediately. Use fire safety equipment if applicable.
OPEN FLAME	Open flame in use, may cause fire.	hair, clothing, paper, synthetic materials	Tie back hair and loose clothing. Follow teacher's instruction on lighting and extinguishing flames.	Notify your teacher immediately. Use fire safety equipment if applicable.

 Eye Safety Proper eye protection should be worn at all times by anyone performing or observing science activities.

 Clothing Protection This symbol appears when substances could stain or burn clothing.

 Animal Safety This symbol appears when safety of animals and students must be ensured.

 Handwashing After the lab, wash hands with soap and water before removing goggles.

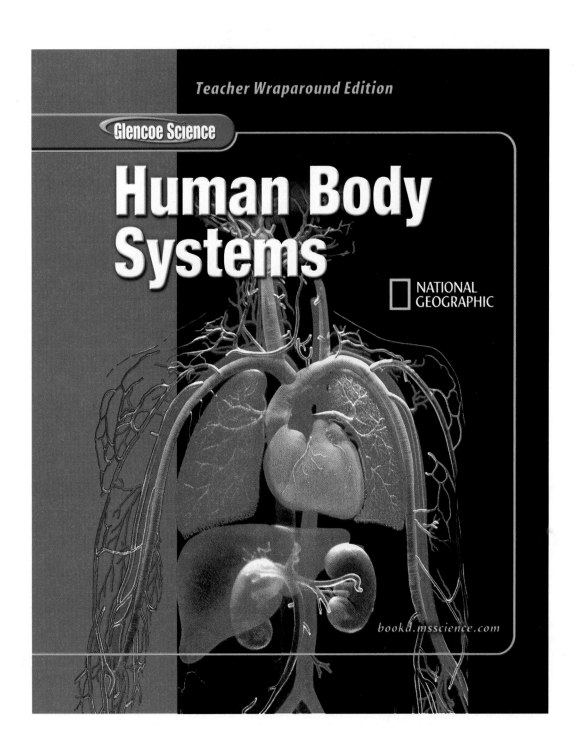

Teacher Wraparound Edition

Glencoe Science

Human Body Systems

NATIONAL GEOGRAPHIC

bookd.msscience.com

Glencoe

New York, New York   Columbus, Ohio   Chicago, Illinois   Peoria, Illinois   Woodland Hills, California

Glencoe Science

Human Body Systems

Parts of several human body systems are shown here. Although each system has a different role, they function together to maintain homeostasis. A human needs all systems operating together in order to survive.

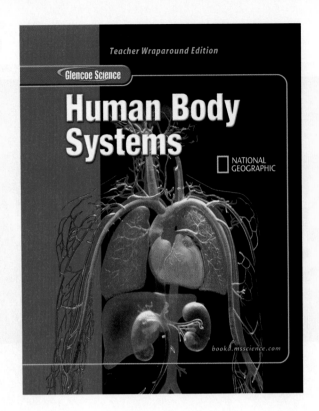

Teacher Wraparound Edition

Glencoe Science

Human Body Systems

NATIONAL GEOGRAPHIC

bookd.msscience.com

 Glencoe

The McGraw·Hill Companies

Send all inquiries to:
Glencoe/McGraw-Hill
8787 Orion Place
Columbus, OH 43240-4027

ISBN 0-07-861743-X (Student Edition)
ISBN 0-07-861744-8 (Teacher Wraparound Edition)

Printed in the United States of America.

2 3 4 5 6 7 8 9 10 027/055 09 08 07 06

Authors

Education Division
Washington, D.C.

Edward Ortleb
Science Consultant
St. Louis, MO

Dinah Zike
Educational Consultant
Dinah-Might Activities, Inc.
San Antonio, TX

Series Consultants

CONTENT

Connie Rizzo, MD, PhD
Department of Science/Math
Marymount Manhattan College
New York, NY

MATH

Michael Hopper, DEng
Manager of Aircraft Certification
L-3 Communications
Greenville, TX

Teri Willard, EdD
Mathematics Curriculum Writer
Belgrade, MT

READING

Elizabeth Babich
Special Education Teacher
Mashpee Public Schools
Mashpee, MA

SAFETY

Aileen Duc, PhD
Science 8 Teacher
Hendrick Middle School, Plano ISD
Plano, TX

Sandra West, PhD
Department of Biology
Texas State University-San Marcos
San Marcos, TX

ACTIVITY TESTERS

Nerma Coats Henderson
Pickerington Lakeview Jr. High
School
Pickerington, OH

Mary Helen Mariscal-Cholka
William D. Slider Middle School
El Paso, TX

**Science Kit and Boreal
Laboratories**
Tonawanda, NY

Series Reviewers

Maureen Barrett
Thomas E. Harrington Middle
School
Mt. Laurel, NJ

Cory Fish
Burkholder Middle School
Henderson, NV

Amy Morgan
Berry Middle School
Hoover, AL

Dee Stout
Penn State University
University Park, PA

Darcy Vetro-Ravndal
Hillsborough High School
Tampa, FL

Glencoe Science 15-Book Series

Teach science your way!

With the 15 Life, Earth, and Physical Science titles in our modular series, you can select the science topics you want to cover and customize your science curriculum in any way you choose.

A Life's Structure and Function
1. Exploring and Classifying Life
2. Cells
3. Cell Processes
4. Cell Reproduction
5. Heredity
6. Adaptations over Time

B From Bacteria to Plants
1. Bacteria
2. Protists and Fungi
3. Plants
4. Plant Reproduction
5. Plant Processes

C Animal Diversity
1. Introduction to Animals
2. Mollusks, Worms, Arthropods, Echinoderms
3. Fish, Amphibians, and Reptiles
4. Birds and Mammals
5. Animal Behavior

D Human Body Systems
1. Structure and Movement
2. Nutrients and Digestion
3. Circulation
4. Respiration and Excretion
5. Control and Coordination
6. Regulation and Reproduction
7. Immunity and Disease

E Ecology
1. Interactions of Life
2. The Nonliving Environment
3. Ecosystems
4. Conserving Resources
5. Conserving Life

Multi-Level Review and Assessment

Each chapter provides five pages of review and testing to help you evaluate students' knowledge and ability to apply science concepts.

Section Review

- Summary pinpoints important concepts in the section.
- Skill-based questions promote critical thinking skills.

Study Guide

- Main idea summary of each section
- Concept mapping activity to help students visualize the main ideas

Chapter Review

- Using Vocabulary
- Checking Concepts
- Thinking Critically
- Performance Activities
- Applying Math

Standardized Test Practice

- Multiple Choice
- Short Response/ Grid In
- Open-Ended Questions

Dynamic Instruction

The consistent instructional strategies in each chapter strengthen students' learning—from the beginning of each chapter where students see "Chapter Preview," to the end where they have a chance to test the knowledge they have acquired and prepare for the next lesson.

Chapter Opener

- *Chapter Preview* introduces the main concepts.
- *Science Journal* promotes critical-thinking skills
- *Dinah Zike's Foldables*™ let students create interactive study guides.
- *Launch Labs* give students an opportunity to explore new ideas.

Section Opener

- *What You'll Learn* introduces main concepts.
- *Why It's Important* provides an answer to "Why do we have to learn this?"
- *Review Vocabulary* reviews a term that helps students better understand section content.
- *New Vocabulary* highlights new terms students will learn in the section.

Labs

- *Labs* allow students to design their own experiments or follow well-tested procedures, enabling them to learn and practice science processes.
- *MiniLABS* offer students quick and easy-to-do ways to clarify concepts and reinforce skills.

Assessment

Glencoe Science offers the Glencoe Assessment Advantage, a system designed to give you all the tools you need to prepare your students for success in any testing situation.

In the *Student Edition*

Section Review and **Applying Math** questions appear in every chapter.

Chapter Review questions help you evaluate students' knowledge and ability to apply science concepts.

Standardized Test Practice questions at the end of each chapter provide students with additional opportunities to practice their test-taking skills.

In the *Teacher Wraparound Edition*

Assessments located throughout the *Teacher Wraparound Edition* provide methods for assessing students' comprehension with Performance, Process, and Content exercises.

Teacher Classroom Resources

Performance Assessment in the Science Classroom
- Guidelines for assessing the performance of a task
- Reproducible activities for evaluating students
- Sample rubrics and checklists

Fast File **Chapter Resources** provides six pages of assessment for every chapter including *Testing Concepts, Applying Concepts,* and *Writing Skills.*

Technology Support

MindJogger Videoquizzes are interactive video quizzes set in game show format. Each is designed for the full range of student learning styles.

Exam*View*® Pro Testmaker CD-ROM for Windows® and Macintosh® provides an easy way to create, edit, and customize your tests. Select your own test items by objective from two different levels of difficulty, or write and edit your own. Translate tests from English to Spanish and vice versa.

Rubrics

The following rubrics are sample scoring devices for short response and open-ended questions.

Short Response

Points	Description
2	The student demonstrates a thorough understanding of the science of the task. The response may contain minor flaws that do not detract from the demonstration of a thorough understanding.
1	The student has provided a response that is only partially correct.
0	The student has provided a completely incorrect solution or no response at all.

Open Ended

Points	Description
4	The student demonstrates a thorough understanding of the science of the task. The response may contain minor flaws that do not detract from the demonstration of a thorough understanding.
3	The student demonstrates an understanding of the science of the task. The response is essentially correct and demonstrates an essential but less than thorough understanding of the science.
2	The student demonstrates only a partial understanding of the science of the task. Although the student may have used the correct approach to a solution or may have provided a correct solution, the work lacks an essential understanding of the underlying science concepts.
1	The student demonstrates a very limited understanding of the science of the task. The response is incomplete and exhibits many flaws.
0	The student provides a completely incorrect solution or no response at all.

Time-Saving Teacher Resources

Glencoe Science provides an extensive array of support materials and resources designed to help you create and customize your science course quickly and easily.

FAST FILE Chapter Resources

For each chapter, Chapter Resources contain key reproducible masters along with additional teaching strategies, teacher support, and answer keys.

Teacher Wraparound Edition

The *Teacher Wraparound Edition* is your key to the teaching resources available. In addition to teaching strategies and suggestions, the *Teacher Wraparound Edition* provides a guide for all print and software materials available for each lesson.

Transparencies

Color Transparencies provides three types of transparencies for use while teaching each chapter. The *Section Focus Transparencies* are designed to generate interest and focus students' attention on the topic being presented in the section. The *Teaching Transparency* for each chapter addresses a major concept that will benefit from an extra visual learning aid. The *Assessment Transparency* for each chapter is set up to resemble standardized tests.

Exam*View*® Pro Testmaker CD-ROM

This CD-ROM will help you create, edit, and customize tests. In addition, it will help you create multiple versions of tests, translate tests from English to Spanish and vice versa, and build tests aligned with state standards.

Video Labs

These VHS cassettes contain step-by-step procedures for selected *Student Edition* labs. They also contain lab safety skills, teacher support, and troubleshooting advice.

TeacherWorks™

This CD-ROM is your all-in-one resource center. Personalize a lesson plan, access resources from the *Teacher Wraparound Edition,* connect to the Internet, or make a to-do list. These are only a few of the many features that can assist you in the planning and organizing of your lessons.

StudentWorks™

This CD-ROM is a valuable resource for students to access content online and use online resources to continue learning chapter concepts.

This CD-ROM brings Microsoft® PowerPoint® presentations right to your door. With the large number of graphics provided, students can use a visual approach to learning chapter content.

Guided Reading Audio Program

The Guided Reading Audio Program has been updated to StudentWorks Plus™.

Virtual Labs CD-ROM Program

The Virtual Labs CD-ROM contains a collection of labs that allow students to complete labs that are too expensive, take too long to complete, or might be too dangerous in a classroom laboratory.

This website is a portal to hundreds of prescreened Internet sites (Web links) that correlate to content in the text. Visit this link to find interactive activities that review chapter concepts and to access the *Student Edition* online.

Mc Graw Hill Learning Network mhln.com

mhln.com is an online teaching and learning space for teachers, students, and parents.

Differentiated Instruction

Teaching Strategies

Following each suggested assessment and activity, ability levels are supplied to accommodate all students. For a key to the Teaching Strategies designations, see the C page before each chapter.

Identifying Misconceptions

These short, diagnostic, and perscriptive lessons target common science misconceptions.

Multiple Learning Styles

Look for these italicized designations under various activities to help you target your lessons to each student's preferred learning style.

- *Kinesthetic* learners learn through touch, movement, and manipulating objects.
- *Visual-Spatial* learners think in terms of images, illustrations, and models.
- *Interpersonal* learners understand and work well with other people.
- *Intrapersonal* learners can analyze their own strengths and weaknesses and may prefer to work on their own.
- *Linguistic* learners write clearly and easily understand the written word.
- *Logical-Mathematical* learners understand numbers easily and have highly-developed reasoning skills.

Daily Interventions

Found at the end of each chapter section, this feature is designed to intercept students who are struggling and prescribe a system to help them get back on track. *Reteach* provides reinforcement of the section's concepts through visual activities.

Differentiated Instruction

These activities present various teaching strategies designed to help you meet the special needs of students with learning disabilities, physical challenges, visual impairment, and hearing impairment. *Challenge* activities provide opportunities for students who excel to engage in activities and research projects that extend the chapter's concepts. English-language learners in the classroom will also find exercises that bridge the gap between language barriers and the chapter content.

Cultural Diversity

These readings provide insights into the unique ways in which people of different ethnicities and cultural heritage have approached science. The intent of these features is to build awareness and appreciation for the global community in which we live.

Inquiry-Based Science

The call for more inquiry-based science by the *National Science Education Standards* has been met by Glencoe Science.

Glencoe Science recognizes the importance of conducting inquiry-based science activities in the classroom. The process of doing inquiry models actual science practice, encouraging problem-solving strategies and developing critical thinking skills. Inquiry gets students actively involved in the learning process by allowing them to determine materials, procedures, or the topics and questions they want to investigate.

Inquiry can range from a very structured activity for those students who need more guidance to a more open-ended approach where students lead the investigations. Glencoe Science recognizes that the inquiry activities suggested will not look the same in every classroom. We encourage teachers to modify the suggested activities in a manner that best supports your students.

Glencoe also provides teachers with *Alternative Inquiry Labs,* teaching strategies or suggestions for making existing labs more inquiry-based.

Research-Based Learning Strategies

Glencoe Science incorporates the most current and applicable educational research on science learning and follows recommendations from the American Association for the Advancement of Science and the National Science Teachers Association. The following research-based strategies can be found throughout the text.

Learning Strategies

The following research-based strategies can be found throughout the text:

- **Using Prior Knowledge** Glencoe Science encourages students to use their prior knowledge to learn information because this adds relevance to the material. Students are referred back to other parts of the text or to their own real-life experiences.

- **Practicing Important Tasks** By offering students an opportunity to practice important tasks using a variety of labs and activities in the *Student Edition, Teacher Wraparound Edition,* ancillaries and technology, Glencoe Science makes learning fun and relevant for students.

- **Using Visuals to Communicate, Organize, and Reinforce Learning** High-quality art and photos throughout the text communicate concepts more efficiently and reinforce learning, while allowing students to organize information.

White Paper

The Glencoe Science White Paper outlines the educational strategies on which this program was based. This document provides specific examples from the *Student Edition, Teacher Wraparound Edition,* ancillary program, and technology resources, highlighting extensive use of educationally sound strategies that help students learn science.

- **Motivating Students to Achieve** Active strategies and real-world experiences motivate students to achieve. Throughout Glencoe's programs, students are encouraged to apply their knowledge in ways that will motivate them to learn.

- **Developing Decoding and Reading Comprehension Strategies** Throughout the text, students are supplied with caption questions, reading checks, and other strategies to aid in comprehension.

- **Using Study Strategies** Through the use of highlighting, outlining, note-taking, summarizing, and other such strategies, students can monitor their own progress and organize information more effectively, thereby increasing their scientific literacy. These strategies are found throughout the text and ancillaries.

The use of these strategies within Glencoe Science will help teachers to achieve the goals set forth by the *National Science Education Standards.*

Glencoe Science White Paper

Research-Based Strategies Used to Develop

Glencoe Science 15-Book Series for Life, Earth, and Physical Science

Field Research and Testing

Feedback from students, teachers, curriculum supervisors, department chairpersons, parents, learning specialists, and science content experts was invaluable in the development of this program. The following pre-publication and post-publication research was conducted.

Prior to Publication

- Detailed classroom teacher and curriculum supervisor **surveys** were conducted by independently contracted researchers.

- A **nationwide panel** of science teachers, curriculum supervisors, and department chairpersons provided countless hours of feedback and assistance throughout program development.

- A wide range of **educator and content reviewers** provided in-depth reviews of and suggestions for manuscripts and pre-publication versions of the program.

- **Face-to-face interviews** with science teachers provided insight into teachers' day-to-day challenges.

After Publication

- Field tests were conducted in which students and teachers used a pre-publication manuscript in the classroom.

- Follow-up interviews, observations, and surveys of Glencoe Science users provide ongoing opportunities for program development and verification of program success.

Field-Test Results

- Field-test research indicates that test scores increased among students using Glencoe Science programs.

- Nine out of ten students earned higher scores after using Glencoe programs.

- Scores improved among both male and female students.

- Scores improved among both minority and non-minority students.

- Overall, the gap between the average pre-test score and a perfect score closed by 33 percent. Stated differently, on average, **scores increased 77 percent after students used the Glencoe program.**

KS Studios

National Education Standards

Correlation of *Glencoe Science* to the National Science Education Standards.

Content Standard	Chapter and Section
(UCP) Unifying Concepts and Processes	
1. Systems, order, and organization	A1-1, A1-2, A1-3, A1-4, A2-1, A2-2, A2-3, A3-1, A3-2, A3-3, A4-1, A4-2, A4-3, A5-1, A5-2, A5-3, A6-1, A6-2, A6-3, B1-1, B2-1, B2-2, B4-1, B4-2, B4-3, B5-1, B5-2, C1-1, C2-1, C2-2, C2-3, C2-4, C3-1, C3-2, C3-3, C3-4, C4-1, C4-2, C5-1, C5-2, D1-1, D1-2, D1-3, D2-1, D2-2, D3-1, D3-2, D3-3, D4-1, D4-2, D5-1, D5-2, D6-1, D6-2, D6-3, E1-1, E1-2, E1-3, E2-1, E2-2, E3-1, E3-2, E3-3
2. Evidence, models, and explanation	A1-1, A1-2, A1-3, A1-4, A2-1, A2-2, A2-3, A3-1, A3-2, A3-3, A4-1, A4-2, A4-3, A5-1, A5-2, A5-3, A6-1, A6-2, A6-3, B1-1, B2-1, B2-2, B3-2, B4-1, B4-2, B4-3, B5-1, B5-2, C1-1, C1-2, C1-3, C2-1, C2-2, C2-4, C3-1, C3-2, C3-3, C3-4, C4-1, C4-2, C5-1, C5-2, D1-1, D1-2, D1-3, D2-1, D3-1, D3-2, D3-3, D4-1, D4-2, D5-1, D5-2, D6-1, D6-2, D6-3, D7-1, D7-2, D7-3, E1-1, E1-2, E1-3, E2-1, E2-2, E3-1, E3-2, E3-3, E4-1, E4-2, E4-3, E5-1, E5-2
3. Change, constancy, and measurement	A1-1, A1-2, A1-3, A1-4, A2-1, A2-2, A3-1, A3-2, A3-3, A4-1, A4-3, A5-1, A5-2, A5-3, A6-1, A6-2, A6-3, B2-1, B2-2, B4-1, B4-2, B4-3, B5-1, B5-2, C1-1, C2-1, C2-2, C2-4, C3-1, C3-2, C3-3, C3-4, C4-1, C4-2, C5-1, C5-2, D1-1, D1-2, D1-3, D3-1, D3-2, D3-3, D4-1, D4-2, D5-1, D5-2, D6-1, D6-2, D6-3, E1-1, E1-2, E1-3, E2-1, E2-2, E3-1, E3-2, E3-3, E4-1, E4-2, E4-3, E5-1, E5-2
4. Evolution and equilibrium	A4-3, A5-2, A5-3, A6-1, A6-2, A6-3, B2-1, C3-1, C3-2, C3-3, C3-4, C4-1, C5-1, C5-2, E1-2, E1-3, E2-1, E3-1
5. Form and function	A1-1, A1-2, A1-3, A1-4, A2-1, A2-2, A2-3, A3-1, A3-2, A3-3, A4-3, A5-1, A5-2, A5-3, A6-1, A6-2, A6-3, B1-1, B1-2, B2-1, B2-2, B3-1, B3-2, B3-3, B4-1, B4-2, B4-3, B5-1, B5-2, C1-1, C1-2, C1-3, C2-1, C2-2, C2-3, C2-4, C3-2, C3-3, C3-4, C4-1, C4-2, D1-1, D1-2, D1-3, D3-1, D3-2, D3-3, D4-1, D4-2, D5-1, D5-2, D6-1, D6-2, D6-3, D7-1, D7-2, D7-3, E1-2, E1-3, E2-2, E3-1, E3-2, E3-3, E5-1, E5-2
(A) Science as Inquiry	
1. Abilities necessary to do scientific inquiry	A1-1, A1-2, A1-3, A1-4, A2-1, A2-2, A2-3, A3-1, A3-2, A3-3, A4-1, A4-2, A4-3, A5-1, A5-2, A5-3, A6-1, A6-2, A6-3, B1-1, B1-2, B2-1, B2-2, B3-1, B3-2, B3-3, B4-1, B4-2, B4-3, B5-1, B5-2, C1-1, C1-2, C1-3, C2-1, C2-2, C2-3, C2-4, C3-1, C3-2, C3-3, C3-4, C4-1, C4-2, C5-1, C5-2, D1-1, D1-2, D1-3, D2-1, D2-2, D3-1, D3-2, D3-3, D4-1, D4-2, D5-1, D5-2, D6-1, D6-2, D6-3, D7-1, D7-2, D7-3, E1-1, E1-2, E1-3, E2-1, E2-2, E3-1, E3-2, E3-3, E4-1, E4-2, E4-3, E5-1, E5-2
2. Understandings about scientific inquiry	A1-1, A1-2, A1-3, A1-4, A2-1, A2-2, A2-3, A3-1, A3-2, A3-3, A4-1, A4-3, A5-1, A5-3, A6-1, A6-2, A6-3, B1-1, B2-1, B2-2, B3-1, B4-1, B4-2, B4-3, B5-1, B5-2, C1-2, C1-3, C2-1, C2-2, C2-3, C2-4, C3-1, C3-2, C3-3, C3-4, C4-1, C4-2, C5-1, C5-2, D1-1, D1-2, D1-3, D2-1, D2-2, D3-1, D3-2, D3-3, D4-1, D4-2, D5-1, D5-2, D6-1, D6-2, D6-3, D7-1, D7-3, E5-1, E5-2, E1-1, E1-2, E1-3, E2-1, E2-2, E3-1, E3-2, E3-3, E4-1, E4-2, E4-3
(B) Physical Science	
1. Properties and changes of properties in matter	A3-1
2. Motions and forces	D1-2
3. Transfer of energy	D1-3, D2-1, D2-2, D6-3, E2-1, E2-2, E2-3
(C) Life Science	
1. Structure and function in living systems	A1-2, A1-3, A2-1, A2-2, A2-3, A3-1, A3-2, A3-3, A4-1, A4-2, A4-3, A5-1, A5-2, A5-3, A6-1, A6-3, B1-1, B2-1, B3-1, B3-2, B3-3, B4-1, B4-2, B4-3, B5-1, B5-2, C1-1, C1-2, C1-3, C2-1, C2-2, C2-3, C2-4, C3-1, C3-2, C3-3, C3-4, C4-1, D1-1, D1-2, D1-3, D2-1, D2-2, D3-1, D3-2, D3-3, D4-1, D4-2, D5-1, D5-2, D6-1, D6-2, D6-3, D7-1, D7-2, D7-3, E1-2, E1-3, E2-2, E2-3, E3-1, E3-2, E3-3, E5-1
2. Reproduction and heredity	A1-2, A2-3, A4-1, A4-2, A4-3, A5-1, A5-2, A5-3, B1-1, B2-1, B3-1, B3-2, B3-3, B4-1, B4-2, B4-3, C1-2, C2-1, C2-2, C2-3, C2-4, C3-1, C3-2, C3-3, C3-4, C4-1, C5-2, D1-1, D1-2, D1-3, D6-1, D6-2, D7-1, D7-2, D7-3, E1-1, E1-2, E1-3
3. Regulation and behavior	A1-2, A2-1, A3-2, A4-1, A4-2, A4-3, B1-1, B1-2, B2-1, B3-1, B3-2, B3-3, B5-1, B5-2, C1-1, C1-2, C1-3, C2-1, C2-2, C2-3, C2-4, C3-1, C3-2, C3-3, C3-4, C4-1, C5-1, D1-2, D1-3, D2-1, D2-2, D3-1, D3-2, D3-3, D4-1, D4-2, D5-1, D5-2, D6-1, D6-2, D6-3, D7-1, D7-2, D7-3, E1-2, E2-2, E3-1, E3-2, E3-3
4. Populations and ecosystems	A6-1, B1-1, B1-2, B2-1, B3-1, B3-2, B3-3, B4-3, C1-2, C1-3, C4-1, C5-2, E1-2, E1-3, E2-2, E3-1, E3-2, E3-3, E5-1
5. Diversity and adaptations of organisms	A1-4, A2-3, A4-2, A6-1, A6-3, B1-1, B1-2, B2-1, B3-1, B3-2, B3-3, B4-1, B4-2, B4-3, B5-2, C1-1, C1-2, C1-3, C2-2, C2-3, C2-4, C3-1, C3-2, C3-3, C3-4, C4-1, C5-1, C5-2, D1-1, D1-2, D1-3, D2-1, D2-2, D3-1, D3-2, D3-3, D5-1, D5-2, D6-3, D7-1, D7-2, D7-3, E1-2, E1-3, E2-2, E2-3, E3-3, E5-1

Content Standard	Chapter and Section
(D) Earth and Space Science	
1. Structure of the Earth system	E2-1, E2-2, E2-3
2. Earth's history	A1-3, A6-1, A6-2
3. Earth in the solar system	E2-3
(E) Science and Technology	
1. Abilities of technological design	B1-2
2. Understandings about science and technology	B1-2
(F) Science in Personal and Social Perspectives	
1. Personal health	A5-2, A6-2, B1-2, B2-2, C3-2, C4-2, D1-1, D1-2, D1-3, D2-1, D2-2, D5-1, D7-1, D7-2, D7-3
2. Populations, resources, and environments	A2-3, B4-3, E1-2, E1-3, E3-3, E4-1, E4-2, E4-3, E5-1, E5-2
3. Natural hazards	A5-3, D7-2
4. Risks and benefits	B1-2, C2-3, C3-4, D7-2, D7-3, E5-1, E5-2
5. Science and technology in society	A5-3, B1-2, C3-4, D7-2, D7-3
(G) History and Nature of Science	
1. Science as a human endeavor	A5-2, A6-1, A6-3, B3-2, D1-3, D2-2, D3-3, D7-3
2. Nature of science	A1-1, A3-3, A5-1, A6-1, A6-2, A6-3, B3-2, B4-3, C1-1, D1-3, D2-2, D3-3, D7-1, D7-3
3. History of science	A1-3, A1-4, A2-2, A2-3, A3-3, A5-1, A6-1, A6-3, B3-2, B4-3, C5-2, D4-2, D5-1

How Glencoe Science Aligns with the National Science Education Standards

The correlations at the left and above show the close alignment between Glencoe Science and the grade-appropriate standards. Glencoe Science allows students to discover concepts within each of the content standards and gives students opportunities to make connections among the science disciplines. Hands-on activities and inquiry-based lessons reinforce the science processes emphasized in the standards.

How Glencoe Science Aligns with the NCTM Standards for Grades 6–8

Throughout Glencoe Science, each Applying Math activity provides students with the opportunity to practice and apply some of the mathematical concepts and applications described in the NCTM Standards. These activities serve to reinforce mathematical skills in real-life situations, thus preparing students to meet their needs in an ever-changing world.

Correlation of *Glencoe Science* to NCTM Standards

Math Standard	Page
1. Number and Operations	A-35, A-46, A-74, A-93, A-123, A-133, A-151, A-181, B-57, B-112, B-119, B-135, B-145, C-25, C-33, C-52, C-67, C-82, C-129, C-155, D-11, D-31, D-59, D-87, D-133, D-141, D-147, D-171, D-201, E-31, E-40, E-59, E-80, E-121, E-150
2. Algebra	A-35, A-46, A-93, A-181, B-57, B-112, B-119, C-25, C-52, D-133, E-40, E-80, E-121
3. Geometry	A-46, D-11
4. Measurement	A-35, A-46, A-63, D-59, E-40, E-80
5. Data Analysis and Probability	A-35, A-93, A-133, A-151, A-181, B-27, B-57, B-89, B-119, B-135, B-145, C-67, C-101, C-129, C-155, D-31, D-59, D-87, D-113, D-141, D-171, D-201, E-40, E-59, E-89, E-121, E-150
6. Problem Solving	A-46, A-93, A-123, B-27, B-89, C-25, C-33, C-101, D-59, D-133, D-201, E-31, E-40, E-59, E-150
7. Reasoning and Proof	C-82, E-31
8. Communication	A-179, D-167
9. Connections	A-35, A-46, A-63, A-74, A-93, A-123, A-133, A-151, A-181, B-27, B-57, B-112, B-119, B-135, B-145, C-25, C-33, C-52, C-67, C-129, C-155, D-59, D-87, D-133, D-141, D-147, D-171, E-40, E-59, E-80, E-121
10. Representation	A-133, E-40

Foldables™

Foldables™ are easy-to-make, three-dimensional, interactive graphic organizers that students create out of simple sheets of paper. These unique hands-on tools for studying and reviewing were created exclusively for Glencoe by education specialist Dinah Zike.

Research Behind Foldables™

According to research (Bransford, 1979; Corno, 1994), study strategies help students understand, organize, remember and apply new information presented in science textbooks. Some study strategies include concept mapping, highlighting, outlining, note taking, summarizing, and underlining (Peverly, Brobst, Graham & Shaw, 2003). Glencoe Science offers Dinah Zike's Foldables™ Study Organizers as an organizational tool and study guide for students.

Foldables™

- Build prereading skills
- Encourage active reading and writing
- Summarize content for review

FOLDABLES™ Study Organizer

Primary and Secondary Succession Make the following Foldable to help you illustrate the main ideas about succession.

STEP 1 **Fold** a vertical sheet of paper in half from top to bottom.

For more ideas on how to incorporate Foldables™ into your lessons consult **Dinah Zike's _Teaching Science with Foldables™_**

Educational Partnerships

NATIONAL GEOGRAPHIC

Some topics in the chapter either require or benefit from a larger, more detailed visual explanation. The National Geographic Society has created *Visualizing* features that call out an important concept from the chapter and illustrate it in a way that will inform, excite, and motivate your students.

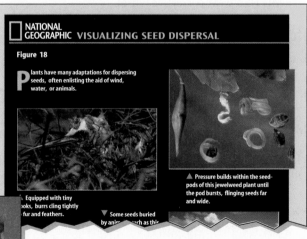

NATIONAL GEOGRAPHIC VISUALIZING SEED DISPERSAL

Figure 18

Plants have many adaptations for dispersing seeds, often enlisting the aid of wind, water, or animals.

▲ Pressure builds within the seedpods of this jewelweed plant until the pod bursts, flinging seeds far and wide.

Equipped with tiny hooks, burrs cling tightly to fur and feathers.

▼ Some seeds buried by animals such as this

TIME SCIENCE AND HISTORY SCIENCE CAN CHANGE THE COURSE OF HISTORY!

Overcoming the Odds

TIME

TIME magazine brings science topics and history together to further explain the chapter's main ideas and show how science relates to real life.

Safety in the Laboratory

All activities are designed to minimize dangers in the laboratory. Careful laboratory planning and management by both the instructor and the student are essential to a safe laboratory experience. **Local, state, and federal laboratory safety laws and regulations must be strictly followed.** The information provided here is one of the many resources to which you can refer for information about laboratory safety.

Classroom and Laboratory Preparation

1. Store equipment properly and securely and other thing.
   a. Clean and dry all equipment before storing.
   b. Protect electronic equipment and microscopes from dust, humidity, and extreme temperatures.
   c. Number, catalog, and organize equipment.
2. Ensure adequate work space for each student.
3. Ensure adequate classroom and storeroom ventilation.
4. Explain and post safety and evacuation guidelines along with expectations of conduct.
5. Ensure that all safety equipment is functioning properly and is clearly visible.
6. Provide hot plates as a heat source whenever possible. If gas burners are used, know where the central gas supply shutoff valve is located.
7. Ensure that each workstation has a GFCI-protected electrical source.
8. Provide safety goggles consistent with ANSI Standard Z87.1 for each student, including students who wear corrective lenses.

Before Each MiniLAB or Lab

1. Arrange the lab in such a way that equipment and supplies are clearly labeled and easily accessible.
2. Have available only equipment and supplies needed to complete the assigned investigation.
3. Review the procedure with students, emphasizing any caution statements or safety symbols that appear.
4. Be sure all students know the proper procedures to follow if an accident should occur.

After the MiniLAB or Lab

1. Be certain that students have returned all equipment and disposed of broken glassware and chemicals properly.
2. Be sure that all hot plates and electrical connections are off.

Storage of Chemicals

Be sure to store all chemicals properly. The following are guidelines commonly used. Your school, city, county, or state may have additional requirements for handling chemicals. It is the responsibility of each teacher to become informed of the rules or guidelines in effect in his or her area.

1. Separate chemicals by reaction type. Strong acids should be stored together. Likewise, strong bases should be stored together and should be separated from acids. Oxidants should be stored away from easily oxidized materials, and so on.
2. Be sure all chemicals are stored in labeled containers indicating contents, concentration, source, date purchased (or prepared), any precautions for handling and storage, and expiration date.
3. Hazardous chemicals require special storage containers and conditions. Be sure to know which chemicals those are and the accepted practices for your area. Some substances must be stored outside the building.

Disposal of Chemicals

Local, state, and federal laws regulate the proper disposal of chemicals. These laws should be consulted before chemical disposal is attempted. Although many substances encountered in the science classroom can be flushed down the drain with plenty of water, it is not safe to assume that this is always true.

DISCLAIMER

Glencoe Publishing Company makes no claims to the completeness of this discussion of laboratory safety and chemical storage. The material presented is not all-inclusive, nor does it address all of the hazards associated with handling, storing, and disposing of chemicals, or with laboratory management.

Preparation of Solutions

It is important to use safe laboratory techniques when handling all chemicals. Always check the MSDS (Material Safety Data Sheet) for each chemical before using it in the classroom. Many substances might appear harmless, but might be toxic, corrosive, or very reactive. Chemicals should never be ingested. Use proper techniques to smell any chemical, wear safety goggles and an apron in the laboratory, and observe the following precautions.

1. **Dilution of Acids and Bases** When diluting acids with water, always add the acids to the water. Never add water to acids. When sulfuric acid and sodium hydroxide are added to water, a large amount of thermal energy is released. Use extra care when handling these substances.

2. **Poisonous and Corrosive Liquids or Vapors** Use a fume hood if possible. Examples include hydrochloric acid, acetic acid, nitric acid, and ammonium hydroxide.

3. **Poisonous and Corrosive to Eyes, Lungs, and Skin** Examples include acids, bases, silver nitrate, iodine, and potassium permanganate.

Bromthymol blue: Add 0.5 g bromthymol blue powder to 500 mL distilled water to make a BTB stock solution. Dilute 40 mL BTB stock solution to 2 L with distilled water. Solution should be bright blue. If not, add one drop of NaOH at a time, swirling to mix. Check color.

Hydrochloric acid (HCL) solution: To make a 5% solution, add 13.6 mL concentrated HCl to 73 mL water while stirring. To make a $0.1M$ solution, add 1 mL concentrated hydrochloric acid to 100 mL water while stirring.

Iodine solution/Iodine stain: Dilute 1 part Lugol's solution with 15 parts water.

Lugol's solution: Dissolve 10 g potassium iodide in 100 mL distilled water. Then add and dissolve 5 g iodine. Store in dark bottle. Keeps indefinitely.

Phenolphthalein indicator: From a drug store, buy a package of any laxative that contains phenolphthalein. To make 1% solution, mash 4 tablets and pour the powder into 10 mL of rubbing alcohol. Let mixture soak for 15 minutes. Pour liquid into and store in a dropper bottle.

Potassium permanganate: For a $0.01M$ solution of potassium permanganate, dissolve 0.15 g $KMnO_4$ in 100 mL water.

Red cabbage concentrate: Put 5 leaves of red cabbage in a pot. Add 1 L of water, bring to a boil, and simmer until water turns a deep purple. Pour liquid through a strainer or piece of cheesecloth into a storage bottle. Keep refrigerated.

Salt solution: For a 3.5% salt (NaCl) solution that simulates the concentration of ocean water, dissolve 35 g of salt (NaCl) in 965 mL of water. For a 1% solution (weak), dissolve 1 g of salt (NaCl) in 99 mL of water. For a 6% solution, dissolve 6 g of salt (NaCl) in 94 mL of water.

Silver nitrate solution: To make a 10% solution, put 5 g of silver nitrate in 50 mL of distilled water.

Sugar solution: Add 1 tablespoon of sugar to 1 cup of warm water in a deep jar or flask. Stir to dissolve.

Sodium hydroxide (dilute): To make a 1% solution, dissolve 1 g NaOH in 99 mL of water.

Equipment and Materials List

Refer to the Chapter Organizer in front of each chapter for a list of equipment and materials used for each laboratory activity in the chapter.

Consumables			
Material	**Launch Lab (Chapter)**	**MiniLAB (Chapter-Section)**	**Lab (Chapter-Section)**
alcohol, rubbing			7-2
aluminum foil		3-2	
ammonia, household, clear			7-3
animal kidney, large			4-2
apple			7-2
baking soda	6		7-3
cardboard tube		4-1	
cheese		2-1	
clay			4-2
cloth, cotton		2-2	
coffee filter			7-3
cornstarch			2-1
cotton ball(s)	7		7-2
filter paper	6	4-2	
food coloring, red			3-3
food flavoring, peppermint	7		
fruits, cubed		2-1	
gauze		3-2	
gravel, fine		4-2	
hydrogen peroxide		7-2	
iodine, 2% tincture			2-1
lemon juice			7-3
liquid bandage solution		3-2	
meat		2-1	
milk, low-fat			3-3
newspaper			1-3, 7-2
orange juice			7-3
paper towel roll or other tube			4-2
peanuts		2-1	
potato chips		2-1	
pretzels		2-1	
red cabbage			7-3
salt	6		
sandpaper			7-2
soap			7-2
sugar			2-2
toothpick(s)		5-2	
vegetables		2-1	
vinegar	6		7-3
weighing paper			2-1, 2-2
wire screen		4-2	
yeast, dry		7-2	
Nonconsumables			
bicycle pump			4-2
cooking pot			7-3
dissecting tray			4-2
map	3		
marbles		4-1	
mortar and pestle			2-2
penny		7-1	
scalpel			4-2
sports bottle			4-2
stirrer, wooden			2-1
tape measure			6-3

Glencoe Science

Human Body Systems

NATIONAL GEOGRAPHIC

bookd.msscience.com

Glencoe

New York, New York   Columbus, Ohio   Chicago, Illinois   Peoria, Illinois   Woodland Hills, California

HOW TO...
Use Your Science Book

Before You Read

- **Chapter Opener** Science is occurring all around you, and the opening photo of each chapter will preview the science you will be learning about. The **Chapter Preview** will give you an idea of what you will be learning about, and you can try the **Launch Lab** to help get your brain headed in the right direction. The **Foldables** exercise is a fun way to keep you organized.

- **Section Opener** Chapters are divided into two to four sections. The **As You Read** in the margin of the first page of each section will let you know what is most important in the section. It is divided into four parts. **What You'll Learn** will tell you the major topics you will be covering. **Why It's Important** will remind you why you are studying this in the first place! The **Review Vocabulary** word is a word you already know, either from your science studies or your prior knowledge. The **New Vocabulary** words are words that you need to learn to understand this section. These words will be in **boldfaced** print and highlighted in the section. Make a note to yourself to recognize these words as you are reading the section.

Glencoe Science

Human Body Systems

NATIONAL GEOGRAPHIC

As You Read

- **Headings** Each section has a title in large red letters, and is further divided into blue titles and small red titles at the beginnings of some paragraphs. To help you study, make an outline of the headings and subheadings.

- **Margins** In the margins of your text, you will find many helpful resources. The **Science Online** exercises and **Integrate** activities help you explore the topics you are studying. **MiniLabs** reinforce the science concepts you have learned.

- **Building Skills** You also will find an **Applying Math** or **Applying Science** activity in each chapter. This gives you extra practice using your new knowledge, and helps prepare you for standardized tests.

- **Student Resources** At the end of the book you will find **Student Resources** to help you throughout your studies. These include **Science, Technology,** and **Math Skill Handbooks,** an **English/Spanish Glossary,** and an **Index.** Also, use your **Foldables** as a resource. It will help you organize information, and review before a test.

- **In Class** Remember, you can always ask your teacher to explain anything you don't understand.

FOLDABLES™ Study Organizer

Science Vocabulary Make the following Foldable to help you understand the vocabulary terms in this chapter.

STEP 1 Fold a vertical sheet of notebook paper from side to side.

STEP 2 Cut along every third line of only the top layer to form tabs.

STEP 3 Label each tab with a vocabulary word from the chapter.

Build Vocabulary As you read the chapter, list the vocabulary words on the tabs. As you learn the definitions, write them under the tab for each vocabulary word.

Look For...

FOLDABLES™

At the beginning of every section.

In Lab

Working in the laboratory is one of the best ways to understand the concepts you are studying. Your book will be your guide through your laboratory experiences, and help you begin to think like a scientist. In it, you not only will find the steps necessary to follow the investigations, but you also will find helpful tips to make the most of your time.

- Each lab provides you with a **Real-World Question** to remind you that science is something you use every day, not just in class. This may lead to many more questions about how things happen in your world.

- Remember, experiments do not always produce the result you expect. Scientists have made many discoveries based on investigations with unexpected results. You can try the experiment again to make sure your results were accurate, or perhaps form a new hypothesis to test.

- Keeping a **Science Journal** is how scientists keep accurate records of observations and data. In your journal, you also can write any questions that may arise during your investigation. This is a great method of reminding yourself to find the answers later.

Look For...
- **Launch Labs** start every chapter.
- **MiniLabs** in the margin of each chapter.
- **Two Full-Period Labs** in every chapter.
- **EXTRA Try at Home Labs** at the end of your book.
- the **Web site** with **laboratory demonstrations.**

Before a Test

Admit it! You don't like to take tests! However, there *are* ways to review that make them less painful. Your book will help you be more successful taking tests if you use the resources provided to you.

- Review all of the **New Vocabulary** words and be sure you understand their definitions.

- Review the notes you've taken on your **Foldables,** in class, and in lab. Write down any question that you still need answered.

- Review the **Summaries** and **Self Check questions** at the end of each section.

- Study the concepts presented in the chapter by reading the **Study Guide** and answering the questions in the **Chapter Review.**

Look For...

- **Reading Checks** and **caption questions** throughout the text.
- the **Summaries** and **Self Check questions** at the end of each section.
- the **Study Guide** and **Review** at the end of each chapter.
- the **Standardized Test Practice** after each chapter.

Let's Get Started

To help you find the information you need quickly, use the Scavenger Hunt below to learn where things are located in Chapter 1.

1. What is the title of this chapter?

2. What will you learn in Section 1?

3. Sometimes you may ask, "Why am I learning this?" State a reason why the concepts from Section 2 are important.

4. What is the main topic presented in Section 2?

5. How many reading checks are in Section 1?

6. What is the Web address where you can find extra information?

7. What is the main heading above the sixth paragraph in Section 2?

8. There is an integration with another subject mentioned in one of the margins of the chapter. What subject is it?

9. List the new vocabulary words presented in Section 2.

10. List the safety symbols presented in the first Lab.

11. Where would you find a Self Check to be sure you understand the section?

12. Suppose you're doing the Self Check and you have a question about concept mapping. Where could you find help?

13. On what pages are the Chapter Study Guide and Chapter Review?

14. Look in the Table of Contents to find out on which page Section 2 of the chapter begins.

15. You complete the Chapter Review to study for your chapter test. Where could you find another quiz for more practice?

Teacher Advisory Board

The Teacher Advisory Board gave the editorial staff and design team feedback on the content and design of the Student Edition. They provided valuable input in the development of the 2005 edition of *Glencoe Science.*

John Gonzales
Challenger Middle School
Tucson, AZ

Rachel Shively
Aptakisic Jr. High School
Buffalo Grove, IL

Roger Pratt
Manistique High School
Manistique, MI

Kirtina Hile
Northmor Jr. High/High School
Galion, OH

Marie Renner
Diley Middle School
Pickerington, OH

Nelson Farrier
Hamlin Middle School
Springfield, OR

Jeff Remington
Palmyra Middle School
Palmyra, PA

Erin Peters
Williamsburg Middle School
Arlington, VA

Rubidel Peoples
Meacham Middle School
Fort Worth, TX

Kristi Ramsey
Navasota Jr. High School
Navasota, TX

Student Advisory Board

The Student Advisory Board gave the editorial staff and design team feedback on the design of the Student Edition. We thank these students for their hard work and creative suggestions in making the 2005 edition of *Glencoe Science* student friendly.

Jack Andrews
Reynoldsburg Jr. High School
Reynoldsburg, OH

Peter Arnold
Hastings Middle School
Upper Arlington, OH

Emily Barbe
Perry Middle School
Worthington, OH

Kirsty Bateman
Hilliard Heritage Middle School
Hilliard, OH

Andre Brown
Spanish Emersion Academy
Columbus, OH

Chris Dundon
Heritage Middle School
Westerville, OH

Ryan Manafee
Monroe Middle School
Columbus, OH

Addison Owen
Davis Middle School
Dublin, OH

Teriana Patrick
Eastmoor Middle School
Columbus, OH

Ashley Ruz
Karrer Middle School
Dublin, OH

The Glencoe middle school science Student Advisory Board taking a timeout at COSI, a science museum in Columbus, Ohio.

Contents

In each chapter, look for these opportunities for review and assessment:
- **Reading Checks**
- **Caption Questions**
- **Section Review**
- **Chapter Study Guide**
- **Chapter Review**
- **Standardized Test Practice**
- **Online practice at bookd.msscience.com**

Student Resources

Cross-Curricular Readings/Labs

available as a video lab

Content Details

Labs/Activities

INTEGRATE

Science Online

Standardized Test Practice

Content Details

D ◆ 1

Human Genome

Introduction

This feature introduces students to scientific inquiry by capturing their interest and then guiding them through the steps scientists are using to sequence the human genome. Scientists working on this project use scientific methods to answer the question "What is the DNA sequence of the entire human genome?" These scientists gathered background information about DNA, genes, chromosome, and DNA sequencing technology to help answer the question. They use up-to-date technology to perform the work quickly and accurately, and multiple trials to check their results. Results are analyzed and communicated also.

1 Motivate

Have students discuss recent media coverage of information concerning the human genome. Provide recent newspaper or news magazine articles for students to examine. Write responses on the board as students respond to the following question: **What have you heard or read in the news about the human genome?**

Human Genome

Figure 1 DNA contains two types of paired bases, adenine-thymine and cytosine-guanine.

By applying scientific methods and using technology, scientists completed the task of mapping the human genome. All of the DNA in an organism makes up its genome. Although knowing the human genome allows for the possibilities of earlier diagnosis, better treatments, and even cures for many types of disorders, it also brings with it many questions about ethics and social values that cannot be answered by science. This feature presents information about the scientific achievements involved in sequencing the human genome. It also presents some questions raised by people in different fields that require careful consideration.

Genes and DNA

The human genome has approximately 30,000 genes. Genes are made of a complex chemical called DNA. In DNA there are four different substances—called bases—that only occur in two types of pairs. The number of paired bases and their order is unique for each species.

Figure 2 In 1983, the Nobel Prize in Medicine was awarded to Dr. Barbara McClintock for her discovery of "jumping genes."

Before the 1950s, scientists could only look at a human cell's nucleus under a microscope and try to count the number of gene-containing chromosomes in it. In 2000, scientists finally determined the order of the three billion DNA bases on all the human chromosomes.

Unraveling the Code

How did scientists determine such a complex and lengthy sequence? Many discoveries about DNA were made before the order of the bases could be determined.

Curriculum Connection

Health Have students research different health-related conditions, such as weight control, various types of cancer, or a particular genetic disorder, to see if the conditions are controlled by a person's genetic make-up, by a person's actions, or by a combination of these two factors. Have students present their findings to the class. Remind students to use up-to-date sources to find information.

Dr. Barbara McClintock made one such discovery. She first recognized jumping DNA—stretches of DNA that can move around and between chromosomes—in Indian corn in the 1940s. In the 1980s, other scientists confirmed her findings. Scientists now hypothesize that this jumping DNA might be related to diseases such as hemophilia, leukemia, and breast cancer.

The Human Genome Project

An international effort to determine the human genome began in October of 1990. For many years, scientists did not have the technology to study chromosomes at the DNA level. In the 1970s and 1980s, computers were improved so that large amounts of data could be stored in small amounts of space. It takes three gigabytes of computer memory to store one human genome. This does not include additional information about the genome, only the order of bases.

Figure 3 Sequencing small segments of DNA was one part of the Human Genome Project.

DNA Sequencing

To determine the order of bases on a chromosome—a chromosome may be up to 250 million bases long—scientists sequence the DNA. First, chromosomes are broken into shorter pieces. Then, the fragments are analyzed to determine the bases. Finally, a computer is used to assemble the short sequences into long stretches, look for errors, and find other information.

What is science?

Science is concerned only with ideas or hypotheses that can be tested. Test results can be considered useful only if they are observable and repeatable. For scientists to learn whether an idea is correct or not, there must be observations or experiments that can show the idea to be true or false. For example, to make a working draft of the DNA sequence on the human genome, scientists identified 90 percent of the genes on each chromosome. Other scientists checked this information. The DNA sequence was not accepted until other scientists repeated it many times. Even before a working draft of the DNA sequence was completed, scientists checked their results multiple times.

Figure 4 This computer display shows some of the sequence results of The Human Genome Project.

THE NATURE OF SCIENCE D ◆ 3

2 Teach

Content Background

DNA sequencing technology allows scientists to "read" the sequence of nucleotide bases that make up DNA. Rapid changes in sequencing technology have increased the speed and accuracy of sequencing. Two sequencing methods were developed but the one that is used most often is called Sanger method. This method makes large-scale production sequencing possible. It mimics what occurs during DNA replication in cells. It begins with a DNA fragment. Part of this fragment's sequence is known. Terminators—nucleotides with fluorescent markers—are used during replication and allow scientists to identify replicated fragments of the original DNA fragment. In this way scientists can read the DNA sequences.

Discussion

How might Barbara McClintock's work have prevented confusion for scientists working on the genome project? Answers will vary. Students should note that without McClintock's work, scientists might have been perplexed by the appearance of a particular gene at different places within the genome.

Visual Learning

Figure 4 This figure shows the computer-generated results of three trials of sequencing of a 43 base-pair stretch of DNA. The groupings of three letters above the tracings indicate the results of each trial, and the top row of letters shows the "consensus sequence," or agreed upon results of the three trials. Ask students to note how frequently the scientists were not able to determine a consensus from the three trials. Use this example to engage students in a discussion of the importance of multiple trials in any experiment or investigation.

The NATURE OF SCIENCE

Figure 5 Using up-to-date equipment allows scientists to obtain better results.

Better Science

Scientists are always striving for better experiments and more accurate observations that will increase their understanding. This means that scientific knowledge may change as scientists learn more. Recognition that the working draft of the human genome contained gaps and errors was an example of this. Scientific knowledge is the most reliable information people currently have. Although scientific knowledge is dependable, it is not certain or eternal.

Limits of Science

Accepted theories change as scientists learn more about the world. This book describes the human body, but there is no information about how a person should behave or how they should think about their body. Science is not qualified to teach morality or spirituality.

Knowing the entire sequence of the human genome can help people in many ways. It can improve diagnoses of diseases and lead to the development of new medicines. Gene therapy—altering an organism's genes—may someday be used to treat or prevent disease. Science is the most reliable way of acquiring objective knowledge about the world, but it is not the only way. There are certain kinds of knowledge that science cannot uncover and some questions that are too complex for science alone to answer.

Technological Limits

Sometimes science cannot answer a question or solve a problem because scientists do not have the necessary tools or skills. Recall that scientists could not sequence the human genome until a complete understanding of DNA was learned and the computer technology to store the information was available. Many questions that scientists cannot answer today may be answered in the future as new technology is developed.

Figure 6 These are some of the computers used to sequence the human genome.

Differentiated Instruction

Gifted Have students extend the Quick Demo activity by investigating the length of a gene in the human genome and calculating the number of possible sequence combinations for that length of DNA. Challenge the students to use a simple computer program or to program a scientific calculator to assist them in their calculations. **L3** **IS** **Logical-Mathematical**

What Science Can't Answer

Even if there were no technical limits, science still could answer only certain kinds of questions. The questions that science can answer are those about facts—about the way things are in the world. But science cannot answer questions about values—how things "should be". Scientific discoveries can raise questions about values. Human genome research, for example, has raised many ethical, legal, and social issues. Some questions raised by this research are:

- Who will be able to find out about a person's genome and how will the information be used?
- Should genetic testing for a disease be performed when no treatment is available?
- How will knowledge that someone may develop a genetic disease affect that person? How will society regard such an individual?
- Do genes make people behave in certain ways? Can they always control their behavior?

Science may provide information that can help people understand issues better, but people have to make their own decisions based on their own values and beliefs.

Figure 7 Many decisions must be made about the application of information gained from the Human Genome Project.

You Do It

In this book, you will learn about human body systems. Some of this information has been known for centuries. Other information is from recent discoveries, such as the understanding of genetic links to certain disorders. Gene therapy is a way to treat, cure, or prevent genetically linked disease by altering a person's genes. Today, research in gene therapy is just beginning. But someday it may be available to help people with genetic diseases. Research this topic and debate it with your classmates. Consider such questions as, "What is normal and what is a disorder? Who decides? Are disabilities diseases? Do they need to be cured or prevented?" Early attempts at gene therapy will be very expensive. "Who will pay for the therapies? Who will get these therapies?"

If you had access to information about your genome, would you share that information? What circumstances would make you more or less likely to share information about your DNA with others? Answers will vary. Students may be unfamiliar with concepts relating to health insurance, and may have a hard time relating to workplace discrimination because of health issues. Some explanation of these concepts may be required.

Use Science Words

Word Origin The word *gigabyte* is combination of *giga-* from a Greek word for giant and *–byte*, which is eight binary digits that are processed as a unit by a computer. A *gigabyte* is defined as 1,073,741,824 bytes.

3 Assess

Use the questions in the You Do It to assess understanding. Answers should relate to the use of gene therapy to treat various disorders, the cost of gene therapy, and the methods of delivering gene therapy to those who need it.

You Do It

Help students locate up-to-date sources to use for the research suggested in the exercise. Divide students into small groups and assign each group one of the questions raised in the feature. Have each group present background information about the aspect of gene therapy they researched, and to present an opinion on the issue. Remind the students that there are no right or wrong answers to the questions in the feature. COOP LEARN **IS** **Interpersonal**

Section/Objectives	Standards		Labs/Features
Chapter Opener	**National**	**State/Local**	**Launch Lab:** Effects of Muscles on Movement , p. 7
	See pp. 16T–17T for a Key to Standards.		**Foldables**, p. 7
Section 1 The Skeletal System 🕐 2 sessions 📦 1 block 1. **Identify** five functions of the skeletal system. 2. **Compare and contrast** movable and immovable joints.	National Content Standards: UCP.1–UCP.3, UCP.5, A.1, A.2, C.1, C.2, C.5, F.1		**Science Online**, p. 10 **Applying Math:** Volume of Bones, p. 11
Section 2 The Muscular System 🕐 2 sessions 📦 1 block 3. **Identify** the major function of the muscular system. 4. **Compare** and contrast the three types of muscles. 5. **Explain** how muscle action results in the movement of body parts.	National Content Standards: UCP.1–UCP.3, UCP.5, A.1, A.2, B.2, B.3, C.1–C.3, C.5, F.1		**Science Online**, p. 15 **Visualizing Human Body Levers,** p. 16 **MiniLAB:** Comparing Muscle Activity, p. 18
Section 3 The Skin 🕐 3 sessions 📦 1.5 blocks 6. **Distinguish** between the epidermis and dermis of the skin. 7. **Identify** the skin's functions. 8. **Explain** how skin protects the body from disease and how it heals itself.	National Content Standards: UCP.1–UCP.3, UCP.5, A.1, A.2, B.3, C.1–C.3, C.5, F.1, G.1, G.2		**Integrate Career**, p. 21 **MiniLAB:** Recognizing Why You Sweat, p. 22 **Integrate Chemistry**, p. 23 **Lab:** Measuring Skin Surface, p. 25 **Lab:** Similar Skeletons, p. 26 **Oops! Accidents in Science:** First Aid Dolls, p. 28

Lab Materials	Reproducible Resources	Section Assessment	Technology
Launch Lab: table and chair	**Chapter FAST FILE Resources** Foldables Worksheet, p. 17 Directed Reading Overview, p. 19 Note-taking Worksheets, pp. 33–36	GLENCOE'S ASSESSMENT ADVANTAGE	TeacherWorks includes: • Interactive Teacher Edition • Lesson Planner with calendar • Access to all program blacklines • Correlations to standards • Web links
	Chapter FAST FILE Resources Transparency Activity, p. 46 Enrichment, p. 30 Reinforcement, p. 27 Directed Reading, p. 20 Lab Activity, pp. 9–11 **Life Science Critical Thinking/ Problem Solving,** p. 14 **Mathematics Skill Activities,** p. 17	Portfolio Visual Learning, p. 10 Performance Applying Math, p. 11 Applying Skills, p. 13 Content Challenge, p. 12 Section Review, p. 13	Section Focus Transparency Virtual Labs CD-ROM Guided Reading Audio Program Interactive Chalkboard CD-ROM
MiniLAB: book, table, meterstick *Need materials?* Contact Science Kit at 1-800-828-7777 or www.sciencekit.com on the Internet.	**Chapter FAST FILE Resources** Transparency Activity, p. 47 MiniLAB, p. 3 Enrichment, p. 31 Reinforcement, p. 28 Directed Reading, p. 20 Transparency Activity, pp. 49–50 Lab Activity, pp. 13–16 **Home and Community Involvement,** p. 49	Portfolio Reteach, p. 19 Performance MiniLAB, p. 18 Applying Skills, p. 19 Content Challenge, p. 16 Section Review, p. 19	Section Focus Transparency Teaching Transparency Virtual Labs CD-ROM Guided Reading Audio Program Interactive Chalkboard CD-ROM
MiniLAB: magnifying lens, clear plastic sandwich bag, tape Lab: large sheets of newspaper (10), scissors, tape, meterstick or ruler Lab: diagrams of a variety of mammal skeletons	**Chapter FAST FILE Resources** Transparency Activity, p. 48 MiniLAB, p. 4 Enrichment, p. 32 Reinforcement, p. 29 Directed Reading, pp. 21, 22 Lab Worksheet, pp. 5–6, 7–8 **Cultural Diversity,** p. 15 **Lab Management and Safety,** p. 67	Portfolio Visual Learning, p. 22 Performance MiniLAB, p. 22 Applying Math, p. 24 Content Challenge, p. 23 Section Review, p. 24	Section Focus Transparency Virtual Labs CD-ROM Guided Reading Audio Program Interactive Chalkboard CD-ROM Video Lab

End of Chapter Assessment

GLENCOE'S ASSESSMENT ADVANTAGE

Blackline Masters	Technology	Professional Series
Chapter FAST FILE Resources Chapter Review, pp. 39–40 Chapter Tests, pp. 41–44 **Standardized Test Practice, pp. 7–10**	MindJogger Videoquiz Virtual Labs CD-ROM ExamView® Pro Testmaker TeacherWorks CD-ROM Interactive Chalkboard CD-ROM	**Performance Assessment in the Science Classroom (PASC)**

Transparencies

Section Focus

Section Focus Transparency 1 Cloud Catchers

If you've ever watched a skyscraper being built, you may have noticed the first part to go up is the metal frame that supports the building. After the skyscraper is completed, the frame usually cannot be seen.

1. What is the function of the frame in the picture?
2. How is the function of this metal frame similar to your "frame"?

L2

Section Focus Transparency 2 No Sweat

Just after World War II, an English neurosurgeon named Sir Ludwig Guttman organized a competition for people in wheelchairs. Today, opportunities exist for everyone to participate in a variety of sports and recreation at all levels.

1. Name a body system that helps people to move.
2. What do hitting a tennis ball and a heartbeat have in common? How are they different?

L2

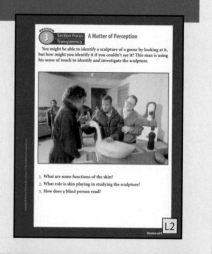

Section Focus Transparency 3 A Matter of Perception

You might be able to identify a sculpture of a goose by looking at it, but how might you identify it if you couldn't see it? This man is using his sense of touch to identify and investigate the sculpture.

1. What are some functions of the skin?
2. What role is skin playing in studying the sculpture?
3. How does a blind person read?

L2

This is a representation of key blackline masters available in the Teacher Classroom Resources. See Resource Manager boxes within the chapter for additional information.

Assessment

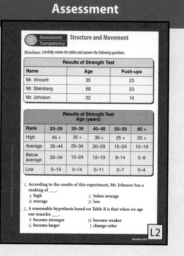

Assessment Transparency Structure and Movement

Directions: Carefully review the tables and answer the following questions.

Results of Strength Test

Name	Age	Push-ups
Mr. Vincent	35	23
Mr. Steinberg	68	23
Mr. Johnson	22	16

Results of Strength Test Age (years)

Rank	20–29	30–39	40–49	50–59	60 +
High	45 +	35 +	30 +	25 +	20 +
Average	35–44	25–34	20–29	15–24	10–19
Below average	20–34	15–24	12–19	8–14	5–9
Low	0–19	0–14	0–11	0–7	0–4

1. According to the results of this experiment, Mr. Johnson has a ranking of ____.
   A high   C below average
   B average   D low
2. A reasonable hypothesis based on Table B is that when we age our muscles ____.
   F become stronger   H become weaker
   G become larger   J change color

L2

Teaching

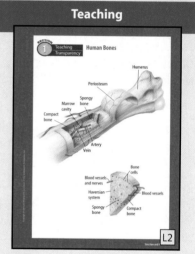

Teaching Transparency 1 Human Bones

Humerus
Periosteum
Spongy bone
Marrow cavity
Compact bone
Artery
Vein
Bone cells
Blood vessels and nerves
Haversian system
Spongy bone
Blood vessels
Compact bone

L2

Key to Teaching Strategies

The following designations will help you decide which activities are appropriate for your students.

L1 Level 1 activities should be appropriate for students with learning difficulties.

L2 Level 2 activities should be within the ability range of all students.

L3 Level 3 activities are designed for above-average students.

ELL ELL activities should be within the ability range of English-Language Learners.

COOP LEARN Cooperative Learning activities are designed for small group work.

LS Multiple Learning Styles logos, as described on page 12T, are used throughout to indicate strategies that address different learning styles.

P These strategies represent student products that can be placed into a best-work portfolio.

PBL Problem-Based Learning activities apply real-world situations to learning.

Hands-on Activities

Student Text Lab Worksheet

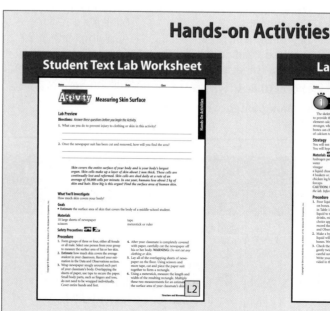

Activity Measuring Skin Surface

Lab Preview
Directions: Answer these questions before you begin the Activity.
1. What can you do to prevent injury to clothing or skin in this activity?

2. Once the newspaper suit has been cut and removed, how will you find the area?

Skin covers the entire surface of your body and is your body's largest organ. Skin cells make up a layer of skin about 2 mm thick. These cells are continually lost and replaced. Skin cells are shed daily at a rate of an average of 50,000 cells per minute. In one year, humans lose about 2 kg of skin and hair. How big is this organ? Find the surface area of human skin.

What You'll Investigate
How much skin covers your body?

Goals
- Estimate the surface area of skin that covers the body of a middle-school student.

Materials
10 large sheets of newspaper
scissors
tape
meterstick or ruler

Safety Precautions

Procedure
1. Form groups of three or four, either all female or all male. Select one person from your group to measure the surface area of his or her skin.
2. Estimate how much skin covers the average student in your classroom. Record your estimation in the Data and Observations section.
3. Wrap newspaper snugly around each part of your classmate's body. Overlapping the sheets of paper, use tape to secure the paper. Small body parts, such as fingers and toes, do not need to be wrapped individually. Cover entire hands and feet.
4. After your classmate is completely covered with paper, carefully cut the newspaper off his or her body. WARNING: Do not cut any clothing or skin.
5. Lay all of the overlapping sheets of newspaper on the floor. Using scissors and more tape, cut and piece the paper suit together to form a rectangle.
6. Using a meterstick, measure the length and width of the resulting rectangle. Multiply these two measurements for an estimate of the surface area of your classmate's skin.

L2

Laboratory Activities

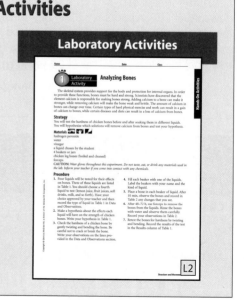

Laboratory Activity 1 Analyzing Bones

The skeletal system provides support for the body and protection for internal organs. In order to provide these functions, bones must be hard and strong. Scientists have discovered that the element calcium is responsible for making bones strong. Adding calcium to a bone can make it stronger, while removing calcium will make the bone weak and brittle. The amount of calcium in bones can change over time. Certain types of hard physical exercise and work can result in a gain of calcium to bones, while certain diseases and diets can result in a loss of calcium from bones.

Strategy
You will test the hardness of chicken bones before and after soaking them in different liquids.
You will hypothesize which solutions will remove calcium from bones and test your hypothesis.

Materials
hydrogen peroxide
water
vinegar
a liquid chosen by the student
4 beakers or jars
chicken leg bones (boiled and cleaned)
forceps
CAUTION: Wear gloves throughout this experiment. Do not taste, eat, or drink any materials used in the lab. Inform your teacher if you come into contact with any chemicals.

Procedure
1. Four liquids will be tested for their effects on bones. Three of these liquids are listed in Table 1. You should choose a fourth liquid to test (lemon juice, fruit juices, soft drinks, milk, and so forth). Have your choice approved by your teacher and then record the type of liquid in Table 1 in Data and Observations.
2. Make a hypothesis about the effects each liquid will have on the strength of chicken bones. Write your hypothesis in Table 1.
3. Check the hardness of a chicken bone by gently twisting and bending the bone. Be careful not to crack or break the bone. Write your observations on the lines provided in the Data and Observations section.
4. Fill each beaker with one of the liquids. Label the beakers with your name and the kind of liquid.
5. Place a bone in each beaker of liquid. After 10 min, observe the bones and record in Table 2 any changes that you see.
6. After 48–72 h, use forceps to remove the bones from the liquids. Rinse the bones with water and observe them carefully. Record your observations in Table 2.
7. Retest the bones for hardness by twisting and bending. Record the results of the test in the Results column of Table 1.

L2

Meeting Different Ability Levels

Content Outline

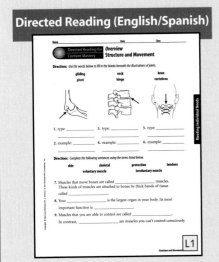

Note-taking Worksheet — **Structure and Movement**

Section 1   The Skeletal System

L2

Reinforcement

Reinforcement — **The Skeletal System**

L2

Enrichment

Enrichment — **Bones of Animals**

L3

Directed Reading (English/Spanish)

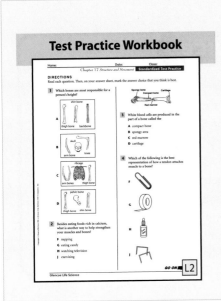

Directed Reading for Content Mastery — *Overview* **Structure and Movement**

L1

Study Guide

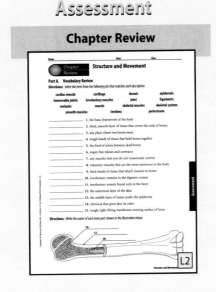

Study Guide

Features
- Contains a study guide page for each section of the chapter
- Reviews key concepts
- Includes answer pages

L2

Reading Essentials

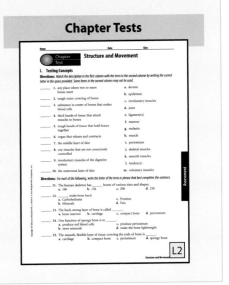

Reading Essentials for Glencoe Science
An Interactive Student Workbook

Features
- Condensed core content
- Actively involves students in reading
- Reinforces key vocabulary

L1

Assessment

Test Practice Workbook

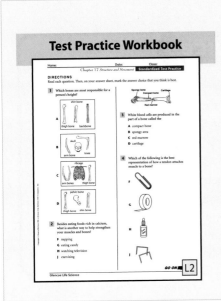

Chapter 17 Structure and Movement **Standardized Test Practice**

L2

Glencoe Life Science

Chapter Review

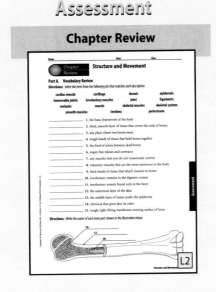

Chapter Review — **Structure and Movement**

Part A. Vocabulary Review

L2

Chapter Tests

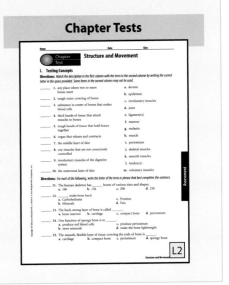

Chapter Test — **Structure and Movement**

I. Testing Concepts

L2

Science Content Background

 ## The Skeletal System
Human Skeletons

Humans have endoskeletons—skeletons inside the body. The skeleton consists of the appendicular skeleton and the axial skeleton. The appendicular skeleton is made up of arm and leg bones and the girdler that attaches them to the body. The axial skeleton is made up of the skull, backbone, ribs, and breastbone.

 ## The Muscular System
Muscle Contractions

The contraction of a muscle cell involves a chemical called acetylcholine, which is released by the ends of the motor neurons. This action sends an impulse over the surface and into the interior of the muscle fiber. Calcium ions are released, which results in muscle contraction.

 ## The Skin

The skin is stretchable, tough, and selectively permeable. The epidermis is only about 30 to 60 cells thick. The dermis varies from 1 to 3 mm in thickness. The surface area of the skin is nearly 1.2 m² for an adolescent.

The Dermis

The dermis has two layers. The upper papillary layer is composed of connective tissue and has many small blood vessels and nerves. The folding of this layer produces ridges on the skin's surface, including fingerprints. The lower reticular layer is made of dense connective tissue with many collagen fibers. This layer also contains the sweat glands, oil glands, and hair follicles.

Sweat Glands

Sweat glands can be found in large numbers on the hands, feet, chest, and neck. Perspiration is similar to weak urine. The oil (sebaceous) glands secrete an oil composed of fats, salts, proteins, and water that lubricates the skin and reduces evaporation of water from the skin's surface. As the oil and sweat mix on the skin's surface, they form a protective layer that inhibits the growth of harmful bacteria and fungi.

Hair

The hair follicles produce masses of epidermal cells that are pushed up through the follicle. These cells then flatten and die. The amount of melanin in the cells gives hair its color. Because hair comes from the skin, it is considered an appendage of the skin.

chapter content resources

Internet Resources
For additional content background, visit
bookd.msscience.com to:
- access your book online
- find references to related articles in popular science magazines
- access Web links with related content background
- access current events with science journal topics

Print Resources
Biology (6th Edition), by Neil A. Campbell, Jane B. Reece, Pearson Benjamin Cummings Publishing, 2001
Human Anatomy & Physiology (5th Edition), by Elaine N. Marieb, Pearson Benjamin Cummings Publishing Company, 2000
Principles of Human Physiology, by William J. Germann, Cindy L. Stanfield, Pearson Benjamin Cummings Publishing, 2001

IDENTIFYING > Misconceptions

Find Out What Students Think

Students may think that . . .

The muscular system is unrelated to other body systems.

When asked about the structure and function of muscles, most students tend to think only about the importance of muscles in movement. Often they don't understand the importance of muscles in the functioning of other systems or the role of the nervous system in controlling the muscular system.

Discussion

Ask students to explain what muscles do. Most will note the importance of muscles in gross motor movement. Record their responses on the board or on the overhead projector. Then ask students to consider other roles muscles play in the body. For example, shivering is a result of muscle contractions. These contractions release heat, which helps warm the body. Have students speculate on other processes that might depend on the movement of muscles. L2

Promote Understanding

Activity

Show students how to take a pulse by lightly placing two fingers on the major artery on the neck and counting the number of pulses in 6 seconds. By adding a zero to this number, the number of beats per minute (heart rate) can be determined. A similar process can be used to determine the respiration rate. L2

• Have students determine and record their at-rest pulse and respiration rates.

• Have those who are able exercise vigorously for 30 seconds. You might have students jump up and down or jog in place.

• When you call time, again have students determine and record their pulse and respiration rates.

Have students compare their at-rest and after-exercise pulse and respiration rates. Emphasize that the data they have collected illustrate that the muscular system is related to both the circulatory and respiratory systems. As muscle activity increased, so too did pulse and respiration rate. Remind students that increased breathing brings needed oxygen into the body and expels waste carbon dioxide. The increase in heart rate quickly moves this oxygen to working muscles. Explain that it is the nervous system that causes these increased rates. As the nervous system senses a buildup of carbon dioxide and other waste products in muscle cells, it causes the body to increase breathing and heart rate.

As an extension, discuss with students how muscles support other systems. An example of this would be muscles aiding in digestion by moving food and undigested material through the digestive track.

Summing

Ask students to describe activities that would cause heart rate to increase. If necessary, ask students what happens to their heart rates when they are frightened. Again point out the connections between the muscular system and the cardiovascular and nervous systems. L2

Assess

After completing the chapter, see *Identifying Misconceptions* in the Study Guide at the end of the chapter.

Structure and Movement

Chapter Vocabulary

Science Journal Student responses will vary, but may be creative. It would be impossible for humans to exist without structure and movement.

INTERACTIVE CHALKBOARD with Image Bank

PowerPoint® Presentations

This CD-ROM is an editable Microsoft® PowerPoint® presentation that includes:
- a pre-made presentation for every chapter
- interactive graphics
- animations
- audio clips
- image bank
- all new section and chapter questions
- Standardized Test Practice
- transparencies
- pre-lab questions for all labs
- Foldables directions
- links to bookd.msscience.com

chapter preview

sections

1 The Skeletal System

2 The Muscular System

3 The Skin
   Lab *Measuring Skin Surface*
   Lab *Similar Skeletons*
   Virtual Lab *What are the major bones in the human body?*

How are you like a building?

Internal and external structures support both buildings and the human body. Bones support us instead of steel or wood. The covering of a building protects the inside from the outside environment. Your skin protects your body's internal environment.

Science Journal Imagine that your body did not have a support system. Describe how you might perform your daily activities.

Theme Connection

Energy When the skeletal and muscular systems work to produce movement, energy is used and work is done. Food is processed by the digestive system and converted into glucose. The chemical energy in glucose is used by muscles and transformed into mechanical energy.

About the Photo

Structure If a building's structural support was severely damaged, the building would collapse. The importance of the skeleton and skin in the human body can be compared to the structural framework and external structure of a building.

Start-Up Activities

Effect of Muscles on Movement

The expression "Many hands make light work" is also true when it comes to muscles in your body. In fact, hundreds of muscles and bones work together to bring about smooth, easy movement. Muscle interactions enable you to pick up a penny or lift a 10-kg weight.

1. Sit on a chair at an empty table and place the palm of one hand under the edge of the table.

2. Push your hand up against the table. Do not push too hard.

3. Use your other hand to feel the muscles located on both sides of your upper arm, as shown in the photo.

4. Next, place your palm on the top of the table and push down. Again, feel the muscles in your upper arm.

5. **Think Critically** Describe in your Science Journal how the different muscles in your upper arm were working during each movement.

Structure and Movement
Without skin, muscle and bone each of us would be a formless mass. Make the following Foldable to help you understand the function of skin, muscle and bone in structure and movement.

STEP 1 Fold a sheet of paper in half lengthwise. Make the back edge about 5 cm longer than the front edge.

STEP 2 Turn the paper so the fold is on the bottom. Then, fold it into thirds.

STEP 3 Unfold and cut only the top layer along both folds to make three tabs. Label the Foldable as shown.

Read and Write As you read this chapter, write the functions that skin, muscle, and bone each have in structure and movement.

 Preview this chapter's content and activities at bookd.mssscience.com

---

Purpose Use the Launch Lab to introduce students to muscles. L2 ELL COOP LEARN LS Kinesthetic

Preparation Clear tables of anything that could spill or break before students begin the lab.

Materials table, chair

Teaching Strategy Inform students that they will learn more about the muscular and skeletal systems as they read the chapter. This lab may also be done by student pairs.

Think Critically

Possible answers: When pushing up on the table, the top of the upper arm muscles feel hard. When pushing down, the muscles on the back of the upper arm feel hard.

Assessment

Process Ask students to observe and decide where the largest muscles in their bodies are located. The largest muscles are located where they can move the limbs and other large parts of the body, such as the buttocks. Use **Performance Assessment in the Science Classroom,** p. 89. L2

 Dinah Zike Study Fold

Student preparation materials for this Foldable are available in the **Chapter *Fast File* Resources.**

section 1

The Skeletal System

Living Bones

Often in a horror movie, a mad scientist works frantically in his lab while a complete human skeleton hangs silently in the corner. When looking at a skeleton, you might think that bones are dead structures made of rocklike material. Although these bones are no longer living, the bones in your body are very much alive. Each is a living organ made of several different tissues. Like all the other living tissues in your body, bone tissue is made of cells that take in nutrients and use energy. Bone cells have the same needs as other body cells.

Functions of Your Skeletal System All the bones in your body make up your **skeletal system,** as shown in **Figure 1.** It is the framework of your body and has five major functions.

Figure 1 The 206 bones of the human body are connected, forming a framework called the skeleton.

1. The skeleton gives shape and support to your body.

2. Bones protect your internal organs. For example, ribs surround the heart and lungs, and the skull encloses the brain.

3. Major muscles are attached to bone and help them move.

4. Blood cells are formed in the center of many bones in soft tissue called red marrow.

5. Major quantities of calcium and phosphorous compounds are stored in the skeleton for later use. Calcium and phosphorus make bones hard.

Bone Structure

Several characteristics of bones are noticeable. The most obvious are the differences in their sizes and shapes. The shapes of bones are inherited. However, a bone's shape can change when the attached muscles are used.

Looking at bone through a magnifying glass will show you that it isn't smooth. Bones have bumps, edges, round ends, rough spots, and many pits and holes. Muscles and ligaments attach to some of the bumps and pits. In your body blood vessels and nerves enter and leave through the holes. Internal characteristics, how a bone looks from the inside, and external characteristics, how the same bone looks from the outside, are shown in **Figure 2.**

A living bone's surface is covered with a tough, tight-fitting membrane called the **periosteum** (per ee AH stee um). Small blood vessels in the periosteum carry nutrients into the bone. Cells involved in the growth and repair of bone also are found in the periosteum. Under the periosteum are two different types of bone tissue—compact bone and spongy bone.

Compact Bone Directly under the periosteum is a hard, strong layer called compact bone. Compact bone gives bones strength. It has a framework containing deposits of calcium phosphate. These deposits make the bone hard. Bone cells and blood vessels also are found in this layer. This framework is living tissue and even though it's hard, it keeps bone from being too rigid, brittle, or easily broken.

Figure 2 Bone is made of layers of living tissue. Compact bone is arranged in circular structures called Haversian systems—tiny, connected channels through which blood vessels and nerve fibers pass.

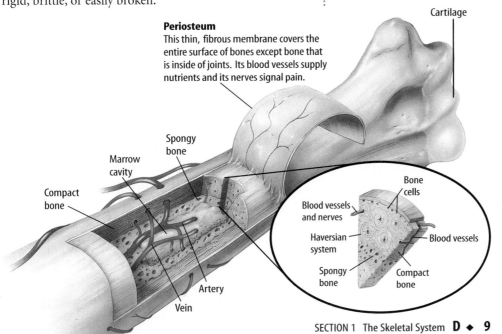

Periosteum
This thin, fibrous membrane covers the entire surface of bones except bone that is inside of joints. Its blood vessels supply nutrients and its nerves signal pain.

Cartilage

Spongy bone

Marrow cavity

Compact bone

Artery

Vein

Bone cells

Blood vessels and nerves

Haversian system

Blood vessels

Spongy bone

Compact bone

Quick Demo

Building Columns

Materials 4-in × 6-in index cards, tape, books

Estimated Time 10 minutes

Procedure Construct one rectangular column and one cylindrical tube. Stand the structures on a flat surface and balance books on top of each one. Have students predict which structure collapses first. Relate this strength to the long, round bones of the human body. L2

Use Science Words

Word Usage Have students find nonscientific meanings of the use of the word *skeleton*. Refer to such idioms as *skeleton outline, skeleton crew,* and *skeleton structure.* L2

Teacher FYI

Osteoporosis A condition in which bones become porous and thin, resulting in reduced bone mass is osteoporosis. Factors that increase the risk of this condition include being female, being Caucasian, having chronic low calcium intake, lacking exercise, being underweight, and smoking.

Differentiated Instruction

English-Language Learners Ask students to interview a physician to find out what the most common fractures are, and how they occur. Have the students give an oral presentation to the class about what they have learned.

Curriculum Connection

Health Fractures are breaks or cracks in bones. When the broken bone isn't completely separated, it is called a greenstick fracture. Complete fractures occur when the broken bone is completely separated, but the broken ends do not pierce the skin. Compound, or open, fractures occur when the ends of the broken bone pierce the skin. Have students find out how each type of fracture is treated. L2

Figure 3 Cartilage is replaced slowly by bone as solid tissue grows outward. Over time, the bone reshapes to include blood vessels, nerves, and marrow. **Describe** *the type of bone cell that builds up bone.*

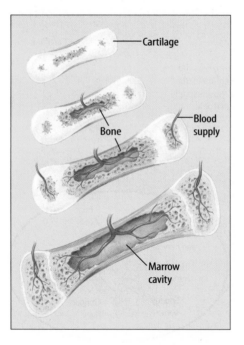

Cartilage

Bone

Blood supply

Marrow cavity

Spongy Bone Spongy bone is located toward the ends of long bones such as those in your thigh and upper arm. Spongy bone has many small, open spaces that make bones lightweight. If all your bones were completely solid, you'd have greater mass. In the centers of long bones are large openings called cavities. These cavities and the spaces in spongy bone are filled with a substance called marrow. Some marrow is yellow and is composed of fat cells. Red marrow produces red blood cells at an incredible rate of 2 million to 3 million cells per second.

Cartilage The ends of bones are covered with a smooth, slippery, thick layer of tissue called **cartilage.** Cartilage does not contain blood vessels or minerals. Nutrients are delivered to cartilage by nearby blood vessels. Cartilage is flexible and important in joints because it acts as a shock absorber. It also makes movement easier by reducing friction that would be caused by bones rubbing together. Cartilage can be damaged because of disease, injury, or years of use. People with damaged cartilage experience pain when they move.

Reading Check *What is cartilage?*

Bone Formation

Although your bones have some hard features, they have not always been this way. Months before your birth, your skeleton was made of cartilage. Gradually the cartilage broke down and was replaced by bone, as illustrated in **Figure 3.** Bone-forming cells called osteoblasts (AHS tee oh blasts) deposit the minerals calcium and phosphorus in bones, making the bone tissue hard. At birth, your skeleton was made up of more than 300 bones. As you developed, some bones fused, or grew together, so that now you have only 206 bones.

Healthy bone tissue is always being formed and re-formed. Osteoblasts build up bone. Another type of bone cell, called an osteoclast, breaks down bone tissue in other areas of the bone. This is a normal process in a healthy person. When osteoclasts break bone down, they release calcium and phosphorus into the bloodstream. This process maintains the elements calcium and phosphorus in your blood at about the levels they need to be. These elements are necessary for the working of your body, including the movement of your muscles.

Joints

What will you do during your lunch break today? You may sit at a table, pick up a sandwich, bite off a piece of a carrot and chew it, and walk to class. All of these motions are possible because your skeleton has joints.

Anyplace where two or more bones come together is a **joint.** The bones making up healthy joints are kept far enough apart by a thin layer of cartilage so that they do not rub against each other as they move. The bones are held in place at these joints by a tough band of tissue called a **ligament.** Many joints, such as your knee, are held together by more than one ligament. Muscles move bones by moving joints.

Applying Math — Calculate Volume

VOLUME OF BONES The Haversian systems found in the cross section of your bones are arranged in long cylinders. This cylindrical shape allows your bones to withstand great pressure. Estimate the volume of a bone that is 36 cm long and is 7 cm in diameter.

Solution

1 *This is what you know:* The bone has a shape of a cylinder whose height, *h*, measures 36 cm and whose diameter is 7.0 cm.

2 *This is what you need to find out:* What is the volume of the cylinder?

3 *This is the procedure you need to use:*
- Volume = $\pi \times (\text{radius})^2 \times \text{height}$, or $V = \pi \times r^2 \times h$
- A radius is one-half the diameter $\left(\frac{1}{2} \times 7 \text{ cm}\right)$, so $r = 3.5$ cm, $h = 36$ cm, and $\pi = 3.14$.
- Substitute in known values and solve.
  $3.14 \times (3.5 \text{ cm})^2 \times 36 \text{ cm} = 1{,}384.74 \text{ cm}^3$
- The volume of the bone is approximately 1,384.74 cm³.

4 *Check your answer:* Divide your answer by 3.14 and then divide that number by $(3.5)^2$. This number should be the height of the bone.

Practice Problems

1. Estimate the volume of a bone that has a height of 12 cm and a diameter of 2.4 cm.

2. If a bone has a volume of 314 cm³ and a diameter of 4 cm, what is its height?

For more practice, visit
bookd.msscience.com/
math_practice

Make a Model

Ligaments Use two cardboard paper towel tubes and rubber bands to model how ligaments hold bones together at a joint.
L2 ELL IS **Visual-Spatial**

Applying Math

National Math Standards
Correlation to Mathematics Objectives
1
Use equations to determine time from average speed and distance measurements.

Teaching Strategy
Use division to find unit rates and ratios in proportional relationships such as speed, density, price, and recipes.

Answers to Practice Problems
1. 54 cm³
2. 25 cm

Teacher FYI

Arthroscopic Surgery During arthroscopic surgery, an arthroscope (surgical instrument used to visually examine the interior of a joint) is inserted through an incision and the surgeon looks around inside the joint. Repair of the joint is done through the incision by means of instruments designed to be used with the arthroscope.

Curriculum Connection

Language Arts Have students look up *periosteum* and *osteoblast* in the dictionary. Have volunteers explain how the root of the word reflects its meaning. The root word *osteo* means "bone"; the root word *peri* means "surrounding"; the root word *blast* means "bud" or "germ." The periosteum surrounds the bone; the osteoblasts are bone-forming cells. L2 IS **Linguistic**

Use an Analogy

Lubricants Moving parts of machines require protection from friction. Lubricants such as oil and grease and other coatings serve to reduce the wear of the parts. Moving parts of the body at bone joints have spaces between the bones. These spaces have lubricants called synovial fluids and sacs of fluids—the bursae and synovial sheaths—to reduce friction between bone surfaces.

Teacher FYI

Forming Skull Joints The joints between the bones of the skull are called sutures. In an infant, the bones are held together by fibrous connective tissue and there is some flexibility between the bones. In later years, the tissue is replaced by bone and the skull becomes a hard, solid protective case for the brain.

Discussion

Importance of Joints If your hand had no joints, how would this affect you? Possible answer: You would not be able to pick up, hold, or turn objects.

Immovable Joints Refer to **Figure 4** as you learn about different types of joints. Joints are broadly classified as immovable or movable. An immovable joint allows little or no movement. The joints of the bones in your skull and pelvis are classified as immovable joints.

Movable Joints All movements, including somersaulting and working the controls of a video game, require movable joints. A movable joint allows the body to make a wide range of motions. There are several types of movable joints—pivot, ball and socket, hinge, and gliding. In a pivot joint, one bone rotates in a ring of another bone that does not move. Turning your head is an example of a pivot movement.

A ball-and-socket joint consists of a bone with a rounded end that fits into a cuplike cavity on another bone. A ball-and-socket joint provides a wider range of motion than a pivot joint does. That's why your legs and arms can swing in almost any direction.

A third type of joint is a hinge joint. This joint has a back-and-forth movement like hinges on a door. Elbows, knees, and fingers have hinge joints. Hinge joints have a smaller range of motion than the ball-and-socket joint. They are not dislocated as easily, or pulled apart, as a ball-and-socket joint can be.

A fourth type of joint is a gliding joint in which one part of a bone slides over another bone. Gliding joints also move in a back-and-forth motion and are found in your wrists and ankles and between vertebrae. Gliding joints are used the most in your body. You can't write a word, use a joystick, or take a step without using a gliding joint.

Figure 4 When a basketball player shoots a ball, several types of joints are in action.
Describe other activities that use several types of joints.

- Skull
- Immovable joints
- Shoulder
- Ball-and-socket joint
- Vertebrae
- Gliding joint
- Arm
- Pivot joint
- Knee
- Hinge joint

Science Journal

Mechanical Joints at Home Have students make lists in their Science Journals of mechanical joints found at and around the home that are similar to joints found in the body. Examples include: door hinge—elbow; swivel chair—wrist; and wind vane—skull on vertebra. L2 IS **Visual-Spatial**

Differentiated Instruction

Challenge Have students write a brief report on the hyoid bone located in the anterior part of the neck. It is the only bone in the body that is not part of a joint with another bone. L3

Moving Smoothly When you rub two pieces of chalk together, their surfaces begin to wear away, and they get reshaped. Without the protection of the cartilage at the end of your bones, they also would wear away at the joints. Cartilage helps make joint movement easier. It reduces friction and allows bones to slide more easily over each other. Shown in **Figure 5,** pads of cartilage, called disks, are located between the vertebrae in your back. They act as a cushion and prevent injury to your spinal cord. A fluid that comes from nearby blood vessels also lubricates the joint.

✓ **Reading Check** *Why is cartilage important?*

Common Joint Problems Arthritis is the most common joint problem. The term *arthritis* describes more than 100 different diseases that can damage the joints. About one out of every seven people in the United States suffers from arthritis. All forms of arthritis begin with the same symptoms: pain, stiffness, and swelling of the joints.

Two types of arthritis are osteoarthritis and rheumatoid arthritis. Osteoarthritis results when cartilage breaks down because of years of use. Rheumatoid arthritis is an ongoing condition in which the body's immune system tries to destroy its own tissues.

Figure 5 A colored X ray of the human backbone shows disks of cartilage between the vertebrae.

✓ **Reading Check**

Answer Cartilage makes joint movement easier by reducing friction that allows bones to slide more easily over each other.

3 Assess

DAILY INTERVENTION

Check for Understanding
Intrapersonal If your hand had no joints, how would this affect you? Possible answer: You would not be able to pick up, hold, or turn objects. L2

Reteach
Bones Bring in the leg and wing bones of cooked chicken or turkey and allow students to examine the ends of the bones for cartilage. Have them note the smooth and slippery surface that facilitates movement, but also notice the firmness needed for support. L2 ELL LS

Visual-Spatial

✓ **Assessment**

Oral Have students infer the functions of a fluid-filled cavity between two cartilage surfaces. The cavity cushions the cartilage and keeps the surfaces from rubbing against each other. Use **Performance Assessment in the Science Classroom,** p. 89. L2

---

section 1 review

Summary

Living Bones
- The skeletal system is the framework of your body and has five major functions.

Bone Structure
- A tough membrane called the periosteum covers a bone and supplies nutrients to it.
- Compact bone is hard bone located directly under the periosteum.
- Spongy bone is lightweight and located toward the ends of long bones.
- Cartilage covers the ends of bones and acts as a shock absorber.

Bone Formation
- Osteoblasts are bone-forming cells and osteoclasts are cells that break down bone.
- A joint is anyplace where two or more bones come together.
- Ligaments are tough bands of tissue that hold bones together at joints.

Self Check

1. **List** the five major functions of the skeletal system.
2. **Name** and give an example of both a movable joint and an immovable joint.
3. **Explain** the functions of cartilage in your skeletal system.
4. **Describe** ligaments.
5. **Think Critically** A thick band of bone forms around a broken bone as it heals. In time, the thickened band disappears. Explain how this extra bone can disappear over time.

Applying Skills

6. **Make and Use Tables** Use a table to classify the bones of the human body as follows: *long, short, flat,* or *irregular.*
7. **Use graphics software** to make a circle graph that shows how an adult's bones are distributed: *29 skull bones, 26 vertebrae, 25 ribs, four shoulder bones, 60 arm and hand bones, two hip bones,* and *60 leg and feet bones.*

---

section 1 review

1. gives shape and support; protects internal organs; provides place for muscle attachment; produces blood cells; stores minerals
2. movable joint: base of skull, shoulder, hip, elbow, knee, finger, wrist, and ankle; immovable joint: skull and pelvis
3. provides padding; also provides shape for ears and nose
4. tough bands of tissue that hold bones in place
5. Osteoclasts break down the extra bone material.
6. Have students work in pairs to compare their classification tables.
7. Circle graph should show these approximate percentages: skull–14% (50°), vertebral column–13% (47°), rib cage–12% (43°), shoulder–2% (7°), arms and hands–29% (104°), hip–1% (4°), legs and feet–29% (104°).

1 Motivate

INTERACTIVE CHALKBOARD
PowerPoint® Presentations

Bellringer

Section Focus Transparencies also are available on the Interactive Chalkboard CD-ROM.

L2 ELL

SECTION 2 | Section Focus Transparency | No Sweat

Just after World War II, an English neurosurgeon named Sir Ludwig Guttman organized a competition for people in wheelchairs. Today, opportunities exist for everyone to participate in a variety of sports and recreation at all levels.

1. Name a body system that helps people to move.
2. What do hitting a tennis ball and a heartbeat have in common? How are they different?

Structure and Movement

Tie to Prior Knowledge

Sore Muscles Everyone has had sore, overworked muscles. Have students discuss why they think this happens. L1

as you read

What You'll Learn
- **Identify** the major function of the muscular system.
- **Compare and contrast** the three types of muscles.
- **Explain** how muscle action results in the movement of body parts.

Why It's Important
The muscular system is responsible for how you move and the production of heat in your body. Muscles also give your body its shape.

Review Vocabulary
bone: dense, calcified tissue of the skeleton, that is moved by muscles

New Vocabulary
- muscle
- voluntary muscle
- involuntary muscle
- skeletal muscle
- tendon
- cardiac muscle
- smooth muscle

Movement of the Human Body

The golfer looks down the fairway and then at the golf ball. With intense concentration and muscle coordination, the golfer swings the club along a graceful arc and connects with the ball. The ball sails through the air, landing inches away from the flag. The crowd applauds. A few minutes later, the golfer makes the final putt and wins the tournament. The champion has learned how to use controlled muscle movement to bring success.

Muscles help make all of your daily movements possible. **Figure 6** shows which muscles connect some of the bones in your body. A **muscle** is an organ that can relax, contract, and provide the force to move your body parts. In the process, energy is used and work is done. Imagine how much energy the more than 600 muscles in your body use each day. No matter how still you might try to be, some muscles in your body are always moving. You're breathing, your heart is beating, and your digestive system is working.

Figure 6 Your muscles come in many shapes and sizes. Even simple movements require the coordinated use of several muscles. The muscles shown here are only those located directly under the skin. Beneath these muscles are middle and deep layers of muscles.

Section 2 Resource Manager

Chapter FAST FILE Resources
Transparency Activity, pp. 47, 49–50
Directed Reading for Content Mastery, p. 20
Enrichment, p. 31
Lab Activity, pp. 9–11

MiniLAB, p. 3
Reinforcement, p. 28
Home and Community Involvement, p. 49

Muscle Control Your hand, arm, and leg muscles are voluntary. So are the muscles of your face, shown in **Figure 7.** You can choose to move them or not move them. Muscles that you are able to control are called **voluntary muscles.** In contrast, **involuntary muscles** are muscles you can't control consciously. They go on working all day long, all your life. Blood gets pumped through blood vessels, and food is moved through your digestive system by the action of involuntary muscles.

 Reading Check *What is a body activity that is controlled by involuntary muscles?*

Your Body's Simple Machines—Levers

INTEGRATE Physics Your skeletal system and muscular system work together when you move, in the same way that the parts of a bicycle work together when it moves. A machine, such as a bicycle, is any device that makes work easier. A simple machine does work with only one movement, like a hammer. The hammer is a type of simple machine called a lever, which is a rod or plank that pivots or turns about a point. This point is called a fulcrum. The action of muscles, bones, and joints working together is like a lever. In your body, bones are rods, joints are fulcrums, and contraction and relaxation of muscles provide the force to move body parts. Levers are classified into three types—first-class, second-class, and third-class. Examples of the three types of levers that are found in the human body are shown in **Figure 8.**

Figure 7 Facial expressions generally are controlled by voluntary muscles. It takes only 13 muscles to smile, but 43 muscles to frown.

Science Online

Topic: Joint Replacement
Visit bookd.msscience.com for Web links to recent news or magazine articles about replacing diseased joints.

Activity Make a list in your Science Journal of the most commonly replaced joints.

SECTION 2 The Muscular System **D ◆ 15**

Visualizing Human Body Levers

Have students examine the pictures and read the captions. Then ask the following questions.

Which type of lever moves the load in the opposite direction of the effort force? First-class levers move the load in a direction opposite to the effort force.

How could the tennis racquet in the picture be thought of as an extension of a lever arm? If the fulcrum is the shoulder and the load is the tennis ball being struck, then the player's arm and racquet together form the lever arm.

Activity

Finding Levers Have students work in small groups to conduct a search through the classroom, or, if possible, the school building for first-, second- and third-class levers. Have each group prepare a visual to list the different examples of levers they found. Have the students include a diagram of one of the examples. L2

Quick Demo

Classes of Levers

Materials 2-inch thick piece of foam (or other material to simulate the brake pedal of car)

Estimated Time 10 minutes

Procedure Demonstrate the three classes of levers by movements of the foot: first-class—press down on the piece of foam with the ball of the foot to simulate pressing on the brake pedal of a car; second-class—rise up on tiptoe; third-class—rise up on heels.

Figure 8

All three types of levers—first-class, second-class, and third-class—are found in the human body. In the photo below, a tennis player prepares to serve a ball. As shown in the accompanying diagrams, the tennis player's stance demonstrates the operation of all three classes of levers in the human body.

▲ Fulcrum
▼ Effort force
■ Load

FIRST-CLASS LEVER
The fulcrum lies between the effort force and the load. This happens when the tennis player uses his neck muscles to tilt his head back.

THIRD-CLASS LEVER
The effort force is between the fulcrum and the load. This happens when the tennis player flexes the muscles in his arm and shoulder.

SECOND-CLASS LEVER
The load lies between the fulcrum and the effort force. This happens when the tennis player's calf muscles lift the weight of his body up on his toes.

16 ◆ D

Differentiated Instruction

Challenge There are other examples of levers within the human body. Have students research to find out which parts of the human ear work as a lever, and write a paragraph explaining their findings to the class. L3

A Skeletal muscles move bones. The muscle tissue is striated, and attached to bone.

B Cardiac muscle is found only in the heart. The muscle tissue has striations.

C Smooth muscle is found in many of your internal organs, such as the digestive tract. This muscle tissue is nonstriated.

Figure 9 The three types of muscle tissue are skeletal muscle, cardiac muscle, and smooth muscle.

Classification of Muscle Tissue

All the muscle tissue in your body is not the same. The three types of muscles are skeletal, smooth, and cardiac. The muscles that move bones are **skeletal muscles.** They are more common than other muscle types and are attached to bones by thick bands of tissue called **tendons.** When viewed under a microscope, skeletal muscle cells are striated (STRI ay tud), and appear striped. You can see the striations in **Figure 9A.** Skeletal muscles are voluntary muscles. You choose when to walk or when not to walk. Skeletal muscles tend to contract quickly and tire more easily than involuntary muscles do.

The remaining two types of muscles are shown in **Figures 9B** and **9C. Cardiac muscle** is found only in the heart. Like skeletal muscle, cardiac muscle is striated. This type of muscle contracts about 70 times per minute every day of your life. **Smooth muscles** are found in your intestines, bladder, blood vessels, and other internal organs. They are nonstriated, involuntary muscles that slowly contract and relax. Internal organs are made of one or more layers of smooth muscles.

Mini LAB

Purpose Students feel the effects of muscle fatigue. L1

ELL **IS** **Kinesthetic**

Materials book, table, meterstick

Teaching Strategy Students can work with a family member. One person can do the activity while the other holds the meterstick vertically.

Analysis

1. Arm muscles become tired after a relatively short period of activity, heart muscles work continuously.

2. Heart muscles do not tire, but work continuously throughout one's life.

Assessment

Oral Have students infer why muscle contractions of the heart must be rhythmic. Use **Performance Assessment in the Science Classroom,** p. 89. L1

Try at Home

Reading Check

Answer With increased muscle activity, individual muscle cells become larger.

Figure 10 **A** When the flexor (hamstring) muscles of your thigh contract, the lower leg is brought toward the thigh. **B** When the extensor (quadriceps) muscles contract, the lower leg is straightened.
Describe *the class of lever shown to the right.*

Mini LAB

Comparing Muscle Activity

Procedure

1. Hold a light **book** in your outstretched hand over a dining or kitchen **table.**

2. Lift the book from this position to a height of 30 cm from the table 20 times.

Analysis

1. Compare your arm muscle activity to the continuous muscle activity of the heart.

2. Infer whether heart muscles become tired.

Try at Home

Extensors contract (flexors relax)

Flexors contract (extensors relax)

Working Muscles

How do muscles allow you to move your body? You move because pairs of skeletal muscles work together. When one muscle of a pair contracts, the other muscle relaxes, or returns to its original length, as shown in **Figure 10.** Muscles always pull. They never push. When the muscles on the back of your upper leg contract, they shorten and pull your lower leg back and up. When you straighten your leg, the back muscles lengthen and relax, and the muscles on the front of your upper leg contract. Compare how the muscles of your legs work with how the muscles of your arms work.

Changes in Muscles Over a period of time, muscles can become larger or smaller, depending on whether or not they are used. Skeletal muscles that do a lot of work, such as those in your writing hand, become strong and large. For example, many soccer and basketball players have noticeably larger, defined leg muscles. Muscles that are given regular exercise respond quickly to stimuli. Some of this change in muscle size is because of an increase in the number of muscle cells. However, most of this change in muscle size is because individual muscle cells become larger.

In contrast, if you participate only in nonactive pastimes such as watching television or playing computer games, your muscles will become soft and flabby and will lack strength. Muscles that aren't exercised become smaller in size. When someone is paralyzed, his or her muscles become smaller due to lack of exercise.

Reading Check *How do muscles increase their size?*

Cultural Diversity

Acupuncture Acupuncture originated in China more than 2,500 years ago. It is the system of inserting thin needles into the skin at specific body points. Acupuncture has been used to treat a variety of disorders. Have students find out some modern uses of acupuncture. Possible answers: to anesthetize patients for surgery, to cure disease, to relieve pain, to improve health L2

Differentiated Instruction

Visually Impaired Have students use their hand to feel the muscle contraction of muscles in their thigh when the lower leg is brought toward the thigh and when the lower leg is straightened. Have sighted students use **Figure 10** to name the muscles as they are touched.

How Muscles Move Your muscles need energy to contract and relax. Your blood carries energy-rich molecules to your muscle cells where the chemical energy stored in these molecules is released. As the muscle contracts, this released energy changes to mechanical energy (movement) and thermal energy (heat), as shown in **Figure 11.** When the supply of energy-rich molecules in a muscle is used up, the muscle becomes tired and needs to rest. During this resting period, your blood supplies more energy-rich molecules to your muscle cells. The heat produced by muscle contractions helps keep your body temperature constant.

Figure 11 Chemical energy is needed for muscle activity. During activity, chemical energy supplied by food is changed into mechanical energy (movement) and thermal energy (heat).

section 2 review

Summary

Movement of the Human Body
- Muscles are organs that relax, contract, and provide force to move your body parts.

Classification of Muscle Tissue
- Skeletal muscles are striated muscles that move bones.
- Cardiac muscles are striated muscles which are found only in the heart.
- Smooth muscles are found in your internal organs and are nonstriated muscles.

Working Muscles
- Muscles always pull and when one muscle of a pair contracts, the other muscle relaxes.
- Chemical energy is needed for muscle activity.

Self Check

1. **Describe** the function of muscles.
2. **Compare and contrast** the three types of muscle tissue.
3. **Name** the type of muscle tissue found in your heart.
4. **Describe** how a muscle attaches to a bone.
5. **Think Critically** What happens to your upper-arm muscles when you bend your arm at the elbow?

Applying Skills

6. **Concept Map** Using a concept map, sequence the activities that take place when you bend your leg at the knee.
7. **Communicate** Write a paragraph in your Science Journal about the three forms of energy involved in a muscle contraction.

Science Online bookd.msscience.com/self_check_quiz   SECTION 2 The Muscular System **D** ◆ **19**

---

section 2 review

1. movement
2. Skeletal (voluntary) and cardiac (involuntary) have striations; smooth muscle (involuntary) has no striations.
3. cardiac
4. Thick bands of tissue called tendons attach muscles to bones.

5. Muscles in the front (biceps) contract, while muscles in the back (triceps) relax.
6. The muscles on the underside of your thigh contract, and the bottom part of your leg is drawn toward the thigh. At the same time, the muscles on the top of the thigh relax and lengthen.

7. Entries should list the three forms of energy as chemical, mechanical, and thermal. It is the thermal energy of muscle contractions that helps maintain the constant body heat of warm-blooded animals.

Tie to Prior Knowledge

Hot Skin Recall how an adult may have felt your forehead if he or she suspected you had a fever. Because the skin permits excess internal heat to escape from the body, touching the skin serves as a quick way to determine whether you have a high temperature.

as you read

What You'll Learn

- **Distinguish** between the epidermis and dermis of the skin.
- **Identify** the skin's functions.
- **Explain** how skin protects the body from disease and how it heals itself.

Why It's Important

Skin plays a vital role in protecting your body.

Review Vocabulary

vitamin: an inorganic nutrient needed by the body in small quantities for growth, disease prevention, and/or regulation of body functions

New Vocabulary

- epidermis
- dermis
- melanin

Your Largest Organ

What is the largest organ in your body? When you think of an organ, you might imagine your heart, stomach, lungs, or brain. However, your skin is the largest organ of your body. Much of the information you receive about your environment comes through your skin. You can think of your skin as your largest sense organ.

Skin Structures

Skin is made up of three layers of tissue—the epidermis, the dermis, and a fatty layer—as shown in **Figure 12.** Each layer of skin is made of different cell types. The **epidermis** is the outer, thinnest layer of your skin. The epidermis's outermost cells are dead and water repellent. Thousands of epidermal cells rub off every time you take a shower, shake hands, blow your nose, or scratch your elbow. New cells are produced constantly at the base of the epidermis. These new cells move up and eventually replace those that are rubbed off.

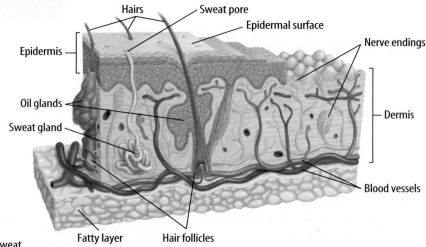

Figure 12 Hair, sweat glands, and oil glands are part of your body's largest organ, the skin.

20 ◆ D CHAPTER 1 Structure and Movement

Melanin Cells in the epidermis produce the chemical melanin (MEL uh nun). **Melanin** is a pigment that protects your skin and gives it color. The different amounts of melanin produced by cells result in differences in skin color, as shown in **Figure 13.** When your skin is exposed to ultraviolet rays, melanin production increases and your skin becomes darker. Lighter skin tones have less protection from the Sun. Such skin burns more easily and may be more susceptible to skin cancer.

Other Skin Layers The **dermis** is the layer of cells directly below the epidermis. This layer is thicker than the epidermis and contains many blood vessels, nerves, muscles, oil and sweat glands, and other structures. Below the dermis is a fatty region that insulates the body. This is where much of the fat is deposited when a person gains weight.

Skin Functions

Your skin is not only the largest organ of your body, it also carries out several major functions, including protection, sensory response, formation of vitamin D, regulation of body temperature, and ridding the body of wastes. The most important function of the skin is protection. The skin forms a protective covering over the body that prevents physical and chemical injury. Some bacteria and other disease-causing organisms cannot pass through the skin as long as it is unbroken. Glands in the skin secrete fluids that can damage or destroy some bacteria. The skin also slows down water loss from body tissues.

Specialized nerve cells in the skin detect and relay information to the brain, making the skin a sensory organ, too. Because of these cells, you are able to sense the softness of a cat, the sharpness of a pin, or the heat of a frying pan.

Mountain Climber
Research the effects of ultraviolet radiation on skin. Mountain climbers risk becoming severely sunburned even in freezing temperatures due to increased ultraviolet (UV) radiation. Research other careers that increase your risk of sunburn. Record your answers in your Science Journal.

Figure 13 Melanin gives skin and eyes their color. The more melanin that is present, the darker the color is. This pigment provides protection from damage caused by harmful UV rays.

INTEGRATE Career

Mountain Climber At higher altitudes the atmosphere is thinner and fewer of the Sun's ultraviolet rays are blocked. Therefore, the skin is exposed to more harmful radiation.

Research Have students name a variety of careers that have an increased risk of sunburn. Ask students what people in these careers can do to reduce their risk of sunburn.

Use an Analogy

Human Body's Thermostat The hypothalamus in the brain acts like a thermostat on a furnace. A furnace's thermostat senses the temperature of the air and turns the furnace on and off to maintain a constant temperature in a home. The hypothalamus receives temperature readings from the skin and relays messages to body parts to maintain a constant temperature.

Activity

Animal Thermoregulation Have students find out how various animals thermoregulate (maintain or regulate their body temperature). Students might investigate dogs panting, elephants fanning ears, and desert lizards escaping into burrows.

Quick Demo

Layers of Skin

Materials glass slide of human skin, microscope

Estimated Time 10 minutes

Procedure Have students look at a slide of human skin to get an idea of the appearance of cells in the different layers and the thickness of the different layers.

Teacher FYI

Losing Epidermis Dandruff flakes are batches of old epidermal cells that are being shed from the surface of the scalp. Batches of the dead cells may harbor bacteria. Scratching the scalp accelerates the formation of new cells to replace the cells that are flaking away.

Differentiated Instruction

Learning Disabled Have students pat a wet cotton ball onto their wrists. Then have them gently blow on the wet surface. The evaporation removes body heat. Relate this experience to the evaporation of perspiration from the skin during hot weather. L1

Purpose to observe water evaporation from skin `L1` `ELL` `LS`
Kinesthetic

Materials clear-plastic bag, tape, magnifying lens

Teaching Strategy Use tape on a roll, rather than from a dispenser. It will be easier for students to manage with one hand.

Safety Precautions Caution students not to wrap the tape too tightly. To prevent skin injury when removing the tape, tape only the bag, not the skin.

Analysis

1. water; from the skin
2. Evaporation of water from the skin cools the skin and helps the body maintain a constant temperature.

Assessment

Performance Have students predict the relative amounts of sweat that would accumulate in the bag under a variety of conditions. Have them design experiments to test their predictions. Use **Performance Assessment in the Science Classroom,** p. 95. `L1`

✓ **Reading Check**

Answer to regulate body temperature and excrete wastes

Discussion

Environmental Sensor How would humans receive information about environmental conditions if they did not have skin? Possible answer: They would have to have other tissues or organs for sensing environmental conditions in order to survive. `L2`

Figure 14 Normal human body temperature is about 37°C. Temperature varies throughout the day. The highest body temperature is reached at about 11 A.M. and the lowest at around 4 A.M. At 43°C (109.5°F) internal bleeding results, causing death.

Heart failure results, causing death
26.4 °C 35.6 36.7 37 37.8 38.9 40
79.5 °F 96 98 98.6 100 102 104

Normal range

Difficult exercise

Cold weather, early morning sleep

Excitement; latter half of menstrual cycle; approximately 37°C is normal for some active adults and children

Recognizing Why You Sweat

Procedure
1. Examine the epidermis and the pores of your skin using a **magnifying lens.**
2. Place a **clear-plastic sandwich bag** on your hand. Use tape to seal the bag around your wrist. **WARNING:** *Do not wrap the tape too tightly.*
3. Quietly study your **text** for 10 min, then look at your hand. Remove the bag.
4. Describe what happened to your hand while it was inside the bag.

Analysis
1. Identify what formed inside the bag. Where did this substance come from?
2. Why does this substance form even when you are not active?

Vitamin D Formation Another important function of skin is the formation of vitamin D. Small amounts of this vitamin are produced in the presence of ultraviolet light from a fatlike molecule in your epidermis. Vitamin D is essential for good health because it helps your body absorb calcium into your blood from food in your digestive tract.

Heat and Waste Exchange Humans can withstand a limited range of body temperatures, as shown in **Figure 14.** Your skin plays an important role in regulating your body temperature. Blood vessels in the skin can help release or hold heat. If the blood vessels expand, or dilate, blood flow increases and heat is released. In contrast, less heat is released when the blood vessels constrict. Think of yourself after running—are you flushed red or pale and shivering?

The adult human dermis has about 3 million sweat glands. These glands help regulate the body's temperature and excrete wastes. When the blood vessels dilate, pores open in the skin that lead to the sweat glands. Perspiration, or sweat, moves out onto the skin. Heat transfers from the body to the sweat on the skin. Eventually, this sweat evaporates, removing the heat and cooling the skin. This system eliminates excess heat produced by muscle contractions.

✓ **Reading Check** *What are two functions of sweat glands?*

As your cells use nutrients for energy, they produce wastes. Such wastes, if not removed from your body, can act as poisons. In addition to helping regulate your body's temperature, sweat glands release water, salt, and other waste products. If too much water and salt are released by sweating during periods of extreme heat or physical exertion, you might feel light-headed or may even faint.

Visual Learning

Figure 14 Have students practice interpreting scientific illustrations by studying this graph and writing a paragraph rephrasing the information it contains. `L2` `LS` **Linguistic and Visual-Spatial** `P`

✓ **Active Reading**

Synthesis Journal In this strategy, each student reflects on a project, a paper, or a performance of his or her experience and plans a personal application. Have each student divide a piece of paper into three sections and label them *What I did, What I learned,* and *How I can use it.* Have students use this strategy for the MiniLAB on this page. `L2`

Skin Injuries and Repair

Your skin often is bruised, scratched, burned, ripped, and exposed to harsh conditions like cold and dry air. In response, the skin produces new cells in its epidermis and repairs tears in the dermis. When the skin is injured, disease-causing organisms can enter the body rapidly. An infection often results.

Bruises Bruises are common, everyday events. Playing sports or working around your house often results in minor injuries. What is a bruise and how does your body repair it?

When you have a bruise, your skin is not broken but the tiny blood vessels underneath the skin have burst. Red blood cells from these broken blood vessels leak into the surrounding tissue. These blood cells then break down, releasing a chemical called hemoglobin. The hemoglobin gradually breaks down into its components, called pigments. The color of these pigments causes the bruised area to turn shades of blue, red, and purple, as shown in **Figure 15.** Swelling also may occur. As the injury heals, the bruise eventually turns yellow as the pigment in the red blood cells is broken down even more and reenters the bloodstream. After all of the pigment is absorbed into the bloodstream, the bruise disappears and the skin looks normal again.

Reading Check *What is the source of the yellow color of a bruise that is healing?*

Cuts Any tear in the skin is called a cut. Blood flows out of the cut until a clot forms over it. A scab then forms, preventing bacteria from entering the body. Cells in the surrounding blood vessels fight infection while the skin cells beneath the scab grow to fill the gap in the skin. In time, the scab falls off, leaving the new skin behind. If the cut is large enough, a scar may develop because of the large amounts of thick tissue fibers that form.

The body generally can repair bruises and small cuts. What happens when severe burns, some diseases, and surgeries result in injury to large areas of skin? Sometimes, not enough skin cells are left that can divide to replace this lost layer. If not treated, this can lead to rapid water loss from skin and muscle tissues, leading to infection and possible death. Skin grafts can prevent such problems. What are skin grafts?

Acidic Skin Oil and sweat glands in your skin cause the skin to be acidic. With a pH between 3 and 5, the growth of potential disease-causing microorganisms on your skin is reduced. What does pH mean? What common substances around your home have a pH value similar to that of your skin? Research to find these answers and then record them in your Science Journal.

Figure 15 Bruising occurs when capillaries and other tiny blood vessels beneath the skin burst.

Acidic Skin pH is a symbol for the measure of acidity or alkalinity of a solution. Substances with pH similar to that of your skin are apples, bananas, cherries, oranges, grapes, and tomatoes.

Reading Check

Answer the breakdown of pigment in red blood cells

Inquiry Lab

Protective Oils

Purpose to explore and observe what happens to your skin when its oil-rich protective film that locks moisture inside the skin and prevents bacteria and other infections is removed

Possible Materials dish soap, moisturizing hand soap, rubbing alcohol, baby oil, dye, non-latex gloves

Estimated Time 1 class session

Teaching Strategies

• Students can wash one hand with dish soap (while wearing a glove on the other hand) and wash the other hand with a moisturizing soap.

• Students can observe what happens when baby oil is applied to the back of one hand, while rubbing alcohol is applied to the back of the other hand.

• Students can predict what happens when a dye is applied to the hand that was treated with baby oil, versus the hand that was treated with rubbing alcohol

• Allow students to explore other questions that arise.

For additional inquiry activities, see *Science Inquiry Labs.*

Differentiated Instruction

Challenge Have students do research to find out about the use of artificial skin for burn victims. Have them write a report about the properties of the artificial skin that helps the patient heal. Artificial skin is a combination of human skin cells and biodegradable polymers. Currently used in treatment of severe burns, artificial skin provides an interactive bandage that covers the wound until a real skin graft can be grown. L3

Teacher FYI

Skin Allergies Contact with certain plants such as poison ivy, poison oak, and poison sumac may produce an inflammation of the skin due to an allergic reaction to the plants. The skin becomes red and itchy, and small blisters develop. Scratching the affected area will cause the blisters to open and may allow infections to develop.

Figure 16 A cancerous growth was removed from the nose of a 69-year-old woman. A piece of skin removed from her scalp was grafted onto her nose to replace the lost skin (top). The skin graft is healing after only one month (bottom).

Skin Grafts Pieces of skin that are cut from one part of a person's body and then moved to the injured or burned area where there is no skin are called skin grafts. This skin graft is kept alive by nearby blood vessels and soon becomes part of the surrounding skin. Successful skin grafts, shown in **Figure 16,** must be taken from the victim's own body or possibly an identical twin. Skin transplants from other sources are rejected in about three weeks.

What can be done for severe burn victims who have little healthy skin left? Since the 1880s, doctors have used the skin from dead humans, called cadavers, to treat such burns temporarily. However, the body usually rejects this skin, so it must be replaced continually until the burn heals.

A recent advancement in skin repair uses temporary grafts from cadavers to prevent immediate infections, while scientists grow large sheets of epidermis from small pieces of the burn victim's healthy skin. After 19 to 21 days, the cadaver skin patch is removed and the new epidermis is applied. With new technologies, severe cases of skin loss or damage that cannot be repaired may no longer be fatal.

section 3 review

Summary

Skin Structures
- The epidermis is the thinnest, outermost layer of skin.
- The dermis is the thick layer below the epidermis. It contains blood vessels, nerves, muscles, oil, and sweat glands.
- Melanin is a pigment that protects your skin and gives it color.

Skin Functions
- Your skin provides protection, and eliminates body wastes.

Skin Injuries and Repair
- A bruise is caused by tiny broken blood vessels underneath the skin.
- When you cut your skin, blood flows out of the cut until a clot forms, causing a scab to protect against bacteria.
- Skin grafts can be made from a cadaver or a victim's healthy skin to repair the epidermis.

Self Check

1. **Compare and contrast** the epidermis and dermis.
2. **List** five of the major functions of the body's largest organ, skin.
3. **Explain** how skin helps prevent disease in the body.
4. **Describe** one way in which doctors are able to repair severe skin damage from burns, injuries, or surgeries.
5. **Think Critically** Why is a person who has been severely burned in danger of dying from loss of water?

Applying Math

6. **Solve One-Step Equations** The skin of eyelids is about 0.5 mm thick. On the soles of your feet, skin is up to 0.4 cm thick. How many times thicker is the skin on the soles of your feet compared to your eyelids?
7. **Calculate** The outermost layers of your skin are replaced every 27 days. How many times per year are your outermost layers of skin replaced?

 Science Online bookd.msscience.com/self_check_quiz

section 3 review

1. epidermis—thin outer layer of the skin, contains melanin; dermis—under the epidermis, is thicker, contains many blood vessels, nerves, and sweat glands
2. protects, regulates body temperature, excretes wastes, serves as sensory organ, forms vitamin D
3. As long as it is unbroken, skin prevents pathogens from entering the body. Glands in the skin secrete fluids that destroy bacteria.
4. A graft of skin from another part of the person's body is moved to the injured area. The graft eventually becomes part of the surrounding skin.
5. The person has lost the skin's protection from loss of water.
6. 8 times
7. 13.5 times

Measuring Skin Surface

Skin covers the entire surface of your body and is your body's largest organ. Skin cells make up a layer of skin about 2 mm thick. These cells are continually lost and re-formed. Skin cells are shed daily at a rate of an average of 50,000 cells per minute. In one year, humans lose about 2 kg of skin and hair. How big is this organ? Find the surface area of human skin.

◉ *Real-World Question*

How much skin covers your body?

Goal
■ **Estimate** the surface area of skin that covers the body of a middle-school student.

Materials
10 large sheets   tape
   of newspaper   meterstick or ruler
scissors

Safety Precautions

◉ *Procedure*

1. Form groups of three or four, either all female or all male. Select one person from your group to measure the surface area of his or her skin.

2. **Estimate** how much skin covers the average student in your classroom. In your Science Journal, record your estimation.

3. Wrap newspaper snugly around each part of your classmate's body. Overlap sheets of paper and use tape to secure them. Cover entire hands and feet. Small body parts, such as fingers and toes, do not need to be wrapped individually.
   WARNING: *Do not cover face. May cause suffocation.*

4. After your classmate is completely covered with paper, carefully cut the newspaper off his or her body. **WARNING:** *Do not cut any clothing or skin.*

5. Lay all of the overlapping sheets of newspaper on the floor. Using scissors and more tape, cut and piece the paper suit together to form a rectangle.

6. Using a meterstick, measure the length and width of the resulting rectangle. Multiply these two measurements for an estimate of the surface area of your classmate's skin.

◉ *Conclude and Apply*

1. Was your estimation correct? Explain.

2. How accurate are your measurements of your classmate's skin surface area? How could your measurements be improved?

3. **Calculate** the skin's volume using 2 mm as the average skin thickness and your calculated surface area from this lab.

Make a table of all data. Find the average area for male groups and then for female groups. Discuss the differences. **For more help, refer to the** Math Skill Handbook.

◉ **Real-World Question**

Purpose Students will estimate the surface area of skin covering a middle school student. L2

Process Skills collect data, predict, measure in SI, analyze results, draw conclusions

Time Required 40 minutes

Safety Precautions Students should use care when cutting the newspaper model off of the student.

◉ **Procedure**

Teaching Strategy Provide printless paper if possible, so the ink does not rub off onto students.

◉ **Conclude and Apply**

1. Answers will vary.
2. Measurements are estimates only. Improvement suggestions will vary.
3. Answers will vary.

☑ **Assessment**

Performance Today scientists are researching methods for producing synthetic skin. This is especially important for burn victims that lose large portions of their skin. Research this topic and report to your class the results of your search. Use **Performance Assessment in the Science Classroom**, p. 143. L2

Communicating
Your Data

Students may want to use a spreadsheet program to record their results.

Real-World Question

Purpose

Internet Students use Internet sites that can be accessed through bookd.msscience.com/internet_lab.

Students can post their findings on the site and get information from other schools around the country about similar skeletal structures among humans and other mammals. L2

Process Skills collect data, identify, write, compare and contrast, infer, describe.

Time Required two days

Make a Plan

Preparation

Internet To run through the steps that the students will follow, visit bookd.msscience.com/internet_lab.

Non-Internet Sources Collect books about mammals. Find realistic models of different mammals to display in the classroom.

Use the Internet

Similar Skeletons

Goals

- **Identify** a skeletal structure in the human body.
- **Write** a list of mammals with which you are familiar.
- **Compare** the identified human skeletal structure to a skeletal structure in each of the mammals.
- **Determine** if the mammal skeletal structure that you selected is similar to the human skeletal structure you identified.
- **Describe** how the mammal skeletal structure is similar to or different from the skeletal structure in a human.

Data Source

Science Online

Visit bookd.msscience.com/internet_lab for Web links to more information about skeletal structures, and for data collected by other students.

Real-World Question

Humans and other mammals share many similar characteristics, including similar skeletal structures. Think about all the different types of mammals you have seen or read about. Tigers, dogs, and household cats are meat-eating mammals. Whales and dolphins live in water. Primates, which include gorillas, chimpanzees, and humans, can walk on two legs. Mammals live in different environments, eat different types of food, and even look different, but they all have hair, possess the ability to maintain fairly constant body temperatures, and have similar skeletal structures. Which skeletal structures are similar among humans and other mammals? How many bones do you have in your hand? What types of bones are they? Do other mammals have similar skeletal structures? Form a hypothesis about the skeletal structures that humans and other mammals have in common.

Make a Plan

1. Choose a specific part of the human skeletal structure to study, such as your hand, foot, skull, leg, or arm.

Alternative Inquiry Lab

Tail Wagging Make this Lab an Inquiry Lab by building on the experience. Encourage your students to use what they have learned to explain why some mammal skeletons have tails, and others do not. Ask students to do research to find out if human skeletons exhibit any evidence of a tail. Have student groups each choose one question to explore.

2. **List** four to six different mammals.

3. Do these mammals possess skeletal structures similar to the human skeleton? Remember, the mammals' skeletons can be similar to that of the human, but the structures can have different functions.

4. **Compare and contrast** the mammal and human skeletal structures. Are the types of bone similar? Is the number of bones the same? Where are these structures located?

● Follow Your Plan

1. Make sure your teacher approves your plan before you start.

2. Visit the link below to post your data.

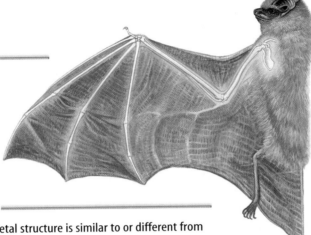

● Analyze Your Data

1. **Describe** how each mammal's skeletal structure is similar to or different from the human skeletal structure you chose.

2. **Record** your data in the data table provided on the Web site.

● Conclude and Apply

1. Visit the link below and compare your data to that of other students. Do other students agree with your conclusions?

2. Do the structures studied have similar functions in the human and the mammals you researched?

Communicating Your Data

Find this lab using the link below. Post your data in the table provided. Compare your data with that posted by other students.

Science Online

bookd.msscience.com/internet_lab

LAB D ◆ 27

● Follow Your Plan

Teaching Strategies

- Have students focus on similar features among humans and mammals. Encourage them to think about human hands, feet, legs, and arms. L2

- Have students determine which mammals have similar limb structures to humans.

Troubleshooting While students can compare mammal skeletal structure to skeletal structure for other non-mammals, be sure to have students compare human skeletal structures to other mammals to draw comparisons.

● Analyze Your Data

1. Answers will vary. Have students compare specific human bones to specific mammal bones to determine whether they are alike or different.

2. Answers will vary. Students should describe how a particular skeletal structure, such as a foot, is similar between a human and a mammal. To do this, they might describe the function of that structure in humans and for that mammal.

● Conclude and Apply

Answers will be individualized and often based on the student's opinion of his or her research. Look for depth and quality of research performed.

✓ Assessment

Content Have students make drawings of the skeletal structures they investigated. Make separate drawings for the human structure and the mammal's structure. Have them label the bones and other physical features in both drawings. Use **Performance Assessment in the Science Classroom**, p. 127. L2

Communicating Your Data

Have students use a word processing program to create a two-column table describing how the human structure and the mammal structure are similar or different. Include descriptions of the labels that are featured on students' drawings of skeletal structures. L2

Content Background

Improving the look, function, and comfort of artificial body parts, or prostheses, is a constant concern for the scientists who develop them. Innovations include myoelectric arms, which are powered by batteries and remaining arm muscles. Bionics connect a prosthesis with the brain through a combination of computer sensors in the prosthesis and nerve cells in the remainder of the limb. Bionics allow limited reactions to some stimuli. Special limbs, such as a sprinting leg, have also been developed for individuals who have lost a limb and wish to participate in sports.

Discussion

Handy Joints Imagine the steps involved with selecting your lunch in the school cafeteria, paying for it, and eating it. How would artificial fingers without flexible joints make these tasks difficult? How would a flexible finger help? Possible answers: Difficulty in picking up trays and food, difficulty holding and sorting money and holding eating utensils. In every case, flexibility in the finger would make these tasks easier.

Activity

Prostheses Organize the class into several groups. Each group should research innovations and uses of prostheses in a certain time period: ancient times, the 1800s, 1900–1950, 1950–present, the future. Each group should report their findings to the class.

First Aid Dolls

A fashion doll is doing her part for medical science! It turns out that the plastic joints that make it possible for one type of doll's legs to bend make good joints in prosthetic (artificial) fingers for humans.

Jane Bahor (photo at right) works at Duke University Medical Center in Durham, North Carolina. She makes lifelike body parts for people who have lost legs, arms, or fingers. A few years ago, she met a patient named Jennifer Jordan, an engineering student who'd lost a finger. The artificial finger that Bahor made looked real, but it couldn't bend. She and Jordan began to discuss the problem.

"If only the finger could bend like a doll's legs bend," said Bahor. "It would be so much more useful to you!"

Jordan's eyes lit up. "That's it!" Jordan said. The engineer went home and borrowed one of her sister's dolls. Returning with it to Bahor's office, she and Bahor did "surgery." They operated on the fashion doll's legs and removed the knee joints from their vinyl casings.

"It turns out that the doll's knee joints flexed the same way that human finger joints do," says Bahor. "We could see that using these joints would allow patients more use and flexibility with their 'new' fingers."

Holding On

The new, fake, flexible fingers can bend in the same way that a doll's legs bend. A person can use his or her other hand to bend and straighten the joint. When the joint bends, it makes a sound similar to a cracking knuckle.

Being able to bend prosthetic fingers allows wearers to hold a pen, pick up a cup, or grab a steering wheel. These are tasks that were impossible before the plastic knee joints were implanted in the artificial fingers. "We've even figured out how to insert three joints in each finger, so that now its wearer can almost make a fist," adds Bahor. Just like the doll's legs, the prosthetic fingers stay bent until the wearer straightens them.

Bahor removes a knee joint from a doll. The joint will soon be in a human's prosthetic finger!

Invent Choose a "problem" you can solve. Use what Bahor calls "commonly found materials" to solve the problem. Then make a model or a drawing of the problem-solving device.

Science Online
For more information, visit bookd.msscience.com/oops

Invent Direct students to solve a problem that will impact their everyday lives—something that is important to them. Display everyday items that might be used to solve problems and could provide ideas to students. Instruct students that they are not limited to using display items.

Resources for Teachers and Students

"Rebuilding the Body," by Alexander Newman, *National Geographic World*, February 2000

"Lending a Helping Leg," by Diane Martindale, *Scientific American*, May 2000

"Barbie Lends a Leg," by Sharon Guynup, *Science World*, Sept. 2000

Reviewing Main Ideas

Section 1 The Skeletal System

1. Bones are living structures that protect, support, make blood, store minerals, and provide for muscle attachment.

2. The skull and pelvic joints in adults do not move and are classified as immovable.

3. Movable joints move freely, and include pivot, hinge, ball-and-socket, and gliding joints.

Section 2 The Muscular System

1. Skeletal muscle is voluntary and moves bones. Smooth muscle is involuntary and controls movement of internal organs. Cardiac muscle is involuntary and located only in the heart.

2. Muscles contract—they pull, not push, to move body parts.

3. Skeletal muscles work in pairs—when one contracts, the other relaxes.

Section 3 The Skin

1. The epidermis has dead cells on its surface. Melanin is produced in the epidermis. Cells at the base of the epidermis produce new skin cells. The dermis is the inner layer where nerves, sweat and oil glands, and blood vessels are located.

2. The functions of skin include protection, reduction of water loss, production of vitamin D, and maintenance of body temperature.

3. Glands in the epidermis produce substances that destroy bacteria.

4. Severe damage to skin, including injuries and burns, can lead to infection and death if it is not treated.

Visualizing Main Ideas

Copy and complete the following concept map on body movement.

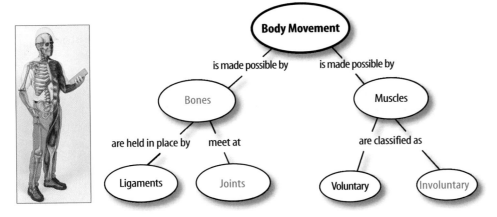

Body Movement — is made possible by — Bones — are held in place by — Ligaments / meet at — Joints

Body Movement — is made possible by — Muscles — are classified as — Voluntary / Involuntary

Science Online bookd.msscience.com/interactive_tutor

CHAPTER STUDY GUIDE **D ◆ 29**

Reviewing Main Ideas

Summary statements can be used by students to review the major concepts of the chapter.

Visualizing Main Ideas

See student page.

Science Online

Visit bookd.msscience.com
/self_check_quiz
/interactive_tutor
/vocabulary_puzzlemaker
/chapter_review
/standardized_test
/field_guide

Assessment Transparency

For additional assessment questions, use the *Assessment Transparency* located in the transparency book.

Assessment

Assessment Transparency — Structure and Movement

Directions: *Carefully review the tables and answer the following questions.*

Results of Strength Test

Name	Age	Push-ups
Mr. Vincent	35	23
Mr. Steinberg	68	23
Mr. Johnson	22	16

Results of Strength Test Age (years)

Rank	20–29	30–39	40–49	50–59	60 +
High	45 +	35 +	30 +	25 +	20 +
Average	35–44	25–34	20–29	15–24	10–19
Below average	20–34	15–24	12–19	8–14	5–9
Low	0–19	0–14	0–11	0–7	0–4

1. According to the results of this experiment, Mr. Johnson has a ranking of ____.
   A high   C below average
   B average   D low

2. A reasonable hypothesis based on Table B is that when we age our muscles ____.
   F become stronger   H become weaker
   G become larger   J change color

Identifying Misconceptions

Assess

Procedure Group students in pairs. Have one student carefully strike the knee of the second student. Have students note the strength of the reaction as measured by the height of the jerk. Then tell one student of the pair to lock his or her right and left hands together and pull. Have the other student strike the other's knee and measure the strength of the reflex. The strength of the reflex should be greater this time.

Expected Outcome Students should understand the interaction of the muscular system with other systems and be able to cite examples of other interactions.

Using Vocabulary

1. periosteum
2. skeletal system
3. epidermis
4. tendons
5. cardiac muscle
6. ligaments
7. muscles
8. voluntary muscles

Checking Concepts

9. A	13. D	17. B
10. D	14. B	18. C
11. A	15. C	19. D
12. A	16. C	

Thinking Critically

20. If there is not enough exposure to sunlight, not enough vitamin D is produced.
21. the severity and size of the burn and the general health of the patient

Using Vocabulary

cardiac muscle p. 17	muscle p. 14
cartilage p. 10	periosteum p. 9
dermis p. 21	skeletal muscle p. 17
epidermis p. 20	skeletal system p. 8
involuntary muscle p. 15	smooth muscle p. 17
joint p. 11	tendon p. 17
ligament p. 11	voluntary muscle p. 15
melanin p. 21	

Match the definitions with the correct vocabulary word.

1. tough outer covering of bone
2. internal framework of the body
3. outer layer of skin
4. thick band of tissue that attaches muscle to a bone
5. muscle found only in the heart
6. a tough band of tissue that holds two bones together
7. organ that can relax and contract to aid in the movement of the body
8. a muscle that you control

Checking Concepts

Choose the word or phrase that best answers the question.

9. Which of the following is the most solid form of bone?
   A) compact   C) spongy
   B) periosteum   D) marrow

10. Where are blood cells made?
    A) compact bone   C) cartilage
    B) periosteum   D) marrow

11. Where are minerals stored?
    A) bone   C) muscle
    B) skin   D) blood

12. What are the ends of bones covered with?
    A) cartilage   C) ligaments
    B) tendons   D) muscle

13. Where are immovable joints found in the human body?
    A) at the elbow   C) in the wrist
    B) at the neck   D) in the skull

14. What kind of joints are the knees, toes, and fingers?
    A) pivot   C) gliding
    B) hinge   D) ball and socket

15. Which vitamin is made in the skin?
    A) A   C) D
    B) B   D) K

16. Where are dead skin cells found?
    A) dermis   C) epidermis
    B) marrow   D) periosteum

17. Which of the following is found in bone?
    A) iron   C) vitamin D
    B) calcium   D) vitamin K

18. Which of the following structures helps retain fluids in the body?
    A) bone   C) skin
    B) muscle   D) a joint

Use the illustration below to answer question 19.

19. Where would this type of muscle tissue be found in your body?
    A) heart   C) stomach
    B) esophagus   D) leg

  Science Online bookd.msscience.com/vocabulary_puzzlemaker

Use the ExamView® Pro Testmaker CD-ROM to:

- create multiple versions of tests
- create modified tests with one mouse click for inclusion students
- edit existing questions and add your own questions
- build tests aligned with state standards using built-in State Curriculum Tags
- change English tests to Spanish with one mouse click and vice versa

Thinking Critically

20. **Explain** why skin might not be able to produce enough vitamin D.

21. **List** what factors a doctor might consider before choosing a method of skin repair for a severe burn victim.

22. **Explain** what a lack of calcium would do to bones.

23. **Concept Map** Copy and complete the following concept map that describes the types and functions of bone cells.

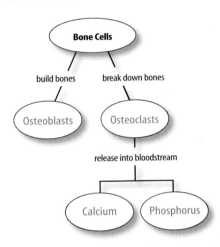

24. **Name** the function of your lower lip's skin that changes when a dentist gives you novocaine before filling a bottom tooth. Why?

25. **Draw Conclusions** The joints in the skull of a newborn baby are flexible, but those of a teenager have fused together and are immovable. Conclude why the infant's skull joints are flexible.

26. **Predict** what would happen if a person's sweat glands didn't produce sweat.

27. **Compare and contrast** the functions of ligaments and tendons.

 Science Online bookd.msscience.com/chapter_review

28. **Form a Hypothesis** Your body has about 3 million sweat glands. Make a hypothesis about where these sweat glands are on your body. Are they distributed evenly throughout your body?

Performance Activities

29. **Display** Research the differences among first-, second-, and third-degree burns. A local hospital's burn unit or a fire department are possible sources of information about burns. Display pictures of each type of burn and descriptions of treatments on a three-sided, free-standing poster.

Applying Math

30. **Bone Volume** Estimate the volume of a hand bone that is 7 cm long and is 1.5 cm in diameter.

Use the graph below to answer question 31.

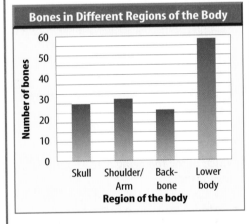

Bones in Different Regions of the Body

31. **Bone Quantity** The total number of bones in the human body is 206. Approximately what percentage of bones is located in the backbone?
    A) 2%   C) 50%
    B) 12%   D) 75%

Thinking Critically

22. Bones lacking calcium become too flexible and misshapen. They also break more easily.

23. See student page.

24. Novocaine numbs the nerves so your skin can no longer sense stimuli such as pressure or pain. Novocaine numbs nerves in the dermis.

25. Accept all reasonable answers. Flexible joints are thought to be helpful during the birthing process.

26. The person would not be able to maintain a constant body temperature or release certain wastes through the skin.

27. Ligaments hold bones in place at joints. Tendons attach muscle to bones.

28. Possible answer: Sweat glands are not evenly distributed on the skin. This is known because when a person exercises, more sweat is found in some areas (face, underarms) than others.

Performance Activities

29. First-degree burns involve only the epidermis; second-degree burns involve the epidermis and dermis; and third-degree burns extend beyond the dermis into the muscle and bone. **Use Performance Assessment in the Science Classroom,** p. 145.

Applying Math

National Math Standards
1, 5
30. 12.4cm³
31. B

FAST FILE

Answer Sheet A practice answer sheet can be found at bookd.msscience.com/answer_sheet.

SAMPLE

Part 1 | Multiple Choice

1. C
2. C
3. B
4. D
5. A
6. C
7. C
8. B
9. B

Part 1 | Multiple Choice

Record your answers on the answer sheet provided by your teacher or on a sheet of paper.

1. Which type of muscle tends to contract quickly and tire more easily?
   A. cardiac muscle   C. skeletal muscle
   B. bladder   D. smooth muscle

Use the table below to answer questions 2 and 3.

Number of Bicycle Deaths per Year		
Year	Male	Female
1996	654	107
1997	712	99
1998	658	99
1999	656	94
2000	605	76

Data from Insurance Institute for Highway Safety

2. If 99% of the people who die in bicycle accidents were not wearing helmets, to the nearest whole number, how many people who died in 1998 were wearing bicycle helmets?
   A. 7   C. 8
   B. 6   D. 9

3. Which year had the greatest total number of bicycle deaths?
   A. 1996   C. 1998
   B. 1997   D. 1999

4. Which of the following is NOT released by sweat glands?
   A. water   C. waste products
   B. salt   D. oil

Test-Taking Tip

Ease Nervousness Stay calm during the test. If you feel yourself getting nervous, close your eyes and take five slow, deep breaths.

Use the illustration below to answer questions 5 and 6.

Ball-and-socket joint   Pivot joint

Gliding joint   Hinge joint

5. Which type of joint do your elbows have?
   A. hinge   C. ball-and-socket
   B. gliding   D. pivot

6. Which type of joint allows your legs and arms to swing in almost any direction?
   A. hinge   C. ball-and-socket
   B. gliding   D. pivot

7. What is the name of the pigment that gives your skin color?
   A. hemoglobin   C. melanin
   B. keratin   D. calcium

8. What does the periosteum do?
   A. connects bones together
   B. covers the surface of bones
   C. produces energy
   D. makes vitamin D

9. Which type of muscle is found in the intestines?
   A. skeletal muscle
   B. smooth muscle
   C. cardiac muscle
   D. tendon

32 ◆ D STANDARDIZED TEST PRACTICE

Part 2 | Short Response/Grid In

10. $300 - 206 = 94$

11. $1/7 = 14\%$

12. Voluntary muscles can be consciously controlled. Involuntary muscles are muscles that cannot be controlled consciously.

13. first-class lever

14. The fulcrum is between the effort force and the load.

15. Heat produced by muscle contractions helps to keep body temperature constant.

16. When the skin is exposed to ultraviolet rays, melanin production increases and the skin becomes darker

Part 2 | Short Response/Grid In

Record your answers on the answer sheet provided by your teacher or on a sheet of paper.

10. At birth, your skeleton had approximately 300 bones. As you developed, some bones fused together. Now you have 206 bones. How many fewer bones do you have now?

11. One in seven people in the United States suffers from arthritis. Calculate the percentage of people that suffer from arthritis.

12. Explain the difference between voluntary and involuntary muscles.

Use the illustration below to answer questions 13 and 14.

13. What type of lever is shown in the photo?

14. Where is the fulcrum?

15. How do muscles help maintain body temperature?

16. Explain what happens when your skin is exposed to ultraviolet rays.

Part 3 | Open Ended

Record your answers on a sheet of paper.

17. Compare and contrast compact and spongy bone.

18. Explain how bone cells help maintain homeostasis.

19. Describe the changes that occur in muscles that do a lot of work. Compare these muscles to the muscles of a person who only does inactive pastimes.

Use the illustration below to answer questions 20 and 21.

20. Identify the injury in the photograph. Describe the sequence of events from the time of injury until the injury disappears.

21. Contrast the injury in the photograph with a cut. Explain why a cut needs to be cleaned but the injury in the photograph does not.

22. What might happen to your body temperature if blood vessels in the skin did not contain smooth muscle?

into the surrounding tissue. These blood cells break down and release hemoglobin. As the hemoglobin gradually breaks down into its component pigments, the color of the bruise changes from blue to red to purple to yellow. Finally the pigment reenters the bloodstream, the bruise disappears, and the skin looks normal again.

20. In a bruise, the skin is not broken, only tiny blood vessels underneath the skin have burst. In a cut, the skin is torn. Blood flows out until a clot forms. Then a scab covers the cut, preventing bacteria from entering the injury. A cut must be cleaned because the skin surface is broken and bacteria could enter the wound. Because the skin is not broken in a bruise, bacteria cannot enter through the skin injury.

21. Blood vessels in the skin can help release or hold heat. Without smooth muscle in the walls, the blood vessels could not change their diameter, that is, they could not constrict (muscle contracts) or dilate (muscle relaxes). When the blood vessels expand or dilate, blood flow increases and heat is released. When you are cold, blood vessels constrict and less heat is released.

Rubrics

For more help evaluating open-ended assessment questions, see the rubric on p. 10T.

Part 3 | Open Ended

17. Compact bone is located directly under the periosteum. Compact bone is a hard, strong layer of bone. Compact bones contain deposits of calcium and phosphate that make the bone hard. Bone cells and blood vessels are also found in this layer. Spongy bone is located toward the ends of long bones. It has many small, open spaces that make bones lightweight. Spongy bone contains marrow. Some marrow is fat. Red marrow makes blood cells.

18. Healthy bone is always being formed and re-formed. As bone is broken down by osteoclasts, calcium and phosphorus deposited in the bone are released into the bloodstream. This process maintains the correct levels of calcium and phosphorus in the blood. Calcium and phosphorus are necessary for the working of the body, including muscle movement.

19. This injury is a bruise. When the skin is bruised, tiny blood vessels underneath the skin have burst. Red blood cells from these vessels leak

Section/Objectives	Standards		Labs/Features
Chapter Opener	**National**	**State/Local**	**Launch Lab:** Model the Digestive Tract, p. 35
	See pp. 16T–17T for a Key to Standards.		**Foldables,** p. 35
Section 1 Nutrition 🕐 2 sessions 📦 1 block 1. **Distinguish** among the six classes of nutrients. 2. **Identify** the importance of each type of nutrient. 3. **Explain** the relationships between diet and health.	National Content Standards: UCP.1, UCP.2, A.1, A.2, B.3, C.1, C.3, C.5, F.1		**Science Online,** p. 38 **MiniLAB:** Comparing the Fat Content of Foods, p. 39 **Applying Science:** Is it unhealthy to snack between meals? p. 40 **Visualizing Vitamins,** p. 41 **Integrate Social Studies,** p. 43 **Lab:** Identifying Vitamin C Content, p. 46
Section 2 The Digestive System 🕐 3 sessions 📦 1.5 block 4. **Distinguish** the differences between mechanical digestion and chemical digestion. 5. **Identify** the organs of the digestive system and what takes place in each. 6. **Explain** how homeostasis is maintained in digestion.	National Content Standards: UCP.1, A.1, A.2, B.1, B.3, C.1, C.3, C.5, F.1, G.1, G.2		**Science Online,** p. 50 **MiniLAB:** Modeling Absorption in the Small Intestine, p. 52 **Integrate Environment,** p. 53 **Lab:** Particle Size and Absorption, p. 54 **Science and Society:** Eating Well, p. 56

Lab Materials	Reproducible Resources	Section Assessment	Technology
Launch Lab: index cards, marker, masking tape, meterstick	**Chapter FAST FILE Resources** Foldables Worksheet, p. 17 Directed Reading Overview, p. 19 Note-taking Worksheets, pp. 31–33	GLENCOE'S ASSESSMENT ADVANTAGE	Teacher**Works** includes: • Interactive Teacher Edition • Lesson Planner with calendar • Access to all program blacklines • Correlations to standards • Web links
MiniLAB: 3 potato chips, pretzels, peanuts; small cubes of fruits, cheese, vegetables, meat; brown grocery bag **Lab:** 4 test tubes, test-tube rack, masking tape, 13 wooden stirrers, graduated cylinder, 2% tincture of iodine, dropper, cornstarch, triple-beam balance, weighing paper, water, glass-marking pencil, 4 types of orange juice in dropper bottles	**Chapter FAST FILE Resources** Transparency Activity, p. 42 MiniLAB, p. 3 Enrichment, p. 29 Reinforcement, p. 27 Directed Reading, p. 20 Lab Worksheet, pp. 5–6 Lab Activity, pp. 9–11 Transparency Activity, pp. 45–46 **Cultural Diversity,** pp. 6, 23 **Mathematics Skill Activities,** p. 47 **Life Science Critical Thinking/ Problem Solving,** pp. 15, 16 **Performance Assessment in the Science Classroom,** p. 66	**Portfolio** Science Journal, p. 40 **Performance** MiniLAB, p. 39 Applying Science, p. 40 Applying Skills, p. 45 **Content** Section Review, p. 45	🔦 Section Focus Transparency 🔦 Teaching Transparency 💿 Virtual Labs CD-ROM 🎧 Guided Reading Audio Program 💿 Interactive Chalkboard CD-ROM 📼 Video Lab
MiniLAB: smooth cotton cloth (25 × 25 cm), cotton terry cloth (25 × 25 cm), bowl, water, measuring cup, 2 containers **Lab:** 3 beakers or jars, 3 thermometers, sugar granules, mortar and pestle, triple-beam balance, stirring rod, sugar cubes, weighing paper, warm water, stopwatch	**Chapter FAST FILE Resources** Transparency Activity, p. 43 MiniLAB, p. 4 Enrichment, p. 30 Reinforcement, p. 28 Directed Reading, pp. 21, 22 Lab Worksheet, pp. 7–8 Lab Activity, pp. 13–15 **Lab Management and Safety,** p. 52 **Home and Community Involvement,** p. 41	**Portfolio** Science Journal, p. 50 Reteach, p. 53 **Performance** MiniLAB, p. 52 Applying Skills, p. 53 **Content** Section Review, p. 53	🔦 Section Focus Transparency 💿 Virtual Labs CD-ROM 🎧 Guided Reading Audio Program 💿 Interactive Chalkboard CD-ROM

End of Chapter Assessment

GLENCOE'S ASSESSMENT ADVANTAGE

Blackline Masters	Technology	Professional Series
Chapter FAST FILE Resources Chapter Review, pp. 35–36 Chapter Tests, pp. 37–40 **Standardized Test Practice,** pp. 11–14	📼 MindJogger Videoquiz 💿 Virtual Labs CD-ROM 💿 ExamView® Pro Testmaker 💿 TeacherWorks CD-ROM 💿 Interactive Chalkboard CD-ROM	**Performance Assessment in the Science Classroom (PASC)**

Transparencies

Section Focus

SECTION 1 Section Focus Transparency — **A World of Food**

Immediate worldwide communication has not only enhanced our quality of life but also enriched our food choices. Colorful, tasty dishes from all over the world can supply your body with the nutrients and energy it needs.

1. Why is eating well-balanced meals important?
2. What foods might be added to the meals above to make them well-balanced?

L2

SECTION 2 Section Focus Transparency — **Pardon Me, but I Digest**

Cows eat quite often—a one-year-old steer may be given almost forty pounds of feed each day. On the other hand, it's not uncommon for a large snake to go more than a month without food. These animals have very different digestive processes to meet different energy needs.

1. In general, why do animals need to eat?
2. Why do you think a snake can go so long without food?

L2

This is a representation of key blackline masters available in the Teacher Classroom Resources. See Resource Manager boxes within the chapter for additional information.

Key to Teaching Strategies

The following designations will help you decide which activities are appropriate for your students.

L1 Level 1 activities should be appropriate for students with learning difficulties.

L2 Level 2 activities should be within the ability range of all students.

L3 Level 3 activities are designed for above-average students.

ELL ELL activities should be within the ability range of English-Language Learners.

COOP LEARN Cooperative Learning activities are designed for small group work.

LS Multiple Learning Styles logos, as described on page 12T, are used throughout to indicate strategies that address different learning styles.

P These strategies represent student products that can be placed into a best-work portfolio.

PBL Problem-Based Learning activities apply real-world situations to learning.

Assessment

Assessment Transparency — **Nutrients and Digestion**

Directions: *Carefully review the table and answer the following questions.*

Ideal Body Weight (kg)—Range for Men and Women

Height (m)	Ages 19–34	Ages 35 +
1.52	44–58	49–62
1.54	46–60	50–65
1.57	47–62	52–67
1.6	48–64	54–69
1.62	?	55–71
1.65	51–68	57–73
1.67	53–70	59–76
1.7	55–72	61–78

1. Based on the information in the table, which of the following should the ideal weight range be for somebody who is 1.62 m tall and 27 years old?
A 53–66   B 49–62   C 50–66   D 48–71
2. These data were collected by studying many different people. If everything remains the same, what would be a healthy weight for someone who is 1.7 m tall and 50 years old?
F 55   G 59   H 72   J 80
3. A reasonable hypothesis using the table is that when we are younger ___.
A our legs and arms weigh more
B we usually weigh more
C our weight never changes
D we usually weigh less

L2

Teaching

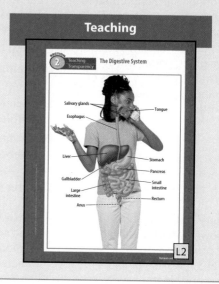

SECTION 2 Teaching Transparency — **The Digestive System**

Salivary glands, Tongue, Esophagus, Liver, Gallbladder, Large intestine, Anus, Stomach, Pancreas, Small intestine, Rectum

L2

Hands-on Activities

Student Text Lab Worksheet

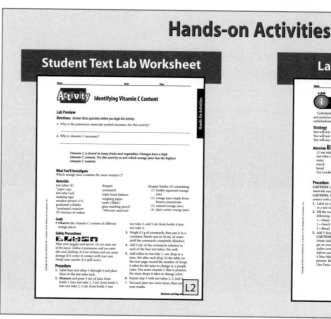

Activity — Identifying Vitamin C Content

Lab Preview

Directions: *Answer these questions before you begin the Activity.*

1. Why is the poisonous materials symbol necessary for this activity?

2. Why is vitamin C necessary?

Vitamin C is found in many fruits and vegetables. Oranges have a high vitamin C content. Try this activity to test which orange juice has the highest vitamin C content.

What You'll Investigate
Which orange juice contains the most vitamin C?

Materials
test tubes (4)
*paper cups
test-tube rack
masking tape
wooden stirrers (13)
*graduated cylinder
*graduated container
2% tincture of iodine

dropper
cornstarch
triple beam balance
weighing paper
water (50mL)
glass-marking pencil
*Alternate materials

dropper bottles (4) containing:
(1) freshly squeezed orange juice
(2) orange juice made from frozen concentrate
(3) canned orange juice
(4) dairy carton orange juice

Goals
• Observe the vitamin C content of different orange juices.

Safety Precautions
Wear your goggles and apron. Do not taste any of the juices. Iodine is poisonous and can stain skin and clothing. It is an irritant and can cause damage if it comes in contact with your eyes. Notify your teacher if a spill occurs.

Procedure
1. Label four test tubes 1 through 4 and place them in the test-tube rack.
2. Measure and pour 5 mL of juice from bottle 1 into test tube 1, 5 mL from bottle 2 into test tube 2, 5 mL from bottle 3 into

test tube 3, and 5 mL from bottle 4 into test tube 4.
3. Weigh 0.3 g of cornstarch, then put it in a container. Slowly mix in 50 mL of water until the cornstarch completely dissolves.
4. Add 5 mL of the cornstarch solution to each of the four test tubes. Stir well.
5. Add iodine to test tube 1, one drop at a time. Stir after each drop. In the table on the next page, record the number of drops it takes for the juice to change to a purple color. The more vitamin C that is present, the more drops it takes to change color.
6. Repeat step 5 with test tubes 2, 3, and 4.
7. Test each juice two more times, then average your results.

Nutrients and Digestion

L2

Laboratory Activities

LAB 1 Laboratory Activity — **Testing for Carbohydrates**

Carbohydrates provide energy for the body. Your body needs more carbohydrates than fats and proteins each day. Foods that contain starch and foods that contain sugar are sources of carbohydrates.

Strategy
You will test foods for starch by using iodine solution.
You will test foods for sugar by using sugar test tablets.
You will use your test results to determine which foods are sources of carbohydrates.

Materials
12 test tubes (18 × 150-mm)
test-tube rack
water
starch
bread
rice (cooked)

egg white (hard-boiled)
potato (cooked)
iodine in dropper bottle
labels
glucose
syrup

honey
milk
molasses
forceps
sugar test tablets

Procedure
CAUTION: *Do not taste, eat, or drink any materials used in the lab.*
CAUTION: *Inform your teacher if you come in contact with any chemicals.*
1. Label six test tubes 1 through 6. Place them in a test-tube rack.
2. Fill the test tubes to about 1 cm with the following:
   1—Water   4—Rice
   2—Starch   5—Egg White
   3—Bread   6—Potato
3. Add 3 drops of iodine to test tubes 1–6. CAUTION: *Iodine is poisonous. Do not inhale iodine fumes. Do not allow iodine to get on your hands. Wash immediately if iodine comes in contact with your skin. Inform your teacher. Examine the color.* A blue-black color means that starch is present. Record the colors in Table 1. (See Data and Observations.)

4. Label the remaining test tubes 7 through 12. Place them in a test-tube rack.
5. Fill these test tubes to a depth of about 1 cm with the following:
   7—Water   10—Honey
   8—Glucose   11—Milk
   9—Syrup   12—Molasses
6. Use forceps to add one sugar test tablet each to test tubes 7–12. CAUTION: *Sugar tablets are poisonous. DO NOT touch the tablet with your fingers. Wash hands immediately if sugar test tablets or solution containing them come in contact with your skin. The test tubes will get hot as the tablets dissolve. Do not remove the test tubes from the test-tube rack. DO NOT TOUCH.*
7. Observe the color of each of the five tubes. Green, yellow, or orange color means that sugar is present. Record the colors in Table 2.

Nutrients and Digestion

L2

Meeting Different Ability Levels

Content Outline

L2

Reinforcement

L2

Enrichment

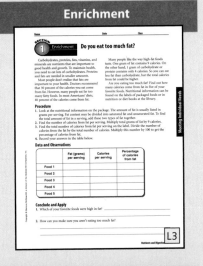

L3

Directed Reading (English/Spanish)

L1

Study Guide

Study Guide

Features
- Contains a study guide page for each section of the chapter
- Reviews key concepts
- Includes answer pages

L2

Reading Essentials

Reading Essentials for Glencoe Science
An Interactive Student Workbook

Features
- Condensed core content
- Actively involves students in reading
- Reinforces key vocabulary

L1

Assessment

Test Practice Workbook

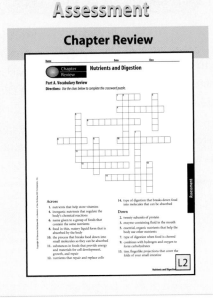

L2

Chapter Review

L2

Chapter Tests

L2

Science Content Background

section 1 Nutrition

Calorie Needs

The rate at which the body consumes energy when at rest is termed the basal metabolic rate. The basal metabolic rate and the physical activity metabolic rate are two of the factors that help determine the number of Calories a person's body requires each day. Other factors include age, body mass, size, sex, endocrine gland activity, and external temperature.

Energy Sources

Carbohydrates and proteins supply about four Calories per gram, and fats supply about nine Calories per gram. Excess sugar is stored in the liver and muscles in the form of glycogen. When energy is required, a series of activities involving the brain, nerves, and adrenal glands brings about the conversion of glycogen to glucose. The amino acids of protein can be converted into carbohydrates, and then these can be utilized as a source of energy. Excess fat stored in the body can oxidize and release energy. This reaction produces a great deal of heat as a waste product.

Vitamins

The role of vitamins as nutrients was not recognized until the early 1900s. During the early years of research, each new vitamin that was identified was given a letter designation. This method proved to be inadequate to correctly classify the substances. Vitamins then were called by their chemical names. Niacin is an example of a vitamin that goes by its chemical name rather than a letter designation.

section 2 The Digestive System

Digestion

The process of transforming foods into usable nutrients is called digestion. This extracellular process takes place in the digestive system, specifically in the stomach and small intestine. Enzymes that serve as catalysts for chemical reactions often require precise environmental conditions, including the proper temperature, pH, and substrate, to be active. For example, the enzyme pepsin, which is found in the stomach, is only active in a medium having a pH of 1.5 to 2.2 and only helps digest proteins.

chapter content resources

Internet Resources
For additional content background, visit
bookd.msscience.com to:
- access your book online
- find references to related articles in popular science magazines
- access Web links with related content background
- access current events with science journal topics

Print Resources
Contemporary Nutrition, by Gordon M. Wardlaw, McGraw-Hill, 2000
The Digestive System, by Carol Ballard, Heinemann Library, 2002
The Human Body for Every Kid, by Janice VanCleave, Wiley, John & Sons, Incorporated, 1995

IDENTIFYING Misconceptions

Find Out What Students Think

Students may think that . . .

Energy comes directly from the food they eat.
Students often think that digestion is a process in which usable energy is released directly from food. Many students do not understand that food must be broken down in the digestive tract into other substances before it is transported to various parts of the body where it can be used to make new substances or broken down for energy release.

Discussion

Have students describe the process of digestion, including what happens to the food they eat, where it goes, and how it is used. Record their ideas on the board or on the overhead projector next to an outline of the digestive system. Keep track of misconceptions, but do not attempt to correct them at this time.

Promote Understanding

Activity

Preparation Prepare a 0.1% starch solution by heating 1 mL soluble starch in 1 L water. Prepare a 0.2% diastase solution by dissolving 2 mL diastase in 1 L water. (Diastase can be purchased from most biological supply houses.)

Procedure Students simulate the digestion of starch in the body. Starch is found in foods such as crackers, rice, and potatoes.

- Have students place two drops of starch solution on each end of a clean glass slide. (One of the sets of drops will serve as a control.)

- Have students add two drops of dilute Lugol's solution to each of the sets of drops. Both sets of drops should turn a pale blue.

John Paul Endress/The Stock Market

- Add one drop of the diastase solution to one of the sets of drops. The diastase will cause the blue of the solution to disappear.

    Ask students why the color disappeared. After some discussion, explain that the changes they observed are similar to the way starch is affected by amylase in the body. Starches are broken down into simple sugars and then transported to different parts of the body where they are used. Emphasize that simple sugars also may be reassembled in the liver and stored as glycogen, or they may be converted into fat molecules and stored throughout the body.

    As an extension, have students brainstorm a list of other foods that are broken down and then used to make new substances. For example, proteins can be broken down into amino acids, which are then assembled in the cells to form new proteins.

Assess

After completing the chapter, see *Identifying Misconceptions* in the Study Guide at the end of the chapter.

Chapter Vocabulary

nutrient, p. 36
protein, p. 37
amino acid, p. 37
carbohydrate, p. 38
fat, p. 39
vitamin, p. 40
mineral, p. 42
food group, p. 44
digestion, p. 47
mechanical digestion, p. 47
chemical digestion, p. 47
enzyme, p. 48
peristalsis, p. 50
chyme, p. 51
villi, p. 52

Science Journal Student responses should include some or all of the following: mouth, esophagus, stomach, small intestine, large intestine, rectum, and anus.

INTERACTIVE CHALKBOARD with Image Bank

PowerPoint® Presentations

This CD-ROM is an editable Microsoft® PowerPoint® presentation that includes:

* a pre-made presentation for every chapter
* interactive graphics
* animations
* audio clips
* image bank
* all new section and chapter questions
* Standardized Test Practice
* transparencies
* pre-lab questions for all labs
* Foldables directions
* links to bookd.msscience.com

Nutrients and Digestion

chapter preview

sections

1 Nutrition
Lab Identifying Vitamin C Content

2 The Digestive System
Lab Particle Size and Absorption

Virtual Lab How can you design a healthful diet?

Intestinal Landscape

This photo may look like a pile of potatoes, but it is a close-up of your small intestine. The wall of the small intestine has many fingerlike projections that soak up substances from digested food. The small intestine is just one of many organs that make up your digestive system.

Science Journal Make a list of all the organs you think are part of your digestive system.

Theme Connection

Energy Energy is a major theme of this chapter. Nutrients contain chemical energy. During digestion, complex food molecules are broken down into simpler forms that body cells can use for metabolism. This process transforms chemical energy into thermal and mechanical energy.

About the Photo

Absorption The inner surface of the small intestine forms many fingerlike projections called villi. On the tip of each villus are thousands of hair-like projections called microvilli. The combination of villi and microvilli increases the absorptive surface area of the small intestine over 6,000 times.

Start-Up Activities

Model the Digestive Tract

Imagine taking a bite of your favorite food. When you eat, your body breaks down food to release energy. How long does it take?

Organs of the Digestive System

Organ	Length	Time
Mouth	8 cm	5 s to 30 s
Pharynx and esophagus	25 cm	10 s
Stomach	16 cm	2 h to 4 h
Small intestine	4.75 m	3 h
Large intestine	1.25 m	2 days

1. Make a label for each of the digestive organs listed here. Include the organ's name, length, and the time it takes for food to pass through it.

2. Working with a partner, place a piece of masking tape that is 6.5 m long on the classroom floor.

3. Beginning at one end of the tape, and in the same order as they are listed in the table, mark the length for each organ. Place each label next to its section.

4. **Think Critically** In your Science Journal, suggest reasons why food spends a different amount of time in each organ.

 FOLDABLES **Study Organizer**

Nutrients in Foods Make the following Foldable to help you organize foods based on the nutrients that they contain.

STEP 1 **Fold** the top of a vertical piece of paper down and the bottom up to divide the paper into thirds. Then, **fold** the paper in half from top to bottom.

STEP 2 **Turn** the paper horizontally, **unfold and label** the six columns as follows: *Proteins, Carbohydrates, Lipids, Water, Vitamins,* and *Minerals.*

Read for Main Ideas As you read the chapter, list foods you eat that provide each of these nutrients in the proper columns.

 Science Online Preview this chapter's content and activities at bookd.msscience.com

Purpose Use the Launch Lab to introduce students to the digestive system. L2 COOP LEARN LS
Visual-Spatial

Preparation Find an area where students can work undisturbed during the activity.

Materials index cards, marking pens, masking tape, meterstick or measuring tape

Teaching Strategies
• Explain that the length of time food spends in the digestive tract varies among individuals and can depend on health conditions.
• After the complete length of the digestive system has been marked off, encourage students to infer how something that long can fit inside their bodies.

Think Critically

The amount of digestion time depends on the type of food. Different foods undergo different chemical processes as they are digested.

Assessment

Process Have students predict what symptoms an infant might exhibit if a birth defect caused a constriction in a portion of the digestive tract. Use **Performance Assessment in the Science Classroom,** p. 93.

 FOLDABLES **Study Organizer** **Dinah Zike** **Study Fold**

Student preparation materials for this Foldable are available in the **Chapter** *FAST FILE* **Resources.**

section 1

Nutrition

Why do you eat?

You're listening to a favorite song on the radio, maybe even singing along. Then all of a sudden, the music stops. You examine the radio to see what happened. The batteries died. You hunt for more batteries and quickly put in the new ones. In the same way that the radio needs batteries to work, you need food to carry out your daily activities—but not just any food. When you are hungry, you probably choose food based on taste and the amount of time you have to eat it. However, as much as you don't want to admit it, the nutritional value of the food you choose is more important than the taste. A chocolate-iced donut might be tasty and quick to eat, yet it provides few of the nutrients your body needs. **Nutrients** (NEW tree unts) are substances in foods that provide energy and materials for cell development, growth, and repair.

Energy Needs Your body needs energy for every activity that it performs. Muscle activities such as the beating of your heart, blinking your eyes, and lifting your backpack require energy. How much energy you need depends on several factors, such as body mass, age, and activity level. This energy comes from the foods you eat. The amount of energy available in food is measured in Calories. A Calorie (Cal) is the amount of heat necessary to raise the temperature of 1 kg of water 1°C. As shown in **Figure 1,** different foods contain different numbers of Calories. A raw carrot may have 30 Cal. This means that when you eat a carrot, your body has 30 Cal of energy available to use. A slice of cheese pizza might have 170 Cal, and one hamburger might have 260 Cal. The number of Calories varies due to the kinds of nutrients a food provides.

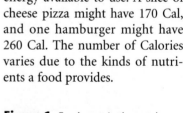

Figure 1 Foods vary in the number of Calories they contain. A hamburger has the same number of Calories as 8.5 average-sized carrots.

Classes of Nutrients

Six kinds of nutrients are available in food—proteins, carbohydrates, fats, vitamins, minerals, and water. Proteins, carbohydrates, vitamins, and fats all contain carbon and are called organic nutrients. In contrast, inorganic nutrients, such as water and minerals, do not contain carbon. Foods containing carbohydrates, fats, and proteins need to be digested or broken down before your body can use them. Water, vitamins, and minerals don't require digestion and are absorbed directly into your bloodstream.

Proteins Your body uses proteins for replacement and repair of body cells and for growth. **Proteins** are large molecules that contain carbon, hydrogen, oxygen, nitrogen and sometimes sulfur. A molecule of protein is made up of a large number of smaller units, or building blocks, called **amino acids.** In **Figure 2** you can see some sources of proteins. Different foods contain different amounts of protein, as shown in **Figure 3.**

Your body needs only 20 amino acids in various combinations to make the thousands of proteins used in your cells. Most of these amino acids can be made in your body's cells, but eight of them cannot. These eight are called essential amino acids. They have to be supplied by the foods you eat. Complete proteins provide all of the essential amino acids. Eggs, milk, cheese, and meat contain complete proteins. Incomplete proteins are missing one or more of the essential amino acids. If you are a vegetarian, you can get all of the essential amino acids by eating a wide variety of protein-rich vegetables, fruits, and grains.

Figure 2 Meats, poultry, eggs, fish, peas, beans, and nuts are all rich in protein.

540 Calories
10 g protein

280 Calories
16 g protein

186 Calories
15 g protein

Figure 3 The amount of protein in a food is not the same as the number of Calories in the food. A taco has nearly the same amount of protein as a slice of pizza, but it usually has about 100 fewer Calories.

SECTION 1 Nutrition **D ◆ 37**

Discussion

Nutrition Are you what you eat? The food you eat supplies materials for the production of new cells, which become part of your body. It also supplies energy, which allows you to do the things you like to do.

Teacher FYI

Oxidation When cells need energy, they oxidize fuels such as carbohydrates and fats. This process results in the formation of carbon dioxide and water, the same products that are formed when a fuel such as gasoline is burned in an engine. Energy is released in this reaction.

Fun Fact

The average rate of protein synthesis is estimated at 500 g per day. This usually is greater than an individual's daily intake and is possible because amino acids are recycled.

Virtual Labs

Diet by Design *How can you design a healthful diet?*

Curriculum Connection

Health Have the school lunchroom manager or a hospital dietitian discuss with students how a balanced diet can be achieved with a variety of foods. Have students work in pairs to list what they ate during the last 24 hours and then evaluate the variety of their diets. L2 COOP LEARN

Science Online

Topic: Dietary Fiber

Visit bookd.msscience.com for Web links to recent news or magazine articles about the importance of fiber in your diet.

Activity In your Science Journal, classify your favorite foods into two groups—*Good source of fiber* and *Little or no fiber.*

Figure 4 These foods contain carbohydrates that provide energy for all the things that you do.
List *the carbohydrates that you've eaten today.*

INTEGRATE Chemistry

Carbohydrates Study the nutrition label on several boxes of cereal. You'll notice that the number of grams of carbohydrates found in a typical serving of cereal is higher than the amounts of the other nutrients. **Carbohydrates** (kar boh HI drayts) usually are the main sources of energy for your body. Each carbohydrate molecule is made of carbon, hydrogen, and oxygen atoms. Energy holds the atoms together. When carbohydrates are broken down in the presence of oxygen in your cells, this energy is released for use by your body.

Three types of carbohydrates are sugar, starch, and fiber, as shown in **Figure 4.** Sugars are called *simple carbohydrates*. You're probably most familiar with table sugar. However, fruits, honey, and milk also contain forms of sugar. Your cells break down glucose, a simple sugar. The other two types of carbohydrates—starch and fiber—are called *complex carbohydrates*. Starch is found in potatoes and foods made from grains such as pasta. Starches are made up of many simple sugars in long chains. Fiber, such as cellulose, is found in the cell walls of plant cells. Foods like whole-grain breads and cereals, beans, peas, and other vegetables and fruits are good sources of fiber. Because different types of fiber are found in foods, you should eat a variety of fiber-rich plant foods. You cannot digest fiber, but it is needed to keep your digestive system running smoothly.

Nutritious snacks can help your body get the nutrients it needs, especially when you are growing rapidly and are physically active. Choose snacks that provide nutrients such as complex carbohydrates, proteins, and vitamins, as well as fiber. Foods high in sugar and fat can have lots of Calories that supply energy, but they provide only some of the nutrients your body needs.

Figure 5 Fat is stored in certain cells in your body. The cytoplasm and nucleus are pushed to the edge of the cell by the fat deposits.

Nucleus   Fat deposit   Cytoplasm

Some foods you might choose for lunch or snacks that are high in fat are outlined in red.

Answer A gram of fat can release twice as much energy as a gram of carbohydrate.

Fats

The term fat has developed a negative meaning for some people. However, **fats,** also called lipids, are necessary because they provide energy and help your body absorb vitamins. Fat tissue cushions your internal organs. A major part of every cell membrane is made up of fat. A gram of fat can release more than twice as much energy as a gram of carbohydrate can. During the digestion process, fat is broken down into smaller molecules called fatty acids and glycerol (GLIH suh rawl). Because fat is a good storage unit for energy, excess energy from the foods you eat is converted to fat and stored for later use, as shown in **Figure 5.**

✓ **Reading Check** *Why is fat a good storage unit for energy?*

Fats are classified as unsaturated or saturated based on their chemical structure. Unsaturated fats are usually liquid at room temperature. Vegetable oils as well as fats found in seeds are unsaturated fats. Saturated fats are found in meats, animal products, and some plants and are usually solid at room temperature. Although fish contains saturated fat, it also has some unsaturated fats that your body needs. Saturated fats have been associated with high levels of blood cholesterol. Your body makes cholesterol in your liver. Cholesterol is part of the cell membrane in all of your cells. However, a diet high in cholesterol may result in deposits forming on the inside walls of blood vessels. These deposits can block the blood supply to organs and increase blood pressure. This can lead to heart disease and strokes.

Mini LAB

Comparing the Fat Content of Foods

Procedure

1. Collect three pieces of each of the following foods: **potato chips; pretzels; peanuts;** and **small cubes of fruits, cheese, vegetables, and meat.**
2. Place the food items on a piece of **brown grocery bag.** Label the paper with the name of each food. Do not taste the foods.
3. Allow foods to sit for 30 min.
4. Remove the items, properly dispose of them, and observe the paper.

Analysis

1. Which items left a translucent (greasy) mark? Which left a wet mark?
2. How are the foods that left a greasy mark on the paper alike?
3. Use this test to determine which other foods contain fats. A greasy mark means the food contains fat. A wet mark means the food contains a lot of water.

Mini LAB

Purpose Students test for fats in foods. L1 ELL LS **Kinesthetic**

Materials 3 potato chips, pretzels, and peanuts; small cubes of fruits, cheeses, vegetables, and meat; brown craft paper or brown paper bag

Teaching Strategy Point out the difference between a water mark and a greasy mark.

Safety Precaution Use only cooked meat.

Analysis

1. Potato chips, peanuts, cheeses, and meat will leave a translucent mark. Pretzels may leave a greasy mark if they are fresh. Fruits and vegetables will leave a wet mark.
2. They have some fat content.
3. Other foods that contain fat include butter, oils, and many crackers and chips.

Assessment

Process Have students test an unknown food item for fat. Use **Performance Assessment in the Science Classroom,** p. 97.

Curriculum Connection

Math Have students calculate the percentage of fat in foods. First have them note the grams of fat in a serving, and then multiply this number by 9, the number of Calories released when fat is oxidized. Divide this number by the total number of Calories in a serving. This yields the percent of Calories from fat. Recommendations are that no more than 30 percent of your Calorie intake should come from fat. L2

Milk Is milk the perfect food? Milk does supply many nutrients but it is not a perfect food, as it lacks certain essential vitamins and minerals. **IS Interpersonal**

Applying Science

Answers

1. Of the snack foods listed, pretzels are the lowest in fat. Other snack foods could be brought into the classroom to compare their fat contents. Students can discuss the difference between fried and baked snacks, and healthier alternatives to their favorite snack foods.

2. Most frozen pizzas are prepared using cheese and pepperoni, which are both high in fat. Ways to make pizza healthier include preparing it fresh at home using low-fat cheese, homemade tomato sauce, turkey pepperoni, and a variety of fresh vegetables.

IDENTIFYING Misconceptions

Vitamin Consumption Students may have the notion that if vitamins are good for you, more is better. Some vitamins should not be taken in high doses. An excess of vitamin A can cause liver and skin problems. Too much vitamin D can cause an imbalance of blood calcium, resulting in digestive, urinary, and nervous system disorders.

Vitamins Organic nutrients needed in small quantities for growth, regulating body functions, and preventing some diseases are called **vitamins.** For instance, your bone cells need vitamin D to use calcium, and your blood needs vitamin K in order to clot.

Most foods supply some vitamins, but no food has them all. Some people feel that taking extra vitamins is helpful, while others feel that eating a well-balanced diet usually gives your body all the vitamins it needs.

Vitamins are classified into two groups, as shown in **Figure 6.** Some vitamins dissolve easily in water and are called water-soluble vitamins. They are not stored by your body so you have to take them daily. Other vitamins dissolve only in fat and are called fat-soluble vitamins. These vitamins are stored by your body. Although you eat or drink most vitamins, some are made by your body. Vitamin D is made when your skin is exposed to sunlight. Some vitamin K and two of the B vitamins are made with the help of bacteria that live in your large intestine.

Applying Science

Is it unhealthy to snack between meals?

Most children eat three meals each day accompanied by snacks in between. Grabbing a bite to eat to satisfy you until your next meal is a common occurrence in today's society, and 20 percent of our energy and nutrient needs comes from snacking. While it would be best to select snacks consisting of fruits and vegetables, most children prefer to eat a bag of chips or a candy bar. Although these quick snacks are highly convenient, many times they are high in fat, as well.

Identifying the Problem

The table on the right lists several snack foods that are popular among adolescents. They are listed alphabetically, and the grams of fat per individual serving is shown. As you examine the chart, can you conclude which snacks would be a healthier choice based on their fat content?

Solving the Problem

1. Looking at the data, what can you conclude about the snack foods you eat? What other snack foods do you eat that are not listed on the chart? How do you think they compare in nutritional value? Which snack foods are healthiest?

2. Pizza appears to be the unhealthiest choice on the chart because of the amount of the fat it contains. Why do you think pizza contains so much fat? List at least three ways to make pizza a healthier snack food.

Fat in Snack Foods	
One Serving	Fat (g)
Candy bar	12
Frozen pizza	30
Ice cream	8
Potato chips	10
Pretzels	1

Differentiated Instruction

Challenge Have students research and report on a particular vitamin deficiency. Their reports should include information about how the vitamin was discovered, the symptoms of a deficiency, and foods that are high in the vitamin. Have students work together to present their findings on a "Vitamins for Good Health" bulletin board. L3
COOP LEARN **IS Linguistic**

Science Journal

Taking Your Vitamins Have students write a paragraph about why it might be a disadvantage to substitute vitamin pills for a proper diet. Their entries should indicate an understanding that other nutrients besides vitamins are needed for maintaining health. A well-balanced diet supplies the range of needed vitamins. L2 **IS Logical-Mathematical** P

NATIONAL GEOGRAPHIC VISUALIZING VITAMINS

Figure 6

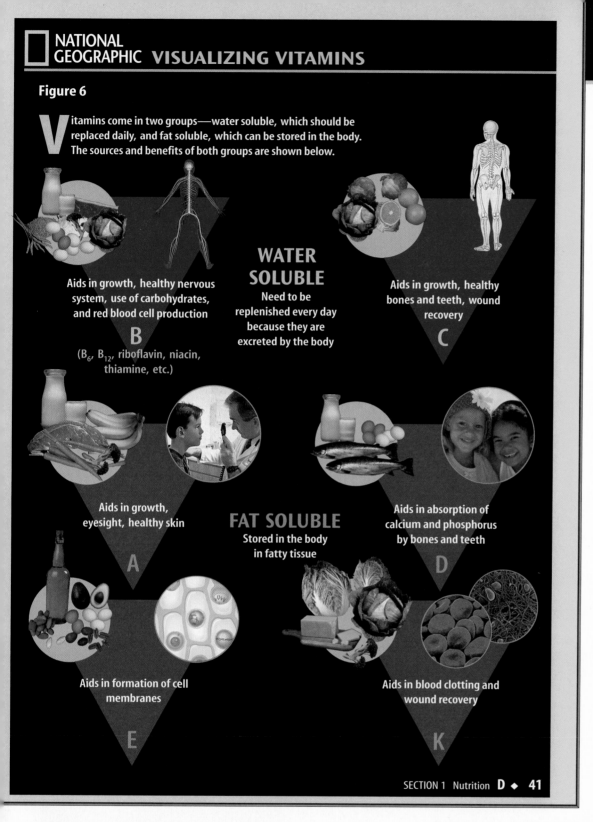

Vitamins come in two groups—water soluble, which should be replaced daily, and fat soluble, which can be stored in the body. The sources and benefits of both groups are shown below.

WATER SOLUBLE
Need to be replenished every day because they are excreted by the body

Aids in growth, healthy nervous system, use of carbohydrates, and red blood cell production

B

(B₆, B₁₂, riboflavin, niacin, thiamine, etc.)

Aids in growth, healthy bones and teeth, wound recovery

C

Aids in growth, eyesight, healthy skin

A

FAT SOLUBLE
Stored in the body in fatty tissue

Aids in absorption of calcium and phosphorus by bones and teeth

D

Aids in formation of cell membranes

E

Aids in blood clotting and wound recovery

K

SECTION 1 Nutrition **D ◆ 41**

Visualizing Vitamins

Have students examine the pictures and read the captions. Then ask the following questions.

Why is it important to eat foods containing vitamin K? A deficiency can lead to excessive bleeding when you are injured and it may take longer for the wound to heal.

What role does vitamin D have in healthy bones? It aids in the absorption of calcium, which is a necessary component of bone tissue.

Activity

Vitamin Needs Have students define the following terms: *beriberi, rickets, scurvy, pellagra, night blindness.* Be sure to have students include which vitamin is deficient in each condition and how the deficiency affects the body. L2

Differentiated Instruction

Challenge Have students research the dangers of vitamin overdose. What effects can high doses of vitamins such as A, C, or E have on the body? Have students answer the question: Why do the Inuit people choose not to eat polar bear liver?

Possible answer: Polar bear liver contains a high amount of vitamin A. As much as 12 times the minimum daily requirement of vitamin A can be found in one gram of polar bear liver. Ingestion of too much vitamin A results in a host of ailments and can even be deadly. L3

Minerals Inorganic nutrients—nutrients that lack carbon and regulate many chemical reactions in your body—are called **minerals.** Your body uses about 14 minerals. Minerals build cells, take part in chemical reactions in cells, send nerve impulses throughout your body, and carry oxygen to body cells. In **Figure 7,** you can see how minerals can get from the soil into your body. Of the 14 minerals, calcium and phosphorus are used in the largest amounts for a variety of body functions. One of these functions is the formation and maintenance of bone. Some minerals, called trace minerals, are required only in small amounts. Copper and iodine usually are listed as trace minerals. Several minerals, what they do, and some food sources for them are listed in **Table 1.**

✓ Reading Check *Why is copper considered a trace mineral?*

Figure 7 The roots of the wheat take in phosphorus from the soil. Then the mature wheat is harvested and used in bread and cereal. Your body gets phosphorus when you eat the cereal.

Phosphorus

Wheat being harvested

Table 1 Minerals		
Mineral	**Health Effect**	**Food Sources**
Calcium	strong bones and teeth, blood clotting, muscle and nerve activity	dairy products, eggs, green leafy vegetables, soy
Phosphorus	strong bones and teeth, muscle contraction, stores energy	cheese, meat, cereal
Potassium	balance of water in cells, nerve impulse conduction, muscle contraction	bananas, potatoes, nuts, meat, oranges
Sodium	fluid balances in tissues, nerve impulse conduction	meat, milk, cheese, salt, beets, carrots, nearly all foods
Iron	oxygen is transported in hemoglobin by red blood cells	red meat, raisins, beans, spinach, eggs
Iodine (trace)	thyroid activity, metabolic stimulation	seafood, iodized salt

Figure 8 About two-thirds of your body water is located within your body cells. Water helps maintain the cells' shapes and sizes. The water that is lost through perspiration and respiration must be replaced.

Water Loss	
Method of Loss	**Amount (mL/day)**
Exhaled air	350
Feces	150
Skin (mostly as sweat)	500
Urine	1,500

Water Have you ever gone on a bike ride on a hot summer day without a bottle of water? You probably were thirsty and maybe you even stopped to get some water. Water is important for your body. Next to oxygen, water is the most important factor for survival. Different organisms need different amounts of water to survive. You could live for a few weeks without food but for only a few days without water because your cells need water to carry out their work. Most of the nutrients you have studied in this chapter can't be used by your body unless they are carried in a solution. This means that they have to be dissolved in water. In cells, chemical reactions take place in solutions.

The human body is about 60 percent water by weight. About two thirds of your body water is located in your body cells. Water also is found around cells and in body fluids such as blood. As shown in **Figure 8,** your body loses water as perspiration. When you exhale, water leaves your body as water vapor. Water also is lost every day when your body gets rid of wastes. To replace water lost each day, you need to drink about 2 L of liquids. However, drinking liquids isn't the only way to supply cells with water. Most foods have more water than you realize. An apple is about 80 percent water, and many meats are 90 percent water.

INTEGRATE Social Studies

Salt Mines The mineral halite is processed to make table salt. In the United States, most salt comes from underground mines. Research to find the locations of these mines, then label them on a map.

Why do you get thirsty? Your body is made up of systems that operate together. When your body needs to replace lost water, messages are sent to your brain that result in a feeling of thirst. Drinking water satisfies your thirst and usually restores the body's homeostasis (hoh mee oh STAY sus). Homeostasis is the regulation of the body's internal environment, such as temperature and amount of water. When homeostasis is restored, the signal to the brain stops and you no longer feel thirsty.

Food Groups

Because no naturally occurring food has every nutrient, you need to eat a variety of foods. Nutritionists have developed a simple system, called the food pyramid, shown in **Figure 9,** to help people select foods that supply all the nutrients needed for energy and growth.

Foods that contain the same type of nutrient belong to a **food group.** Foods have been divided into five groups—bread and cereal, vegetable, fruit, milk, and meat. The recommended daily amount for each food group will supply your body with the nutrients it needs for good health. Using the food pyramid to make choices when you eat will help you maintain good health.

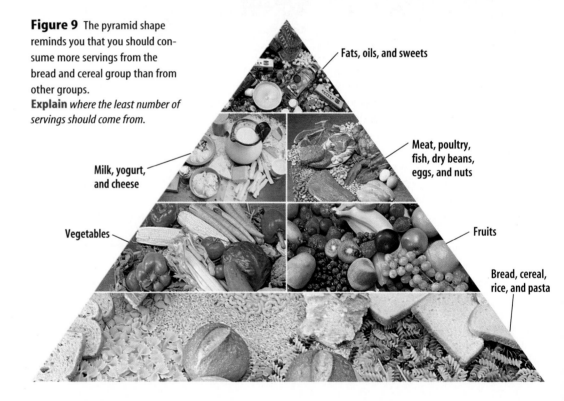

Figure 9 The pyramid shape reminds you that you should consume more servings from the bread and cereal group than from other groups.
Explain *where the least number of servings should come from.*

Fats, oils, and sweets

Meat, poultry, fish, dry beans, eggs, and nuts

Milk, yogurt, and cheese

Vegetables

Fruits

Bread, cereal, rice, and pasta

Cultural Diversity

Diet and Disease Certain cultures have diets that contain little animal fat. Such diets typically result in low intake of cholesterol. These diets may include large amounts of vegetables, fruits, and grains. People of Asia have a lower incidence of heart disease than people in the United States, possibly as a result of having a diet that is lower in fat.

Differentiated Instruction

English-Language Learners Bring a sample school lunch to class. Ask students to list, on a sheet of paper, the foods provided and the food groups they represent. L2

Daily Servings Each day you should eat six to eleven servings from the bread and cereal group, three to five servings from the vegetable group, two to four servings from the fruit group, two to three servings from the milk group, and two to three servings from the meat group. Only small amounts of fats, oils, and sweets should be consumed.

The size of a serving is different for different foods. For example, a slice of bread or one ounce of ready-to-eat cereal is a bread and cereal-group serving. One cup of raw leafy vegetables or one-half cup of cooked or chopped raw vegetables make a serving from the vegetable group. One medium apple, banana, or orange is a fruit serving. A serving from the milk group can be one cup of milk or yogurt. Two ounces of cooked lean meat or one egg is a serving from the meat group.

Food Labels The nutritional facts found on all packaged foods make it easier to make healthful food choices. These labels, as shown in **Figure 10,** can help you plan meals that supply the daily recommended amounts of nutrients and meet special dietary requirements (for example, a low-fat diet).

Figure 10 The information on a food label can help you decide what to eat.

Nutrition Facts
Serving Size 1 Meal

Amount Per Serving	
Calories 330	Calories from Fat 60

	% Daily Value*
Total Fat 7g	10%
Saturated Fat 3.5g	17%
Polyunsaturated Fat 1g	
Monounsaturated Fat 2.5g	
Cholesterol 35mg	12%
Sodium 460mg	19%
Total Carbohydrate 52g	18%
Dietary Fiber 6g	24%
Sugars 17g	
Protein 15g	

Vitamin A 15%	•	Vitamin C 70%	
Calcium 4%	•	Iron 10%	

* Percent Daily Values are based on a 2,000 calorie diet. Your daily values may be higher or lower depending on your calorie needs.

	Calories	2,000	2,500
Total Fat	Less than	65g	80g
Sat Fat	Less than	20g	25g
Cholesterol	Less than	300mg	300mg
Sodium	Less than	2,400mg	2,400mg
Total Carbohydrate		300g	375g
Dietary Fiber		25g	30g

Science Online book d.mssscience.com/self_check_quiz

section 1 review

Summary

Why do you eat?
- Food provides the energy for your body.

Classes of Nutrients
- The nutrients in food fall into six classes.
- Organic nutrients—proteins, vitamins, fats, and carbohydrates—contain carbon.
- Inorganic nutrients—water and minerals—do not contain carbon.

Food Groups
- Foods are divided into groups based on the type of nutrient in the foods.
- The five food groups are bread and cereal, vegetable, fruit, milk, and meat.

Self Check

1. **List** the six classes of nutrients. Give one example of a food source for each class.
2. **Describe** a major function of each class of nutrient.
3. **Discuss** how food choices can positively and negatively affect your health.
4. **Explain** the importance of water in the body.
5. **Think Critically** What foods from each food group would provide a balanced breakfast? Explain.

Applying Skills

6. **Interpret Data** Nutritional information can be found on the labels of most foods. Interpret the labels found on three different types of food products.

Activity

Food Labels Have students read the labels of canned and packaged foods. Discuss the major sources of various nutrients in the foods they eat each day. [L2]
Logical-Mathematical

3 Assess

DAILY INTERVENTION

Check for Understanding
Visual-Spatial Have students research unique sources of proteins and carbohydrates used in different countries. Make labels with the food names and place them in the proper locations on a world map. Examples include amaranth in South America and Africa and taro root in the Pacific Islands. [L3]

Reteach
Food Flash Cards Have students make flash cards with names of fruits or vegetables. On the reverse side, have them identify the major vitamin content of each food. Students can test each other using the flash cards. [L1]
Visual-Spatial

✔ Assessment

Performance Assess students' abilities to make and use tables by having them use **Figure 8** to determine how much water (in liters) is lost through the skin. Use **Performance Assessment in the Science Classroom,** p. 109.

---

section 1 review

1. carbohydrates: bread; proteins: fish; fats: butter; vitamins: fruit; minerals: vegetables; water: juice
2. carbohydrates: source of energy; proteins: growth of cells; fats: source of energy; vitamins: growth; minerals: nerve activity; water: enables chemical reactions to occur
3. Student answers will vary. Accept all correct responses.
4. dissolves and carries nutrients, removes wastes, enables chemical reactions to occur
5. Students should be able to support their answers with information from **Figure 9.**
6. Have pairs of students compare their interpretations.

Real-World Question

Purpose Students test orange juices for vitamin C content. L2
ELL COOP LEARN

Process Skills observe, measure, predict, interpret data, experiment, communicate, compare and contrast

Time Required 50 minutes

Safety Precautions Remind students not to consume any substances used in the lab.

Procedure

Teaching Strategy Have students practice making uniform drops using water before they begin adding drops of iodine to the test tubes. Remind students to rinse test tubes after each trial.

Troubleshooting Warn students not to mix up the test-solution droppers as they are preparing the test tubes.

Conclude and Apply

1. Answers should reflect student results.
2. Results may vary because of freshness, exposure to heat or air, and amount of vitamin C added.

Identifying Vitamin C Content

Vitamin C is found in many fruits and vegetables. Oranges have a high vitamin C content. Try this lab to test which orange juice has the highest vitamin C content.

Real-World Question

Which orange juice contains the most vitamin C?

Goals

■ **Observe** the vitamin C content of different orange juices.

Materials

test tubes (4)	2% tincture of iodine
*paper cups	dropper
test-tube rack	cornstarch
masking tape	triple-beam balance
wooden stirrers (13)	weighing paper
graduated cylinder	water (50 mL)
*graduated container	glass-marking pencil

dropper bottles (4) containing:
(1) freshly squeezed orange juice
(2) orange juice made from frozen concentrate
(3) canned orange juice
(4) dairy carton orange juice
*Alternate materials

Safety Precautions

WARNING: *Do not taste any of the juices. Iodine is poisonous, can stain skin and clothing, and is an irritant that can cause damage if it comes in contact with your eyes. Notify your teacher if a spill occurs.*

Sample Data

Drops of Iodine Needed to Change Color				
Juice	Trial 1	2	3	Average
1 Fresh juice	8	7	8	8
2 Frozen juice	7	8	8	8
3 Canned juice	6	6	6	6
4 Carton juice	4	3	4	4

Procedure

1. Copy the data table shown above.
2. Label four test tubes as shown in the table above and place them in the test-tube rack.
3. **Measure** and pour 5 mL of juice from each bottle into its labeled test tube.
4. **Measure** 0.3 g of cornstarch, then put it in a container. Slowly mix in 50 mL of water until the cornstarch completely dissolves.
5. Add 5 mL of the cornstarch solution to each of the four test tubes. Stir well.
6. Add iodine to test tube 1, one drop at a time. Stir after each drop. Record the number of drops needed to change the juice to purple. The more vitamin C, the more drops needed.
7. Repeat step 6 with test tubes 2, 3, and 4.
8. Empty and clean the test tubes. Repeat steps 3 through 7 two more times, then average your results.

Conclude and Apply

1. **Compare and contrast** the amount of vitamin C in the orange juices tested.
2. **Infer** why the amount of vitamin C varied.

✓ Assessment

Performance To further assess students' abilities to identify vitamin C content, have them test water in which shredded lettuce or shredded cabbage cores have been soaked overnight. Use **Performance Assessment in the Science Classroom,** p. 97.

Communicating Your Data

Have students check the labels of the containers to see how much vitamin C each claims to contain. Have students use a spreadsheet program to enter the comparison between their tests and the information on the labels.

The Digestive System

Functions of the Digestive System

You are walking through a park on a cool, autumn afternoon. Birds are searching in the grass for insects. A squirrel is eating an acorn. Why are the animals so busy? Like you, they need food to supply their bodies with energy. Food is processed in your body in four stages—ingestion, digestion, absorption, and elimination. Whether it is a piece of fruit or an entire meal, all the food you eat is treated to the same processes in your body. As soon as food enters your mouth, or is ingested as shown in **Figure 11,** breakdown begins. **Digestion** is the process that breaks down food into small molecules so that they can be absorbed and moved into the blood. From the blood, food molecules are transported across the cell membrane to be used by the cell. Unused molecules pass out of your body as wastes.

Digestion is mechanical and chemical. **Mechanical digestion** takes place when food is chewed, mixed, and churned. **Chemical digestion** occurs when chemical reactions occur that break down large molecules of food into smaller ones.

as you read

What **You'll Learn**

- **Distinguish** the differences between mechanical digestion and chemical digestion.
- **Identify** the organs of the digestive system and what takes place in each.
- **Explain** how homeostasis is maintained in digestion.

Why **It's Important**

The processes of the digestive system make the food you eat available to your cells.

🔎 **Review Vocabulary**

bacteria: one-celled organism without membrane-bound organelles

New Vocabulary

- digestion
- mechanical digestion
- chemical digestion
- enzyme
- peristalsis
- chyme
- villi

Figure 11 Humans have to chew solid foods before swallowing them, but snakes have adaptations that allow them to swallow their food whole.

SECTION 2 The Digestive System **D ◆ 47**

Bellringer

Section Focus Transparencies also are available on the Interactive Chalkboard CD-ROM.
L2 ELL

SECTION 2 Section Focus Transparency — Pardon Me, but I Digest

Cows eat quite often—a one-year-old steer may be given almost forty pounds of feed each day. On the other hand, it's not uncommon for a large snake to go more than a month without food. These animals have very different digestive processes to meet different energy needs.

1. In general, why do animals need to eat?
2. Why do you think a snake can go so long without food?

Tie to Prior Knowledge

Digestion Remind students that one feature of living things is that they use energy. Discuss with students that food is the source of energy for cell activities, but that it must be processed into usable molecules. This is the function of the digestive system.

Section 2 Resource Manager	
Chapter *FAST FILE* Resources	

Chapter *FAST FILE* Resources

Transparency Activity, p. 43

Directed Reading for Content Mastery, pp. 21, 22

MiniLAB, p. 4

Enrichment, p. 30

Reinforcement, p. 28

Lab Worksheet, pp. 7–8

Lab Activity, pp. 13–15

Lab Management and Safety, p. 52

Home and Community Involvement, p. 41

Quick Demo

Meat Tenderizers

Meat tenderizers often contain the enzyme papain, which is made from papaya juice.

Materials meat tenderizer, two small cubes of beef, sugar, oven, plastic fork

Estimated Time 15 minutes

Procedure Sprinkle some meat tenderizer on a small cube of beef. On another cube of beef, sprinkle some sugar. Heat both pieces in an oven at 250°F until brown. When cooled, have students examine both pieces and probe with a plastic fork to compare tenderness.

Use Science Words

Word Meaning The names of many enzymes are designated with the suffix -ase. For example, the enzyme that is responsible for the conversion of sucrose is called *sucrase*. Have students determine the enzymes for lactose (lactase), lipids (lipase), and amylose (amylase).

Caption Answer

Figure 12 It is free to join with another molecule in another reaction.

✔ Reading Check

Answer Enzymes speed up the rate of chemical digestion.

Enzyme | Molecule A | Molecule B

Temporary complex forms

Unchanged enzyme | Molecule C

The surface shape of an enzyme fits the shape of specific molecules that take part in the reaction.

The enzyme and the molecules join and the reaction occurs between the two molecules.

Following the reaction, the enzyme and the new molecule separate. The enzyme is not changed by the reaction. The resulting new molecule has a new chemical structure.

Figure 12 Enzymes speed up the rate of certain body reactions. During these reactions, the enzymes are not used up or changed in any way.
Explain *what happens to the enzyme after it separates from the new molecule.*

Enzymes

Chemical digestion is possible only because of enzymes (EN zimez). An **enzyme** is a type of protein that speeds up the rate of a chemical reaction in your body. One way enzymes speed up reactions is by reducing the amount of energy necessary for a chemical reaction to begin. If enzymes weren't there to help, the rate of chemical reactions would slow down. Some might not even happen at all. As shown in **Figure 12,** enzymes work without being changed or used up.

Enzymes in Digestion Many enzymes help you digest carbohydrates, proteins, and fats. Amylase (AM uh lays) is an enzyme produced by glands near the mouth. This enzyme helps speed up the breakdown of complex carbohydrates, such as starch, into simpler carbohydrates—sugars. In your stomach, the enzyme pepsin aids the chemical reactions that break down complex proteins into less complex proteins. In your small intestine, a number of other enzymes continue to speed up the breakdown of proteins into amino acids.

The pancreas, an organ on the back side of the stomach, releases several enzymes through a tube into the small intestine. Some of these enzymes continue to aid the process of starch breakdown that started in the mouth. The resulting sugars are turned into glucose and are used by your body's cells. Different enzymes from the pancreas are involved in the breakdown of fats into fatty acids. Others help in the reactions that break down proteins.

✔ Reading Check
What is the role of enzymes in the chemical digestion of food?

48 ◆ **D** **CHAPTER 2** Nutrients and Digestion

Teacher FYI

Enzyme Interactions Nearly every bodily chemical reaction involves enzymes. There is an intricate relationship among enzymes, vitamins, and minerals. Often enzymes cannot function in the absence of specific vitamins or minerals.

Differentiated Instruction

Visually Impaired and Learning Disabled Cut from foam-core board pairs of shapes that fit together as shown in **Figure 12.** Mix up several pairs, and have students find the enzyme for each molecule by matching the shapes. Compare the matching of shapes to a key fitting in a lock or pieces of a puzzle fitting together. L1 IS **Kinesthetic**

Other Enzyme Actions Enzyme-aided reactions are not limited to the digestive process. Enzymes also help speed up chemical reactions responsible for building your body. They are involved in the energy production activities of your muscle and nerve cells. Enzymes also aid in the blood-clotting process. Without enzymes, the chemical reactions of your body would not happen. In fact, you would not exist.

Organs of the Digestive System

Your digestive system has two parts—the digestive tract and the accessory organs. The major organs of your digestive tract—mouth, esophagus (ih SAH fuh guhs), stomach, small intestine, large intestine, rectum, and anus—are shown in **Figure 13.** Food passes through all of these organs. The tongue, teeth, salivary glands, liver, gallbladder, and pancreas, also shown in **Figure 13,** are the accessory organs. Although food doesn't pass through them, they are important in mechanical and chemical digestion. Your liver, gallbladder, and pancreas produce or store enzymes and chemicals that help break down food as it passes through the digestive tract.

Salivary glands
Esophagus
Tongue
Liver
Stomach
Pancreas
Gallbladder
Small intestine
Large intestine
Rectum
Anus

Figure 13 The human digestive system can be described as a tube divided into several specialized sections. If stretched out, an adult's digestive system is 6 m to 9 m long.

IDENTIFYING Misconceptions

Peristalsis Students may think that peristalsis cannot occur in the "weightless" environment of a spacecraft. Because peristalsis is an action controlled by muscles, the lack of gravity does not affect swallowing and the movement of food through the digestive system.

Fun Fact

Birds have a specialized stomach chamber, the gizzard, that contains small stones. These stones aid in grinding food—a process that is needed in the absence of teeth.

Figure 14 About 1.5 L of saliva are produced each day by salivary glands in your mouth. **Describe** *what happens in your mouth when you think about a food you like.*

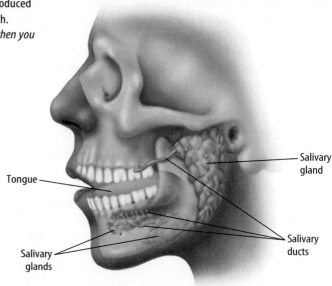

Tongue
Salivary gland
Salivary ducts
Salivary glands

Science Online

Topic: The Stomach

Visit bookd.msscience.com for Web links to information about the role of the stomach during digestion.

Activity Research to find out how antacids provide relief from stomach discomfort.

The Mouth Mechanical and chemical digestion begin in your mouth. Mechanical digestion happens when you chew your food with your teeth and mix it with your tongue. Chemical digestion begins with the addition of a watery substance called saliva (suh LI vuh). As you chew, your tongue moves food around and mixes it with saliva. Saliva is produced by three sets of glands near your mouth, as shown in **Figure 14.** Although saliva is mostly water, it also contains mucus and an enzyme that aids in the breakdown of starch into sugar. Food mixed with saliva becomes a soft mass and is moved to the back of your mouth by your tongue. It is swallowed and passes into your esophagus. Now ingestion is complete, but the process of digestion continues.

The Esophagus Food moving into the esophagus passes over the epiglottis (ep uh GLAH tus). This structure automatically covers the opening to the windpipe to prevent food from entering it, otherwise you would choke. Your esophagus is a muscular tube about 25 cm long. It takes about 4 s to 10 s for food to move down the esophagus to the stomach. No digestion takes place in the esophagus. Mucous glands in the wall of the esophagus keep the food moist. Smooth muscles in the wall move food downward with a squeezing action. These waves of muscle contractions, called **peristalsis** (per uh STAHL sus), move food through the entire digestive tract.

50 ◆ D CHAPTER 2 Nutrients and Digestion

Science Journal

Cavities Have interested students research information about the relationship between sugars in the mouth and cavity-causing bacteria. Have them record in their journals information on the formation of tooth cavities. Some students might like to include diagrams showing the stages of tooth decay. L2 IS **Linguistic** P

The Stomach The stomach, shown in **Figure 15,** is a muscular bag. When empty, it is somewhat sausage shaped with folds on the inside. As food enters from the esophagus, the stomach expands and the folds smooth out. Mechanical and chemical digestion take place in the stomach. Mechanically, food is mixed in the stomach by peristalsis. Chemically, food is mixed with enzymes and strong digestive solutions, such as hydrochloric acid solution, to help break it down.

Specialized cells in the walls of the stomach release about 2 L of hydrochloric acid solution each day. The acidic solution works with the enzyme pepsin to digest protein. The acidic solution has another important purpose—it destroys bacteria that are present in the food. The stomach also produces mucus, which makes food more slippery and protects the stomach from the strong, digestive solutions. Food moves through your stomach in 2 hours to 4 hours and is changed into a thin, watery liquid called **chyme** (KIME). Little by little, chyme moves out of your stomach and into your small intestine.

☑ **Reading Check** *Why isn't your stomach digested by the acidic digestive solution?*

Figure 15 A band of muscle is at the entrance of the stomach to control the entry of food from the esophagus. Muscles at the end of the stomach control the flow of the partially digested food into the first part of the small intestine.

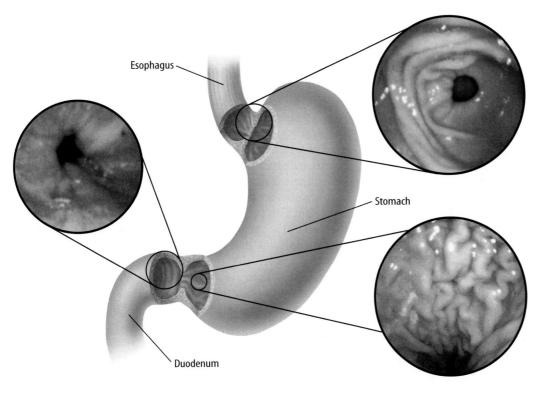

Esophagus

Stomach

Duodenum

Comparison Have students place a spoonful of cooking oil in a glass of warm water. Tell students to add a quarter-spoonful of dishwashing detergent to the glass, then stir. Have students note how the oil is separated into tiny droplets. Relate this to the action of bile on fats in the small intestine. L2

☑ **Reading Check**

Answer It is protected by a mucous coating.

Visual Learning

Figure 15 Why do you think it is important for the entrance and exit of the stomach to be controlled by strong muscles? Possible answer: The muscles at the entrance to the stomach keep partially digested food and stomach acids from moving back into the esophagus. The muscle at the exit of the stomach allows only chyme to leave the stomach, keeping larger food particles in the stomach for further digestion.

Teacher FYI

The Small Intestine The amount of time needed for food undergoing digestion to move through the small intestine is between one and six hours. The small intestine is subdivided into three parts: the duodenum, jejunum, and ileum. Most digestion occurs in the duodenum and most absorption of nutrients takes place in the duodenum and the jejunum. Vitamin B_{12} and bile salts are absorbed in the ileum.

☑ **Active Reading**

Metacognition Journal In this strategy, each student analyzes his or her own thought processes. Have students divide the paper in half. On the left, have them record what they have learned about a topic. On the right, have them record the reason they learned it. Have students write a Metacognition Journal about the digestive system.

Mini LAB

Purpose Students model how villi increase absorption area.

L1 ELL IS **Kinesthetic**

Materials 2 bowls, measuring cup, water, 2 containers, one piece 25-cm × 25-cm smooth cotton cloth, one piece 25-cm × 25-cm cotton terry cloth

Teaching Strategy Cloths should be wrung out completely.

Analysis
1. The terry cloth will absorb more water.
2. The terry cloth's surface of threads is similar to the small intestine's surface of villi.

Assessment

Process Have students compare the absorption of various other cloths and observe differences in their surfaces. Use **Performance Assessment in the Science Classroom,** p. 89.

Figure 16 Hundreds of thousands of densely packed villi give the impression of a velvet cloth surface. If the surface area of your villi could be stretched out, it would cover an area the size of a tennis court.
Infer what would happen to a person's weight if the number of villi were drastically reduced. Why?

Small intestine

Villi

Lymph vessel (collects excess fluid from tissues)

Capillary (bloodstream)

Magnification: 360×

Mini LAB

Modeling Absorption in the Small Intestine

Procedure 🖐️

1. Place one piece of smooth **cotton cloth** (about 25 cm × 25 cm) and a similar-sized piece of **cotton terry cloth** into a **bowl of water.**
2. Soak each for 30 s.
3. Remove the cloths and drain for 1 minute.
4. Wring out each cloth into different containers. Measure the amount of water collected in each.

Analysis
1. Which cloth absorbed the most water?
2. How does the surface of the terry cloth compare to the internal surface of the small intestine?

Try at Home

The Small Intestine Your small intestine is small in diameter, but it measures 4 m to 7 m in length. As chyme leaves your stomach, it enters the first part of your small intestine, called the duodenum (doo AH duh num). Most digestion takes place in your duodenum. Here, a greenish fluid from the liver, called bile, is added. The acid from the stomach makes large fat particles float to the top of the liquid. Bile breaks up the large fat particles, similar to the way detergent breaks up grease.

Chemical digestion of carbohydrates, proteins, and fats occurs when a digestive solution from the pancreas is mixed in. This solution contains bicarbonate ions and enzymes. The bicarbonate ions help neutralize the stomach acid that is mixed with chyme. Your pancreas also makes insulin, a hormone that allows glucose to pass from the bloodstream into your cells.

Absorption of food takes place in the small intestine. Look at the wall of the small intestine in **Figure 16.** The wall has many ridges and folds that are covered with fingerlike projections called **villi** (VIH li). Villi increase the surface area of the small intestine so that nutrients in the chyme have more places to be absorbed. Peristalsis continues to move and mix the chyme. The villi move and are bathed in the soupy liquid. Nutrients move into blood vessels within the villi. From here, blood transports the nutrients to all cells of your body. Peristalsis continues to force the remaining undigested and unabsorbed materials slowly into the large intestine.

Differentiated Instruction

Challenge Have students demonstrate the chemical process involved in neutralizing an acid. First, have them use litmus paper to test a vinegar solution (5 mL in 100 mL water) and a baking soda solution (5 mL in 100 mL water). After the two solutions are combined, have students again test to show that the combined solution is no longer acidic or basic. Note: The reaction will produce bubbles of carbon dioxide gas. L3

The Large Intestine When the chyme enters the large intestine, it is still a thin, watery mixture. The main job of the large intestine is to absorb water from the undigested mass. This keeps large amounts of water in your body and helps maintain homeostasis. Peristalsis usually slows down in the large intestine. The chyme might stay there for as long as three days. After the excess water is absorbed, the remaining undigested materials become more solid. Muscles in the rectum, which is the last section of the large intestine, and the anus control the release of semisolid wastes from the body in the form of feces (FEE seez).

Bacteria Are Important

Many types of bacteria live in your body. Bacteria live in many of the organs of your digestive tract including your mouth and large intestine. Some of these bacteria live in a relationship that is beneficial to the bacteria and to your body. The bacteria in your large intestine feed on undigested material like cellulose. In turn, bacteria make vitamins you need—vitamin K and two B vitamins. Vitamin K is needed for blood clotting. The two B vitamins, niacin and thiamine, are important for your nervous system and for other body functions. Bacterial action also converts bile pigments into new compounds. The breakdown of intestinal materials by bacteria produces gas.

INTEGRATE Environment

Bacteria The species of bacteria that live in your large intestine are adapted to their habitat. What do you think would happen to the bacteria if their environment were to change? How would this affect your large intestine? Discuss your ideas with a classmate and write your answers in your Science Journal.

INTEGRATE Environment

Bacteria If the environment changed, the bacteria might die, preventing the decomposition of undigested material and the manufacture of certain vitamins.

---

section 2 review

Summary

Functions of the Digestive System
- To process food, your body must ingest, digest, absorb, and eliminate it.

Enzymes
- Enzymes aid the chemical reactions of digestion.

Organs of the Digestive System
- The mouth, esophagus, stomach, small intestine, large intestine, rectum, and anus are the major organs of this system.
- The digestive system also has accessory organs that are important to mechanical and chemical digestion.

Bacteria Are Important
- Bacteria help break down intestinal materials and make vitamins.

Self Check

1. **Compare and contrast** mechanical digestion and chemical digestion.
2. **Explain** how activities in the large intestine help maintain homeostasis.
3. **Describe** the function of each of the organs in the digestive tract.
4. **Explain** how the accessory organs aid digestion.
5. **Think Critically** A cracker contains starch. Explain why a cracker begins to taste sweet after it is in your mouth for five minutes without being chewed.

Applying Skills

6. **Recognize Cause and Effect** What would happen to some of the nutrients in chyme if the pancreas did not secrete its solution into the small intestine?

Science Online bookd.mssciencie.com/self_check_quiz

SECTION 2 The Digestive System **D ◆ 53**

---

section 2 review

1. Mechanical digestion—cutting and grinding by teeth, tongue and peristalsis move food; chemical digestion—the chemical breakdown of food into usable nutrients.

2. Water is removed from wastes and returned to the body.

3. mouth—mechanical and chemical digestion; esophagus—moistens food; stomach—mechanical and chemical digestion; small intestine—chemical digestion and food absorption; large intestine—water absorption; rectum and anus—release wastes

4. liver produces digestive juices and bile that breaks up fat particles; pancreas produces digestive juices

5. Starch is broken down into simple sugars by saliva.

6. Chyme would remain acidic in the digestive tract, possibly causing damage.

Particle Size and Absorption

Real-World Question

Purpose Students will observe the relationship between particle size and rate of dissolving. L2
ELL IN **Naturalist**

Process Skills observe and infer, communicate, recognize cause and effect, separate and control variables, interpret data, compare and contrast

Time Required 50 minutes

Procedure

Safety Precautions Remind students not to taste, eat, or drink any materials used in the lab.

Teaching Strategy

Troubleshooting Be sure the water temperature and amount of water is the same in each beaker.

Analyze Your Data

Expected Outcome Most student lab results will show that the ground sugar particles were the quickest to dissolve.

Goals
- **Compare** the dissolving rates of different sized particles.
- **Predict** the dissolving rate of sugar particles larger than sugar cubes.
- **Predict** the dissolving rate of sugar particles smaller than particles of ground sugar.
- Using the lab results, infer why the body must break down and dissolve food particles.

Materials
250-mL beakers or jars (3)
thermometers (3)
sugar granules
mortar and pestle
triple-beam balance
stirring rod
sugar cubes
weighing paper
warm water
stopwatch

Safety Precautions

WARNING: *Do not taste, eat, or drink any materials used in the lab.*

Real-World Question

Before food reaches the small intestine, it is digested mechanically in the mouth and the stomach. The food mass is reduced to small particles. You can chew an apple into small pieces, but you would feed applesauce to a small child who didn't have teeth. What is the advantage of reducing the size of the food material? How does reducing the size of food particles aid the process of digestion?

Procedure

1. Copy the data table below into your Science Journal.

Dissolving Time of Sugar Particles		
Size of Sugar Particles	Mass	Time Until Dissolved
Sugar cube		Answers will vary.
Sugar granules		
Ground sugar particles		

2. Place a sugar cube into your mortar and grind up the cube with the pestle until the sugar becomes powder.
3. Using the triple-beam balance and weighing paper, measure the mass of the powdered sugar from your mortar. Using separate sheets of weighing paper, measure the mass of a sugar cube and the mass of a sample of the granular sugar. The masses of the powdered sugar, sugar cube, and granular sugar should be approximately equal to each other. Record the three masses in your data table.
4. Place warm water into the three beakers. Use the thermometers to be certain the water in each beaker is the same temperature.

Alternative Inquiry Lab

Absorption Rate Students may further investigate absorption rate by determining if factors other than particle size, such as temperature, affect the rate of dissolution. Students can predict the results and then design an experiment to test their hypothesis.

5. Place the sugar cube in a beaker, the powdered sugar in a second beaker, and the granular sugar in the third beaker. Place all the sugar samples in the beakers at the same time and start the stopwatch when you put the sugar samples in the beaker.

6. Stir each sample equally.

7. **Measure** the time it takes each sugar sample to dissolve and record the times in your data table.

▶ Analyze Your Data

1. **Identify** the experiment's constants and variables.

2. **Compare** the rate at which the sugar samples dissolved. What type of sugar dissolved most rapidly? Which was the slowest to dissolve?

▶ Conclude and Apply

1. **Predict** how long it would take sugar particles larger than the sugar cubes to dissolve. Predict how long it would take sugar particles smaller than the powdered sugar to dissolve.

2. **Infer and explain** the reason why small particles dissolve more rapidly than large particles.

3. **Infer** why you should thoroughly chew your food.

4. **Explain** how reducing the size of food particles aids the process of digestion.

*C*ommunicating
Your Data

Write a news column for a health magazine explaining to health-conscious people what they can do to digest their food better.

LAB D ◆ 55

Answers to Questions

1. The size of the beakers, mass of the sugar samples, temperature of the water in the beakers, and the amount of time each sample is stirred are the constants. The three particle sizes of the sugar are the variables.

2. The sugar cube should dissolve the slowest. The ground sugar particles should dissolve in the least amount of time.

Error Analysis Have students compare their results and attempt to explain any significant differences.

▶ Conclude and Apply

1. Answers will vary, but larger sugar cubes would require more time to dissolve than the three samples used in the experiment, and smaller ground granules would require less time.

2. Small particles have much more surface area exposed to a dissolving agent than large particles.

3. Smaller particles of food will digest more easily than larger food particles. Chewing food thoroughly speeds up the digestion process.

4. To be used by the body, foods must be broken down into nutrients. Once digested, the blood carries these nutrients to all the cells of the body.

☑ Assessment

Process Have students investigate and compare the rate of dissolving among table salt, kosher salt, and rock salt. Use **Performance Assessment in the Science Classroom,** p. 97.

*C*ommunicating
Your Data

Articles should emphasize the idea that smaller particles of food will digest more easily than larger food particles. Chewing food thoroughly speeds up the digestion process. To be used by the body, foods must be broken down into nutrients. Once digested, the blood carries these nutrients to all the cells of the body.

Content Background

Early studies of food by nutritionists and food scientists were steeped in the food traditions of the culture from which they came. For instance, food scientists from the West believed a diet high in protein was essential for good health.

Then, in 1991, the U.S. Department of Agriculture introduced a food pyramid that emphasizes grains and a carbohydrate-rich diet. Some nutritionists believe it is still culturally specific to Americans. Thus, some groups have taken the U.S. food pyramid and adapted it to reflect the culture and foodways of different regions and countries.

Discussion

Proper Diets Why might Western nutritionists suggest that Indian women eat more meat and eggs? Possible answer: The U.S. and European diets were based on consuming animal products and foods high in protein.

Investigate the Issue

Ask students to think about the foods they eat every day. Explain to students that different cultural, age, ethnic, and even family groups have distinct food traditions. Give students the following examples of food traditions: Asian-American students might consume a largely plant-based diet with rice being served at most meals. Share with the class an example of a food tradition in your own family. Then, ask students to name a food tradition or food item that they believe is unique to their family or ethnic or cultural group.

TIME SCIENCE AND Society

SCIENCE ISSUES THAT AFFECT YOU!

Eating Well

Does the same diet work for everyone?

Growing up in India in the first half of the twentieth century, R. Rajalakshmi (RAH jah lok shmee) saw many people around her who did not get enough food. Breakfast for a poor child might have been a cup of tea. Lunch might have consisted of a slice of bread. For dinner, a child might have eaten a serving of rice with a small piece of fish. This type of diet, low in calories and nutrients, produced children who were often sick and died young.

Good Diet, Wrong Place

R. Rajalakshmi studied biochemistry and nutrition at universities in India and in Canada. In the 1960s, she was asked to help manage a program to improve nutrition in her country. At that time, North American and European nutritionists suggested foods that were common and worked well for people who lived in these nations.

Thanks to R. Rajalakshmi and other nutritionists, many children in India are eating well and staying healthy.

For example, they told poor Indian women to eat more meat and eggs and drink more orange juice. But Rajalakshmi knew this advice was useless in a country such as India. People there didn't eat such foods. They weren't easy to find. And for the poor, such foods were too expensive.

The Proper Diet for India

Rajalakshmi knew that for the program to work, it had to fit Indian culture. So she decided to restructure the nutrition program. She first found out what healthy middle class people in India ate. She took note of the nutrients available in those foods. Then she looked for cheap, easy-to-find foods that would provide the same nutrients.

Rajalakshmi created a balanced diet of cheap, locally grown fruits, vegetables, and grains. Legumes (plants related to peas and peanuts), vegetables, and an Indian food called dhokla (DOH kluh) were basics. Dhokla is made of grains, legumes, and leafy vegetables. The grains and legumes provided protein, and the vegetables added vitamins and minerals.

Rajalakshmi's ideas were thought unusual in the 1960s. For example, she insisted that a diet without meat could provide all major nutrients. Now we know she was right. But it took persistence to get others to accept her diet about 40 years ago. Because of Rajalakshmi's program, Indian children almost doubled their food intake. And many children who would have been hungry and ill grew healthy and strong.

Report Choose a continent and research what foods are native to that area. Share your findings with your classmates and compile a list of the foods and where they originated. Using the class list, mark the origins of the different foods on a world map.

Science Online

For more information, visit bookd.msscience.com/time

Report Have students research a specific region, such as a continent, and compile a list of foods that are common there. After students write their lists on the board, direct students to note the differences in diets. Which cultures have a mostly plant-based diet and which have a mostly meat-based diet? What might be the reasons for the difference?

Resources for Teachers and Students

American Food Habits in Historical Perspective by Elain N. McIntosh, Ph.D., R.D. Praeger, 1995

Food and Culture: a Reader. Routledge, 1997

Reviewing Main Ideas

Section 1 Nutrition

1. Proteins, carbohydrates, fats, vitamins, minerals, and water are the six nutrients found in foods.

2. Carbohydrates provide energy, proteins are needed for growth and repair, and fats store energy and cushion organs. Vitamins and minerals regulate functions. Water makes up about 60 percent of your body's mass and is used for a variety of homeostatic functions.

3. Health is affected by the combination of foods that make up a diet.

Section 2 The Digestive System

1. Mechanical digestion breaks down food through chewing and churning.

2. Enzymes and other chemicals aid chemical digestion.

3. Digestion breaks down food into substances that cells can absorb and use. Carbohydrates break down into simple sugars; proteins into amino acids; and fats into fatty acids and glycerol.

4. Food is ingested in the mouth. Digestion occurs in the mouth, stomach, and small intestine, with absorption occurring in the small and large intestines. Wastes are excreted through the anus.

5. The accessory digestive organs move and cut up food and supply digestive enzymes and other chemicals, such as bile, needed for digestion.

6. The large intestine absorbs water, which helps the body maintain homeostasis.

Visualizing Main Ideas

Copy and complete the following table indicating good sources of vitamins and minerals.

Vitamin and Mineral Sources

Food Type	Source of Vitamin	Source of Mineral
Milk	D	calcium
Spinach	A, B, C, K	iron
Meat	B	calcium, potassium
Eggs	E	iron, calcium
Carrots	A	sodium

 bookd.msscience.com/interactive_tutor

CHAPTER STUDY GUIDE D ◆ 57

Reviewing Main Ideas

Summary statements can be used by students to review the major concepts of the chapter.

Visualizing Main Ideas

See student page.

Visit **bookd.msscience.com**
/self_check_quiz
/interactive_tutor
/vocabulary_puzzlemaker
/chapter_review
/standardized_test
/field_guide

Assessment Transparency

For additional assessment questions, use the *Assessment Transparency* located in the transparency book.

Assessment

Nutrients and Digestion

Directions: *Carefully review the table and answer the following questions.*

Ideal Body Weight (kg)—Range for Men and Women		
Height (m)	Ages 19–34	Ages 35 +
1.52	44–58	49–62
1.54	46–60	50–65
1.57	47–62	52–67
1.6	48–64	54–69
1.62	?	55–71
1.65	51–68	57–73
1.67	53–70	59–76
1.7	55–72	61–78

1. Based on the information in the table, which of the following should be the ideal weight range be for somebody who is 1.62 m tall and 27 years old?
   A 53–66   B 49–62   C 50–66   D 48–71

2. These data were collected by studying many different people. If everything remains the same, what would be a healthy weight for someone who is 1.7 m tall and 50 years old?
   F 55   G 59   H 72   J 80

3. A reasonable hypothesis using the table is that when we are younger ____.
   A our legs and arms weigh more
   B we usually weigh more
   C our weight never changes
   D we usually weigh less

Nutrients and Digestion

Identifying Misconceptions

Assess

Use this assessment as follow-up to the F page at the beginning of this chapter.

Materials test tubes, starch solution, Lugol's solution, saliva (collected safely)

Procedure Take two large test tubes and add to each some of the starch solution and Lugol's solution. Add saliva to one of the tubes. Explain that saliva contains an enzyme, amylase. (The danger of using body fluids in experiments should be stressed to students.) The blue color in the tube with the saliva should disappear. Ask students what they think happened to the blue color.

Expected Outcome Students should be able to explain that the enzyme helped digest the starch.

Using Vocabulary

1. Peristalsis
2. villi
3. amino acids
4. chyme
5. Digestion
6. carbohydrates
7. Minerals
8. food group
9. Mechanical digestion
10. vitamin

Checking Concepts

11. D
12. C
13. B
14. A
15. D
16. C
17. B
18. A
19. B

Using Vocabulary

amino acid p. 37	mechanical
carbohydrate p. 38	digestion p. 47
chemical digestion p. 47	mineral p. 42
chyme p. 51	nutrient p. 36
digestion p. 47	peristalsis p. 50
enzyme p. 48	protein p. 37
fat p. 39	villi p. 52
food group p. 44	vitamin p. 40

Fill in the blanks with the correct vocabulary word or words.

1. _____ is the muscular contractions of the esophagus.
2. The _____ increase the surface area of the small intestine.
3. The building blocks of proteins are _____.
4. The liquid product of digestion is called _____.
5. _____ is the breakdown of food.
6. Your body's main source of energy is _____.
7. _____ are inorganic nutrients.
8. Pears and apples belong to the same _____.
9. _____ is when food is chewed and mixed.
10. A(n) _____ is a nutrient needed in small quantities for growth and for regulating body functions.

Checking Concepts

Choose the word or phrase that best answers the question.

11. In which organ is water absorbed?
    A) liver
    B) esophagus
    C) small intestine
    D) large intestine

12. What beneficial substances are produced by bacteria in the large intestine?
    A) fats
    B) minerals
    C) vitamins
    D) proteins

13. Which organ makes bile?
    A) gallbladder
    B) liver
    C) stomach
    D) small intestine

14. Where in humans does most chemical digestion occur?
    A) duodenum
    B) stomach
    C) liver
    D) large intestine

15. Which of these organs is an accessory organ?
    A) mouth
    B) stomach
    C) small intestine
    D) liver

16. Which vitamin is found most abundantly in citrus fruits?
    A) A
    B) B
    C) C
    D) K

17. Where is hydrochloric acid solution added to the food mass?
    A) mouth
    B) stomach
    C) small intestine
    D) large intestine

18. Which of the following is in the same food group as yogurt and cheese?

A)

C)

B)

D)

19. Which organ produces enzymes that help in digestion of proteins, fats, and carbohydrates?
    A) mouth
    B) pancreas
    C) large intestine
    D) gallbladder

Science Online bookd.msscience.com/vocabulary_puzzlemaker

Use the Exam*View*® Pro Testmaker CD-ROM to:
- create multiple versions of tests
- create modified tests with one mouse click for inclusion students
- edit existing questions and add your own questions
- build tests aligned with state standards using built-in State Curriculum Tags
- change English tests to Spanish with one mouse click and vice versa

Thinking Critically

Use the figure below to answer question 20.

Nutrition Facts
Serving Size 1 Meal

Amount Per Serving	
Calories 330	Calories from Fat 60

	% Daily Value*
Total Fat 7g	**10%**
Saturated Fat 3.5g	**17%**
Polyunsaturated Fat 1g	
Monounsaturated Fat 2.5g	
Cholesterol 35mg	**12%**
Sodium 460mg	**19%**
Total Carbohydrate 52g	**18%**
Dietary Fiber 6g	**24%**
Sugars 17g	
Protein 15g	

Vitamin A 15%	• Vitamin C 70%
Calcium 4%	• Iron 10%

* Percent Daily Values are based on a 2,000 calorie diet. Your daily values may be higher or lower depending on your calorie needs.

	Calories	2,000	2,500
Total Fat	Less than	65g	80g
Sat Fat	Less than	20g	25g
Cholesterol	Less than	300mg	300mg
Sodium	Less than	2,400mg	2,400mg
Total Carbohydrate		300g	375g
Dietary Fiber		25g	30g

20. **Explain** how the information on the food label above can help you make healthful food choices.

21. **Infer** Food does not enter your body until it is absorbed into the blood. Explain why.

22. **Discuss** the meaning of the familiar statement "You are what you eat." Base your answer on your knowledge of food groups and nutrients.

23. **Explain** Bile's action is similar to that of soap. Use this information to explain how bile works on fats.

24. **Compare and contrast** the three types of carbohydrates—sugar, starch, and fiber.

Performance Activities

25. **Project** Research the ingredients used in antacid medications. Identify the compounds used to neutralize the excess stomach acid. Note the time, and then place an antacid tablet in a glass of vinegar—an acid. Using pH paper, check when the acid is neutralized. Record the time it took for the antacid to neutralize the vinegar. Repeat this procedure with different antacids. Compare your results.

Applying Math

26. **Villi Surface Area** The surface area of the villi in your small intestine is comparable to the area of a tennis court. A tennis court measures 11.0 m by 23.8 m. What is the area of a tennis court—and the surface area of the small intestine's villi—in square meters?

Use the table below to answer question 27.

Recommended Dietary Allowances	
Nutrient	**Percent U.S. RDA**
Protein	2
Vitamin A	20
Vitamin C	25
Vitamin D	15
Calcium (Ca)	less than 2
Iron (Fe)	25
Zinc (Zn)	15
Total fat	5
Saturated fat	3
Cholesterol	0
Sodium	3

27. **Nutrients** A product nutrient label is shown above. Make a bar graph of this information.

Thinking Critically

20. This information can help you plan meals that supply the daily recommended amounts of nutrients and meet special dietary requirements.

21. As food passes through the digestive tract it is broken down into smaller pieces, eventually reaching the molecular level. These molecules are absorbed by the blood, transported to body cells, and used as an energy source.

22. If we eat nutritious food, the body will have good building blocks to use. A poor diet will not supply good building blocks.

23. Bile breaks down fats into smaller droplets, which have an increased surface area; this allows digestion to occur more quickly and easily.

24. Sugar—simple carbohydrate, dissolves in water, tastes sweet; starch and fiber—complex carbohydrates, do not dissolve in water; fiber absorbs water, starch does not.

Performance Activities

25. Common ingredients in antacids include sodium bicarbonate, calcium carbonate, ranitidine hydrochloride, and famotidine. Use **Performance Assessment in the Science Classroom,** p. 115.

Applying Math

National Math Standards
1, 4, 5, 6, 9

26. 11.0 m × 23.8 m = 261.8 m²

27. Check student graphs to ensure consistency with data provided.

Assessment Resources

Reproducible Masters

Chapter *Fast File* Resources
Chapter Review, pp. 35–36
Chapter Tests, pp. 37–40
Assessment Transparency Activity, p. 47

Glencoe Science Web site
Chapter Review Test
Standardized Test Practice

Glencoe Technology
- Assessment Transparency
- Exam*View*® Pro Testmaker
- MindJogger Videoquiz
- Interactive Chalkboard

FAST FILE

Answer Sheet A practice answer sheet can be found at bookd.msscience.com/answer_sheet.

S A M P L E

Part 1 Multiple Choice

1. C	4. D
2. C	5. B
3. A	6. D

Part 2 Short Response

7. Organic nutrients, like proteins, carbohydrates, fats, and vitamins, contain carbon; inorganic nutrients, like minerals and water, do not contain carbon.

Part 1 Multiple Choice

Record your answers on the answer sheet provided by your teacher or on a sheet of paper.

1. How many amino acids are required by your body?
   A. 5   C. 20
   B. 12   D. 50

Use the illustration below to answer questions 2 and 3.

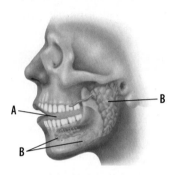

2. How does the organ labeled "A" help break down food?
   A. produces enzymes
   B. produces saliva
   C. moves food around
   D. produces mucus

3. Which of the following is produced by the organs labeled "B"?
   A. saliva   C. hydrochloric acid
   B. bile   D. chyme

Test-Taking Tip

Using Tables Concentrate on what the question is asking from a table, not all the information in the table.

Question 4 Look in the column titled *DV (Daily Values)* to find what the question asks, then follow the row to the *Item* column to find the answer.

Use the table below to answer questions 4 and 5.

Nutrition Facts of Vanilla Ice Cream		
Item	**Amount**	**DV (Daily Values)**
Serving Size	112 g	0
Calories	208	0
Total Fat	19 g	29%
Saturated Fat	11 g	55%
Cholesterol	0.125 g	42%
Sodium	0.90 g	4%
Total Carbohydrates	22 g	7%
Fiber	0 g	0%
Sugars	22 g	n/a
Protein	5 g	n/a
Calcium	0.117 g	15%
Iron	n/a	0%

4. According to the table above, which mineral has the greatest DV?
   A. sodium   C. iron
   B. cholesterol   D. calcium

5. If you had two servings of this vanilla ice cream, how many grams of saturated fat and Daily Value (DV) percentage would you eat?
   A. 11 g, 110%   C. 21 g, 55%
   B. 22 g, 110%   D. 5.5 g, 110%

6. Which of the following is the correct sequence of the organs of the digestive tract?
   A. mouth, stomach, esophagus, small intestine, large intestine
   B. esophagus, mouth, stomach, small intestine, large intestine
   C. mouth, esophagus, small intestine, stomach, large intestine
   D. mouth, esophagus, stomach, small intestine, large intestine

8. teen playing soccer; More water is being lost through the skin (sweat).

9. teen playing soccer; An active person needs more food energy to meet the increased demand for energy.

10. eggs, milk, cheese, and meat

11. Bile breaks up the large fat particles.

12. An essential amino acid is one that cannot be made by the body's cells.

13. These bacteria make vitamin K and two B vitamins, niacin and thiamine. They also convert bile pigments into new compounds.

14. Fats are a good storage unit for energy, help the body absorb vitamins, and cushion internal organs.

15. Enzymes help speed up reactions responsible for building the body, are involved in energy releasing activities of muscles and nerve cells, and aid in blood clotting.

16. $540 \div 180 = 3$

Part 2 | Short Response/Grid In

Record your answers on the answer sheet provided by your teacher or on a sheet of paper.

7. Explain the difference between organic and inorganic nutrients. Name a class of nutrients for each.

Use the photos below to answer questions 8 and 9.

8. During the activity shown above, which of the two teens is losing more body water? Why?

9. Based on the activity shown above, which teen may need more food energy (Calories)? Why?

10. Name three food sources that contain complete proteins.

11. How does bile help in digestion?

12. What is meant by an "essential amino acid"?

13. How do bacteria that live in the large intestine help your body?

14. Explain the importance of fats in the body.

15. Enzymes play an important role in the digestive process. But enzyme-aided reactions are also involved in other body systems. Give an example of how enzymes are used by the body in a way that does not involve the digestive system.

16. A taco has 180 Calories (Cal) and an ice cream sundae has 540 Cal. How many tacos could you eat to equal the number of Calories in the ice cream sundae?

Part 3 | Open Ended

Record your answers on a sheet of paper.

17. Explain what might happen to a child who is deficient in vitamin D. What foods should be eaten to prevent a deficiency in vitamin D?

18. Certain bacteria that do not normally live in the body can make toxins that affect intestinal absorption. Explain what might happen if these bacteria were present in the small and large intestines.

Use the illustration below to answer questions 19 and 20.

19. Identify the food group shown at the base of the food pyramid. Explain why the greatest number of servings should come from this group.

20. Identify the food group at the top of the pyramid. Explain why the least number of servings should come from this group.

21. Antibiotics may be given to help a person fight off a bacterial infection. If a person is taking antibiotics, what might happen to the normal bacteria living in the large intestine? How would this affect the body?

22. Sometimes the esophagus can be affected by a disease in which peristalsis is not normal and the band of muscle at the entrance to the stomach does not work properly. What do you think would happen to food that the person swallowed?

20. The food group at the top of the pyramid is fats, oils, and sweets. The least number of servings should come from this group because they may have lots of Calories that supply energy, but provide only some of the nutrients that the body needs.

21. Antibiotics kill the bacteria that cause the infection, but may also kill some of the bacteria normally in the large intestine. These bacteria produce vitamins and break down intestinal materials, so vitamin production and bacterial breakdown may not occur or may be reduced.

22. The person would have difficulty swallowing food, and, because the muscle at the stomach entrance is not working properly, undigested food could go back up the esophagus.

Rubrics

For more help evaluating open-ended assessment questions, see the rubric on p. 10T.

Part 3 | Open Ended

17. Vitamin D helps bones and teeth absorb calcium and phosphorus, which makes them hard. A child with vitamin D deficiency would not have hard bones and teeth. Good food sources of vitamin D are fortified milk, butter, eggs, fish liver oil, and sunshine on the skin.

18. These bacteria affect intestinal absorption, which would affect absorption of food and water. Water would not be reabsorbed into the body through the intestines, affecting homeostasis. All the nutrients from the food may not be absorbed. Excess food and water in the bowel would cause diarrhea.

19. The food group at the base of the pyramid is the bread, cereal, rice, and pasta group. The greatest number of servings should come from this group because these foods are carbohydrates, which are the main sources of energy for the body.

Section/Objectives	Standards		Labs/Features
Chapter Opener	**National**	**State/Local**	**Launch Lab:** Comparing Circulatory and Road Systems, p. 63 **Foldables**, p. 63 A data-collection lab using Probeware technology can be found in the **Probeware Lab Manual**, pp. 5–8
	See pp. 16T–17T for a Key to Standards.		
Section 1 The Circulatory System 🕐 3 sessions 📦 1.5 blocks 1. **Compare and contrast** arteries, veins, and capillaries. 2. **Explain** how blood moves through the heart. 3. **Identify** the functions of the pulmonary and systemic circulation systems.	National Content Standards: UCP.1–UCP.3, UCP.5, A.1, A.2, C.1, C.3, C.5		**MiniLAB:** Inferring How Hard the Heart Works, p. 65 **Integrate Physics**, p. 69 **Visualizing Atherosclerosis**, p. 70 **Science Online**, p. 71 **Lab:** The Heart as a Pump, p. 73
Section 2 Blood 🕐 2 sessions 📦 1 block 4. **Identify** the parts and functions of blood. 5. **Explain** why blood types are checked before a transfusion. 6. **Give examples** of diseases of blood.	National Content Standards: UCP.1–UCP.3, UCP.5, A.1, A.2, C.1, C.3, C.5		**Science Online**, p. 75 **MiniLAB:** Modeling Scab Formation, p. 76 **Integrate History**, p. 78 **Applying Science:** Will there be enough blood donors?, p. 78
Section 3 The Lymphatic System 🕐 2 sessions 📦 1 block 7. **Describe** the functions of the lymphatic system. 8. **Identify** where lymph comes from. 9. **Explain** how lymph organs help fight infections.	National Content Standards: UCP.1–UCP.5, A.1, A.2, C.1, C.3, C.5, G.1, G.3		**Lab:** Blood Type Reactions, p. 82 **Science and History:** Have a Heart, p. 84

Lab Materials	Reproducible Resources	Section Assessment	Technology
Launch Lab: a city, county, or state map; Science Journal	**Chapter *FAST FILE* Resources** Foldables Worksheet, p. 17 Directed Reading Overview, p. 19 Note-taking Worksheets, pp. 33–37	GLENCOE'S **ASSESSMENT** ADVANTAGE	Teacher**Works** includes: • Interactive Teacher Edition • Lesson Planner with calendar • Access to all program blacklines • Correlations to standards • Web links
MiniLAB: bowl of water, stopwatch or clock **Lab:** watch or clock with second hand *Need materials?* Contact Science Kit at 1-800-828-7777 or www.sciencekit.com on the Internet.	**Chapter *FAST FILE* Resources** Transparency Activity, p. 46 MiniLAB, p. 3 Enrichment, p. 30 Reinforcement, p. 27 Directed Reading, p. 20 Lab Worksheet, pp. 5–6 Lab Activities, pp. 9–12, 13–16 Transparency Activity, pp. 49–50 **Home and Community Involvement,** p. 26	**Portfolio** Assessment, p. 72 **Performance** MiniLAB, p. 65 Applying Skills, p. 72 **Content** Section Review, p. 72 Challenge, p. 70	Section Focus Transparency Teaching Transparency Virtual Labs CD-ROM Guided Reading Audio Program Interactive Chalkboard CD-ROM
MiniLAB: gauze, aluminum foil, liquid bandage solution, dropper, water	**Chapter *FAST FILE* Resources** Transparency Activity, p. 47 MiniLAB, p. 4 Enrichment, p. 31 Reinforcement, p. 28 Directed Reading, p. 20 **Mathematics Skill Activities,** p. 33 **Cultural Diversity,** p. 18	**Portfolio** Challenge, p. 76 **Performance** MiniLAB, p. 76 Applying Math, p. 79 **Content** Section Review, p. 79	Section Focus Transparency Virtual Labs CD-ROM Guided Reading Audio Program Interactive Chalkboard CD-ROM
Lab: simulated blood (10 mL low-fat milk and 10 mL water plus red food coloring), lemon juice, water, droppers, small paper cups, marking pen, 10-mL graduated cylinder	**Chapter *FAST FILE* Resources** Transparency Activity, p. 48 Enrichment, p. 32 Reinforcement, p. 29 Directed Reading, pp. 21, 22 Lab Worksheet, pp. 7–8 **Lab Management and Safety,** p. 69	**Portfolio** Check for Understanding, p. 81 **Performance** Applying Skills, p. 81 **Content** Section Review, p. 81	Section Focus Transparency Virtual Labs CD-ROM Guided Reading Audio Program Interactive Chalkboard CD-ROM Video Lab Probeware Lab

End of Chapter Assessment

GLENCOE'S **ASSESSMENT** ADVANTAGE

Blackline Masters	Technology	Professional Series
Chapter *FAST FILE* Resources Chapter Review, pp. 39–40 Chapter Tests, pp. 41–44 **Standardized Test Practice,** pp. 15–18	MindJogger Videoquiz Virtual Labs CD-ROM Exam*View*® Pro Testmaker TeacherWorks CD-ROM Interactive Chalkboard CD-ROM	**Performance Assessment in the Science Classroom (PASC)**

Transparencies

Section Focus

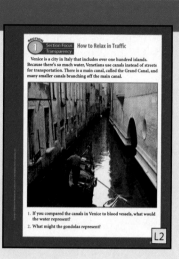

SECTION 1 Section Focus Transparency **How to Relax in Traffic**

Venice is a city in Italy that includes over one hundred islands. Because there's so much water, Venetians use canals instead of streets for transportation. There is a main canal, called the Grand Canal, and many smaller canals branching off the main canal.

1. If you compared the canals in Venice to blood vessels, what would the water represent?
2. What might the gondolas represent?

L2

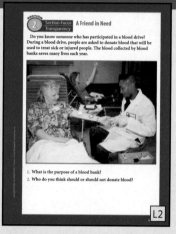

SECTION 2 Section Focus Transparency **A Friend in Need**

Do you know someone who has participated in a blood drive? During a blood drive, people are asked to donate blood that will be used to treat sick or injured people. The blood collected by blood banks saves many lives each year.

1. What is the purpose of a blood bank?
2. Who do you think should or should not donate blood?

L2

SECTION 3 Section Focus Transparency **Here I Come to Save the Day!**

This image shows a cell from the immune system at work. A white blood cell is devouring an invading organism. The only part of the organism that can be seen is at the lower right portion of the photo. It is being sucked into the tube-like extension of the colorful white blood cell.

1. Describe what is happening to the invading organism.
2. What purpose do you think white blood cells serve?

L2

This is a representation of key blackline masters available in the Teacher Classroom Resources. See Resource Manager boxes within the chapter for additional information.

Key to Teaching Strategies

The following designations will help you decide which activities are appropriate for your students.

L1 Level 1 activities should be appropriate for students with learning difficulties.

L2 Level 2 activities should be within the ability range of all students.

L3 Level 3 activities are designed for above-average students.

ELL ELL activities should be within the ability range of English-Language Learners.

COOP LEARN Cooperative Learning activities are designed for small group work.

LS Multiple Learning Styles logos, as described on page 12T, are used throughout to indicate strategies that address different learning styles.

P These strategies represent student products that can be placed into a best-work portfolio.

PBL Problem-Based Learning activities apply real-world situations to learning.

Assessment

Assessment Transparency **Circulation**

Directions: Carefully review the table and answer the following questions.

Regional HIV/AIDS Statistics, December 1998

Region	Individuals living with AIDS/HIV	Individuals newly infected HIV	Women with HIV (%)
South and Southeast Asia	6,700,000	1,200,000	25
Western Europe	500,000	30,000	20
North America	890,000	44,000	20
Sub-Saharan Africa	22,500,000	4,000,000	50
Latin America	1,400,000	160,000	20

1. According to the table, which region has the most people infected and living with AIDS/HIV?
   A Latin America   C North America
   B South & Southeast Asia   D Sub-Saharan Africa
2. According to the table, in which region is 75 percent of the HIV-infected population male?
   F Western Europe   H South & Southeast Asia
   G Sub-Saharan Africa   J North America
3. The total world population of individuals living with HIV/AIDS is 33.4 million. Approximately what percentage of these individuals live in the Sub-Sahara African region?
   A 5%   B 10%   C 70%   D 100%

L2

Teaching

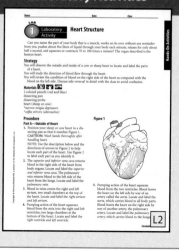

SECTION 1 Teaching Transparency **Pulmonary Circulation**

L2

Hands-on Activities

Student Text Lab Worksheet

Activity **The Heart as a Pump**

Lab Preview
Directions: Answer these questions before you begin the Activity.
1. How is your pulse related to your heart?

2. Why is it important to know your pulse?

The heart is a pumping organ. Blood is forced through the arteries as heart muscles contract and then relax. This creates a series of waves in blood as it flows through the arteries. These waves are called the pulse. Try this activity to learn how physical activity affects your pulse.

What You'll Investigate
What does the pulse rate tell you about the work of the heart?

Materials
watch or clock with second hand
*stopwatch,
*Alternate materials

Goals
• Observe pulse rate.
• Compare pulse rate at rest to rate after jogging.

Procedure
1. Use the table below to record your data.
2. Sit down to take your pulse. Your partner will serve as the recorder.
3. Find your pulse by placing the middle and index fingers over the radial artery in your wrist as shown in Figure 1. WARNING: Do not press too hard.
4. Count each beat of the radial pulse silently for 15 s. Multiply the number of beats by four to find your pulse rate per minute. Have your partner record the number in the data table.
5. Now jog in place for 1 min and take your pulse again. Count the beats for 15 s.
6. Calculate this new pulse rate and have your partner record it in the data table.

Figure 1

Reverse roles with your partner and repeat steps 2 through 6.
8. Collect and record the new data in Table 1.

Data and Observations
Table 1

Pulse Rate		
Pulse rate	Partner's	Yours
At rest		
After jogging		

L2

Laboratory Activities

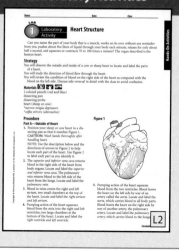

LAB 1 Laboratory Activity **Heart Structure**

Can you name the part of your body that is a muscle, works on its own without any reminder from you, pushes about five liters of liquid through your body each minute, relaxes for only about half a second, and squeezes or contracts 70 to 100 times a minute? The organ described is the human heart.

Strategy
You will observe the outside and inside of a cow or sheep heart to locate and label the parts of a heart.
You will study the direction of blood flow through the heart.
You will review the condition of blood on the right side of the heart as compared with the blood on the left side. Discuss side reversal in detail with the class to avoid confusion.

Materials
2 colored pencils (red and blue)
dissecting pan
dissecting probe
heart (sheep or cow)
*narrow tongue depressors
*coffee stirrers (alternative)

Procedure
Part A—Outside of Heart
1. Position your sheep or cow heart in a dissecting pan so that it matches Figure 1. CAUTION: Wash hands thoroughly after handling heart.
NOTE: Use the description below and the directions of arrows in Figure 2 to help locate each part of the heart. Use Figure 2 to label each part as you identify it.
2. The superior and inferior vena cava return blood to the right side of the heart from body organs. Locate and label the superior and inferior vena cava. The pulmonary vein returns blood to the left side of the heart from the lungs. Locate and label the pulmonary vein.

Figure 1

Pumping action of the heart squeezes blood from the atria into the right and left ventricles, two large chambers at the bottom of the heart. Locate and label the right ventricle and left ventricle.

5. Pumping action of the heart squeezes blood from two ventricles. Blood leaves the heart on the left side by way of an artery called the aorta. Locate and label the aorta, which carries blood to all body parts. Blood leaves the heart on the right side by way of another artery, the pulmonary artery. Locate and label the pulmonary artery, which carries blood to the lungs.

L2

Resource Manager

Meeting Different Ability Levels

Content Outline

L2

Reinforcement

L2

Enrichment

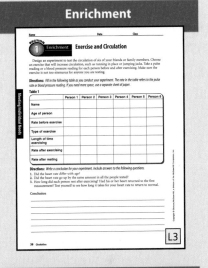

L3

Directed Reading (English/Spanish)

L1

Study Guide

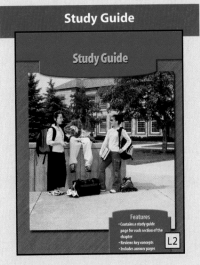

Study Guide

Features
• Contains a study guide page for each section of the chapter
• Reviews key concepts
• Includes answer pages

L2

Reading Essentials

Reading Essentials for Glencoe Science
An Interactive Student Workbook

Features
• Condensed core content
• Actively involves students in reading
• Reinforces key vocabulary

L1

Assessment

Test Practice Workbook

L2

Chapter Review

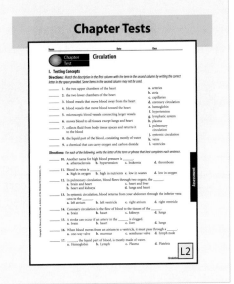

L2

Chapter Tests

L2

Science Content Background

section 1 The Circulatory System
How Materials Move Through the Body

In 1628, William Harvey published his findings, which indicated that blood in the human body follows "a motion as it were in a circle." Pumped by the heart, the blood moved through arteries into the body and returned to the heart via the veins. However, it was still a mystery how the blood made its way from the arteries, through tissues, and into the veins. Not until the invention of the microscope was it discovered that minute vessels, the capillaries, made the connection.

The Heart

The heart is a muscular organ that lies in the thoracic cavity between the lungs. It is enclosed by a protective sac of fibrous tissue, the pericardium.

The initiation of the heartbeat originates within the heart muscle. The sinoatrial node is a modified piece of cardiac muscle tissue located near the superior vena cava. An impulse for this node spreads to the atria of the heart, causing them to contract. Another node (atrioventricular) receives the signal and then transmits it to the ventricles, causing them to contract.

The first human heart transplant was conducted in 1967. The first permanent artificial heart was implanted in 1982, but the patient lived for only three months afterward. In July 2001, a self-contained, battery-powered, titanium and plastic heart was implanted into a man, who lived for thirteen months afterward.

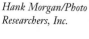

Hank Morgan/Photo Researchers, Inc.

Blood Vessels

A cross section of arteries and veins shows that the walls have three layers. The inner lining of the vessels is covered with two types of tissue; one of these is a network of elastic connective tissue. The middle layer is smooth muscle and elastic tissue. The outer layer is collagenous connective tissue. The middle layer in veins is less developed than it is in arteries, and therefore collapses more easily. Capillaries have walls only one cell thick. This allows materials to diffuse through them. So numerous are the capillaries in the body that most cells are less than one-fourth of a millimeter from a capillary.

Blood Pressure

The pressure in the blood vessels is the result of a greater amount of blood being pumped into the arteries than can be absorbed by the arterioles and capillaries. Blood pressure is measured in millimeters of mercury with a sphygmomanometer. The person taking the blood pressure is listening for the flow of blood to be cut off and then return to normal while taking note of the respective pressures.

> ### Teacher to Teacher
> Edward G. Ezrailson, Ph.D.
> Science Consultant
> Spring, TX
>
> "The discussion of the circulatory system provides an opportunity to integrate the sciences. Supernovas are known to produce elements found in nature. The iron bound to hemoglobin came from deep space in this manner when the planets were formed."
>
> *Edward G. Ezrailson, Ph.D.*

Blood
A Liquid Tissue

The liquid component of blood, plasma, is a complex solution of organic and inorganic substances dissolved in water. Blood is about 90 percent water and eight percent proteins. The remaining two percent is made up of dissolved substances such as electrolytes, gases, and nutrients. Blood characteristics such as pH and sugar content are precisely controlled by the body. The pH of blood is slightly alkaline, and serious problems can occur if the pH changes only slightly. Because blood supplies for transfusions often are in short supply, synthetic substitutes for blood or blood parts are being developed.

The Lymphatic System
Understanding Tissue Fluid

The lymphatic system can be thought of as a branch of the circulatory system. Lymph is blood plasma that has diffused and filtered from the blood capillaries into the spaces between cells. Often the lymph in these spaces is referred to as intercellular or interstitial fluid. Like blood plasma, lymph consists mainly of water, some dissolved substances, and white blood cells called lymphocytes.

Lymph from the interstitial spaces passes through lymph capillaries, larger lymph vessels, lymph nodes, and lymph glands before entering a vein. Lymph is not under great pressure; therefore, external forces are needed to cause it to flow. Gravity plays a role in the movement of lymph above the heart. Other forces include the contraction of smooth muscles in the larger lymphatic vessels, the contraction of skeletal muscles, and the movements of breathing muscles. Backflow of lymph is prevented by valves in the large lymph vessels.

When skin is subjected to continued friction or pressure, a blow, or heat, the blood capillaries

Charles Gupton/The Stock Market

dilate. Lymph accumulates in the injured area, and a liquid-filled blister is formed under the skin. If there is poor circulation in a region of the body, lymph may collect and cause a swelling called edema.

chapter content resources

Internet Resources
For additional content background, visit
bookd.msscience.com to:
- access your book online
- find references to related articles in popular science magazines
- access Web links with related content background
- access current events with science journal topics

Print Resources
Biology (6th Edition), by Neil A. Campbell, Jane B. Reece, Pearson Benjamin Cummings Publishing, 2001
Human Anatomy & Physiology (5th Edition), by Elaine N. Marieb, Pearson Benjamin Cummings Publishing, 2000
Principles of Human Physiology, by William J. Germann, Cindy L. Stanfield; Pearson Benjamin Cummings Publishing, 2001

chapter 3

Chapter Vocabulary

atrium, p. 65
ventricle, p. 65
coronary circulation, p. 65
pulmonary circulation, p. 66
systemic circulation, p. 67
artery, p. 68
vein, p. 68
capillary, p. 69
plasma, p. 74
hemoglobin, p. 75
platelet, p. 75
lymph, p. 80
lymphatic system, p. 80
lymphocyte, p. 80
lymph node, p. 80

Science Journal Student responses may vary, but may include questions about blood, the heart, and lungs.

INTERACTIVE CHALKBOARD with Image Bank

PowerPoint® Presentations

This CD-ROM is an editable Microsoft® PowerPoint® presentation that includes:

- a pre-made presentation for every chapter
- interactive graphics
- animations
- audio clips
- image bank
- all new section and chapter questions
- Standardized Test Practice
- transparencies
- pre-lab questions for all labs
- Foldables directions
- links to bookd.msscience.com

Circulation

chapter preview

sections

1 The Circulatory System
Lab The Heart as a Pump

2 Blood

3 The Lymphatic System
Lab Blood Type Reactions

Virtual Lab What factors affect the likelihood of hypertension?

62 ◆ D

What does a highway have to do with circulation?

Think of this interchange as a simplified way to visualize how your blood travels through your body. Your complex circulatory system also plays an important role in protecting you from disease.

Science Journal Infer how the circulatory system provides your body with the nutrients it needs to stay healthy?

Theme Connection

Stability and Change The circulatory system is a good example of a system that functions to maintain stability and respond to changes in human life processes.

About the Photo

Transportation Systems Highway interchanges, like this one in England, are used in the same way that the circulatory system uses blood vessels. There are about 40 billion microscopic capillaries and they constitute the majority of the body's 100,000 miles of vessels. The circumference of Earth at the equator is about 25,000 miles. If all of the blood vessels in one adult were laid end to end, they would circle the equator four times.

Start-Up Activities

Comparing Circulatory and Road Systems

If you look at an aerial view of a road system, as shown in the photograph, you see roads leading in many directions. These roads provide a way to carry people and goods from one place to another. Your circulatory system is like a road system. Just as roads are used to transport goods to homes and factories, your blood vessels transport substances throughout your body.

1. Look at a map of your city, county, or state.

2. Identify roads that are interstates, as well as state and county routes, using the map key.

3. Plan a route to a destination that your teacher describes. Then plan a different return trip.

4. Draw a diagram in your Science Journal showing your routes to and from the destination.

5. **Think Critically** If the destination represents your heart, what do the routes represent? Draw a comparison between a blocked road on your map and a clogged artery in your body.

Circulation Your body is supplied with nutrients by blood circulating through your blood vessels. Make the following Foldable to help you organize information about circulation.

STEP 1 **Fold** a sheet of paper in half lengthwise. Make the back edge about 5 cm longer than the front edge.

STEP 2 **Turn** the paper so the fold is on the bottom. Then, **fold** it into thirds.

STEP 3 **Unfold and cut** only the top layer along both folds to make three tabs. **Label** the top of the page *Circulation*, and label the three tabs *Pulmonary*, *Coronary*, and *Systemic*.

Read and Write As you read the chapter, write about each section under its tab.

 Preview this chapter's content and activities at bookd.msscience.com

---

Purpose Use the Launch Lab to help students model how the circulatory system transports substances throughout the body.
L2 **LS** **Visual-Spatial**

Preparation Obtain enough maps so that each group can plan a route to and from a different destination.

Materials maps of your city, county, or state; Science Journal

Teaching Strategy Help students interpret the map key. Point out that colors as well as symbols can be used to denote different types of roads.

Think Critically

Possible answer: The routes represent the blood vessels that transport materials to and from the heart.

Assessment

Oral Again refer students to their map's legend. Have them infer why there are different types of roads and how they might be analogous to the circulatory system. Different types of roads carry different amounts of traffic at different speeds. They are analogous to different sizes of blood vessels in the body. Use **Performance Assessment in the Science Classroom**, p. 89.

FOLDABLES **Dinah Zike**
Study Organizer **Study Fold**

Student preparation materials for this Foldable are available in the **Chapter FAST FILE Resources.**

Probeware Labs

This chapter's data-collection lab using Probeware technology is included on the *Video Labs CD-ROM*. See the *Probeware Lab Manual* pages 5–8 for student worksheets.

D ◆ 63

The Circulatory System

as you read

What **You'll Learn**

- **Compare and contrast** arteries, veins, and capillaries.
- **Explain** how blood moves through the heart.
- **Identify** the functions of the pulmonary and systemic circulation systems.

Why **It's Important**

Your body's cells depend on the blood vessels to bring nutrients and remove wastes.

Review Vocabulary
heart: organ that circulates blood through your body continuously

New Vocabulary
- atrium
- ventricle
- coronary circulation
- pulmonary circulation
- systemic circulation
- artery
- vein
- capillary

How Materials Move Through the Body

It's time to get ready for school, but your younger sister is taking a long time in the shower. "Don't use up all the water," you shout. Water is carried throughout your house in pipes that are part of the plumbing system. The plumbing system supplies water for all your needs and carries away wastes. Just as you expect water to flow when you turn on the faucet, your body needs a continuous supply of oxygen and nutrients and a way to remove wastes. In a similar way materials are moved throughout your body by your cardiovascular (kar dee oh VAS kyuh lur) system. It includes your heart, kilometers of blood vessels, and blood.

Blood vessels carry blood to every part of your body, as shown in **Figure 1.** Blood moves oxygen and nutrients to cells and carries carbon dioxide and other wastes away from the cells. Sometimes blood carries substances made in one part of the body to another part of the body where these substances are needed. Movement of materials into and out of your cells occurs by diffusion (dih FYEW zhun) and active transport. Diffusion occurs when a material moves from an area where there is more of it to an area where there is less of it. Active transport is the opposite of diffusion. Active transport requires an input of energy from the cell, but diffusion does not.

Figure 1 The blood is pumped by the heart to all the cells of the body and then back to the heart through a network of blood vessels.

The Heart

Your heart is an organ made of cardiac muscle tissue. It is located behind your breastbone, called the sternum, and between your lungs. Your heart has four compartments called chambers. The two upper chambers are called the right and left **atriums** (AY tree umz). The two lower chambers are called the right and left **ventricles** (VEN trih kulz). During one heartbeat, both atriums contract at the same time. Then, both ventricles contract at the same time. A one-way valve separates each atrium from the ventricle below it. The blood flows only in one direction from an atrium to a ventricle, then from a ventricle into a blood vessel. A wall prevents blood from flowing between the two atriums or the two ventricles. This wall keeps blood rich in oxygen separate from blood low in oxygen. If oxygen-rich blood and oxygen-poor blood were to mix, your body's cells would not get all the oxygen they need.

Scientists have divided the circulatory system into three sections—coronary circulation, pulmonary (PUL muh ner ee) circulation, and systemic circulation. The beating of your heart controls blood flow through each section.

Coronary Circulation Your heart has its own blood vessels that supply it with nutrients and oxygen and remove wastes. **Coronary** (KOR uh ner ee) **circulation,** as shown in **Figure 2,** is the flow of blood to and from the tissues of the heart. When the coronary circulation is blocked, oxygen and nutrients cannot reach all the cells of the heart. This can result in a heart attack.

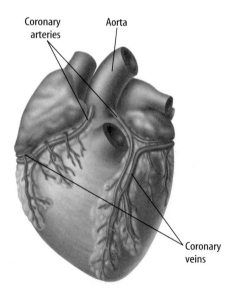

Coronary arteries

Aorta

Coronary veins

Figure 2 Like the rest of the body, the heart receives the oxygen and nutrients that it needs from the blood. The blood also carries away wastes from the heart's cells. On the diagram, you can see the coronary arteries, which nourish the heart.

Mini LAB

Inferring How Hard the Heart Works

Procedure

1. Make a fist and observe its size, which is approximately the size of your heart.
2. Place your fist in a **bowl of water.** Then clench and unclench your fist to cause water to squirt out between your thumb and forefinger.
3. Continue the squeezing action for 3 min. Determine the number of squeezes per minute.

Analysis

1. State how many times you squeezed your fist in 1 min. A resting heart beats approximately 70 times per minute.
2. What can you do when the muscles of your hand and arm get tired? Explain why cardiac muscle does not get tired.

Try at Home

---

2 Teach

Mini LAB

Purpose Students explore heart rate. **L2** **ELL**
LS Logical-Mathematical

Materials bowl of water, stopwatch or clock

Teaching Strategy Students must squeeze at a steady rate throughout the entire minute.

Troubleshooting Place newspaper around the bowl to absorb spilled water.

Analysis

1. Answers will vary, but most will find it difficult to maintain the 70-clenches-per-minute rate.
2. Students can stop or change hands when tired. The heart must beat continuously in order to maintain the body's activities.

Assessment

Process Have students infer the tiring time for cardiac muscles and compare this with the tiring time for skeletal muscles. Use **Performance Assessment in the Science Classroom,** p. 89.

Try at Home

Curriculum Connection

History Galen (born in A.D. 129) was a physician and scientist who wrote about the heart and circulation of blood. Have students find out three things that Galen discovered about the circulatory system as he dissected different animals. Galen described heart valves in detail, noted the differences between arteries and veins, and showed that arteries carry blood, not air, as had been thought for 400 years.

Visual Learning

Figure 3 Direct students to trace the flow of blood through the heart. Then have them explain why this definition of veins is correct or incorrect: "Pulmonary veins are vessels that carry more carbon dioxide than oxygen." The statement is incorrect. In pulmonary circulation the veins carry more oxygen than carbon dioxide. L2 IS **Visual-Spatial**

Quick Demo

The Heart

Materials a beef heart

Estimated Time 10 minutes

Procedure Have students examine the heart. Draw attention to the thick, muscular walls of the ventricles, which are necessary to provide a lifetime of pumping action.

Use Science Words

Word Origins The body's largest artery is the aorta. The name has its origin in the Greek word *aorte*, meaning "to raise or lift." Discuss why this is an appropriate word for this vessel. The aorta rises from the top of the heart.

Blood, high in carbon dioxide and low in oxygen, returns from the body to the heart. It enters the right atrium through the superior and inferior vena cavae.

Oxygen-rich blood travels from the lungs through the pulmonary veins and into the left atrium. The pulmonary veins are the only veins that carry oxygen-rich blood.

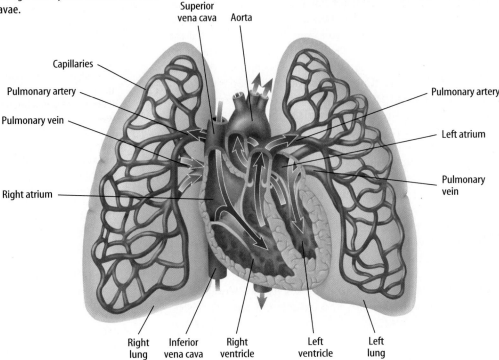

The right atrium contracts, forcing the blood into the right ventricle. When the right ventricle contracts, the blood leaves the heart and goes through the pulmonary arteries to the lungs. The pulmonary arteries are the only arteries that carry blood that is high in carbon dioxide.

The left atrium contracts and forces the blood into the left ventricle. The left ventricle contracts, forcing the blood out of the heart and into the aorta.

Figure 3 Pulmonary circulation moves blood between the heart and lungs.

Pulmonary Circulation The flow of blood through the heart to the lungs and back to the heart is **pulmonary circulation.** Use **Figure 3** to trace the path blood takes through this part of the circulatory system. The blood returning from the body through the right side of the heart and to the lungs contains cellular wastes. The wastes include molecules of carbon dioxide and other substances. In the lungs, gaseous wastes diffuse out of the blood, and oxygen diffuses into the blood. Then the blood returns to the left side of the heart. In the final step of pulmonary circulation, the oxygen-rich blood is pumped from the left ventricle into the aorta (ay OR tuh), the largest artery in your body. Next, the oxygen-rich blood flows to all parts of your body.

Active Reading

Double Bubble Map This strategy uses two bubble maps to compare concepts. Each cluster has qualities that are unique to that idea. In the middle, connecting ideas are similar to both cluster ideas. This technique helps students list common qualities before writing or discussing a topic. Have students design a Double Bubble Map about the circulatory system. L2

Sample map:

from heart to body and back to heart — Pulmonary circulation — from heart to lungs and back to heart — oxygen provided to cells — Pumped by heart — wastes removed in lungs — wastes removed from cells — Systemic circulation — oxygen added

Systemic Circulation Oxygen-rich blood moves to all of your organs and body tissues, except the heart and lungs, by **systemic circulation,** and oxygen-poor blood returns to the heart. Systemic circulation is the largest of the three sections of your circulatory system. **Figure 4** shows the major arteries (AR tuh reez) and veins (VAYNZ) of the systemic circulation system. Oxygen-rich blood flows from your heart in the arteries of this system. Then nutrients and oxygen are delivered by blood to your body cells and exchanged for carbon dioxide and wastes. Finally, the blood returns to your heart in the veins of the systemic circulation system.

Reading Check *What are the functions of the systemic circulation system in your body?*

Internal jugular vein

Carotid artery

Superior vena cava

Aorta

Heart

Inferior vena cava

Aorta

Tissue cells

O_2

CO_2

Plasma

Systemic capillary

Red blood cell

Figure 4 The rate at which blood flows through the systemic circulation system depends on how quickly the left ventricle contracts.
Explain *why the rate changes when a person has been jumping rope.*

SECTION 1 The Circulatory System **D** ◆ **67**

Connective tissue

Connective tissue

Smooth muscle

Elastic connective tissue

Smooth lining

Smooth muscle

Elastic connective tissue

Valve

Artery   Vein   Capillary

Fun Fact

All tissues in the body are nourished by materials from the circulatory system. Every cell is within 0.10 to 0.15 mm from a capillary. Some arteries have such thick walls that they have their own system of capillaries.

Activity

Capillary Walls Have students prepare a brief report on how the one-cell thick capillary walls are held together and why a covering would not be practical. A cementing material holds the cells together. A covering would not easily allow materials to pass in and out of the walls. L2 LS
Logical-Mathematical

Reading Check

Answer Arteries and veins have walls consisting of three layers of tissue. Arteries move blood away from the heart; veins move blood to the heart. Veins have valves that keep blood from flowing backward.

Virtual Labs

Predictors of Hypertension
What factors affect the likelihood of hypertension?

Figure 5 The structures of arteries, veins, and capillaries are different. Valves in veins prevent blood from flowing backward. Capillaries are much smaller. Capillary walls are only one cell thick.

Blood Vessels

In the middle 1600s, scientists proved that blood moves in one direction in a blood vessel, like traffic on a one-way street. They discovered that blood moves by the pumping of the heart and flows from arteries to veins. But, they couldn't explain how blood gets from arteries to veins. Using a new invention of that time, the microscope, scientists discovered capillaries (KAP uh ler eez), the connection between arteries and veins.

Arteries As blood is pumped out of the heart, it travels through arteries, capillaries, and then veins. **Arteries** are blood vessels that carry blood away from the heart. Arteries, shown in **Figure 5,** have thick, elastic walls made of connective tissue and smooth muscle tissue. Each ventricle of the heart is connected to an artery. The right ventricle is connected to the pulmonary artery, and the left ventricle is attached to the aorta. Every time your heart contracts, blood is moved from your heart into arteries.

Veins The blood vessels that carry blood back to the heart are called **veins,** as shown in **Figure 5.** Veins have one-way valves that keep blood moving toward the heart. If blood flows backward, the pressure of the blood against the valves causes them to close. The flow of blood in veins also is helped by your skeletal muscles. When skeletal muscles contract, the veins in these muscles are squeezed and help blood move toward the heart. Two major veins return blood from your body to your heart. The superior vena cava returns blood from your head and neck. Blood from your abdomen and lower body returns through the inferior vena cava.

Reading Check
What are the similarities and differences between arteries and veins?

Science Journal

Blood Vessels Have students write brief descriptions in their own words of arteries, veins, and capillaries. Ask them to write a paragraph contrasting these three types of blood vessels. L2 LS
Linguistic

Capillaries

Arteries and veins are connected by microscopic blood vessels called **capillaries,** as shown in **Figure 5.** The walls of capillaries are only one cell thick. You can see capillaries when you have a bloodshot eye. They are the tiny red lines you see in the white area of your eye. Nutrients and oxygen diffuse into body cells through the thin capillary walls. Waste materials and carbon dioxide diffuse from body cells into the capillaries.

Blood Pressure

If you fill a balloon with water and then push on it, the pressure moves through the water in all directions, as shown in **Figure 6.** Your circulatory system is like the water balloon. When your heart pumps blood through the circulatory system, the pressure of the push moves through the blood. The force of the blood on the walls of the blood vessels is called blood pressure. This pressure is highest in arteries and lowest in veins. When you take your pulse, you can feel the waves of pressure. This rise and fall of pressure occurs with each heartbeat. Normal resting pulse rates are 60 to 100 heartbeats per minute for adults, and 80 to 100 beats per minute for children.

Measuring Blood Pressure Blood pressure is measured in large arteries and is expressed by two numbers, such as 120 over 80. The first number is a measure of the pressure caused when the ventricles contract and blood is pushed out of the heart. This is called the systolic (sihs TAH lihk) pressure. Then, blood pressure drops as the ventricles relax. The second number is a measure of the diastolic (di uh STAH lihk) pressure that occurs as the ventricles fill with blood just before they contract again.

Controlling Blood Pressure Your body tries to keep blood pressure normal. Special nerve cells in the walls of some arteries sense changes in blood pressure. When pressure is higher or lower than normal, messages are sent to your brain by these nerve cells. Then messages are sent by your brain to raise or lower blood pressure—by speeding up or slowing the heart rate for example. This helps keep blood pressure constant within your arteries. When blood pressure is constant, enough blood reaches all organs and tissues in your body and delivers needed nutrients to every cell.

Blood Pressure Some molecules of nutrients are forced through capillary walls by the force of blood pressure. What is the cause of the pressure? Discuss your answer with a classmate. Then write your answer in your Science Journal.

Figure 6 When pressure is exerted on a fluid in a closed container, the pressure is transmitted through the liquid in all directions. Your circulatory system is like a closed container.

Water-filled balloon

Blood Pressure Blood pressure, a force produced by the pumping action of the heart, is exerted by the blood against the walls of the blood vessels. Blood pressure tends to force fluids into capillaries at their artery end (where blood pressure is higher); osmosis tends to force water out of capillaries at their venous end (where blood pressure is lower).

Fun Fact

Systolic pressure is the peak pressure of blood flow caused by the contraction of the ventricles. Diastolic pressure is the low pressure of blood flow produced when the heart relaxes.

Teacher FYI

Pressure The term *pressure* is used in discussions of fluids such as gases and liquids. Pressure is produced when a force is applied to a fluid. The greater the force, the greater the pressure on the fluid, and the smaller the volume it takes up. Usually, the volume of a gas decreases by one-half when the pressure doubles. The volume of liquids changes less dramatically.

Visualizing Atherosclerosis

Have students examine the pictures and read the captions. Then ask the following questions.

How do you think a person with restricted arteries would feel while lifting a heavy object? Possible answers: short of breath, difficulty breathing, dizzy, lightheaded, tiring quickly, chest pain.

How do medicines that thin the blood help a person who is suffering from atherosclerosis? Possible answer: The thinner blood will be able to pass more easily through a restricted passage.

IDENTIFYING Misconceptions

Cholesterol The main component of fatty deposits, atheroma, in arteries is cholesterol, a steroid lipid. Some students will assume that any cholesterol is unhealthy. The liver produces cholesterol, it is a component of nerve cells, and it is involved in the synthesis of certain hormones. Normal levels of cholesterol are essential for good health.

Use an Analogy

Lime Deposits The buildup of fatty deposits in the walls of arteries is similar to the buildup of lime deposits in plumbing pipes. In both cases, the pathway is narrowed and the flow is reduced. If possible, show students an old pipe that is full of this type of deposit.

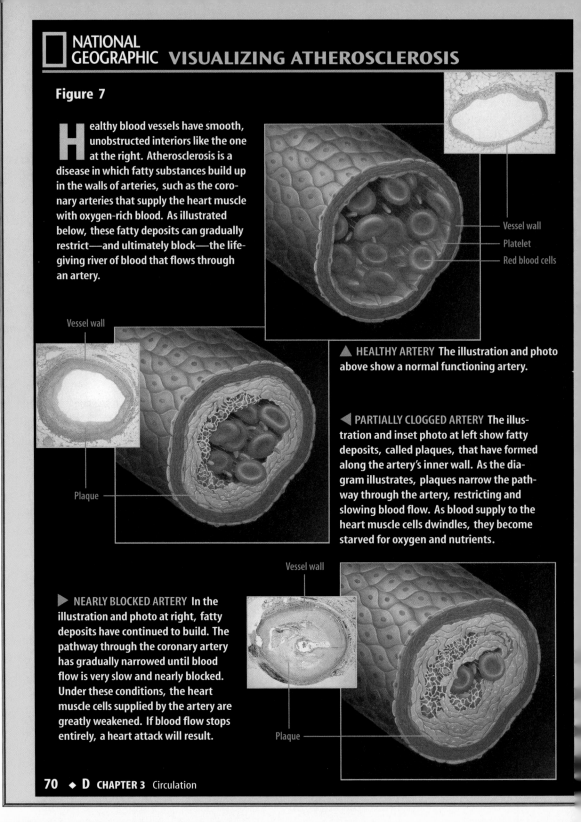

NATIONAL GEOGRAPHIC VISUALIZING ATHEROSCLEROSIS

Figure 7

Healthy blood vessels have smooth, unobstructed interiors like the one at the right. Atherosclerosis is a disease in which fatty substances build up in the walls of arteries, such as the coronary arteries that supply the heart muscle with oxygen-rich blood. As illustrated below, these fatty deposits can gradually restrict—and ultimately block—the life-giving river of blood that flows through an artery.

▲ HEALTHY ARTERY The illustration and photo above show a normal functioning artery.

◀ PARTIALLY CLOGGED ARTERY The illustration and inset photo at left show fatty deposits, called plaques, that have formed along the artery's inner wall. As the diagram illustrates, plaques narrow the pathway through the artery, restricting and slowing blood flow. As blood supply to the heart muscle cells dwindles, they become starved for oxygen and nutrients.

▶ NEARLY BLOCKED ARTERY In the illustration and photo at right, fatty deposits have continued to build. The pathway through the coronary artery has gradually narrowed until blood flow is very slow and nearly blocked. Under these conditions, the heart muscle cells supplied by the artery are greatly weakened. If blood flow stops entirely, a heart attack will result.

70 ◆ **D** **CHAPTER 3** Circulation

Differentiated Instruction

Challenge Have students find statistics on atherosclerosis, and graph the data. This can include percentages in categories such as age, race, gender, countries, or other characteristics that may be associated with the condition. L3

Cardiovascular Disease

Any disease that affects the cardiovascular system—the heart, blood vessels, and blood—can seriously affect the health of your entire body. People often think of cancer and automobile accidents as the leading causes of death in the United States. However, heart disease is the leading cause of death, when you factor in all age groups.

Atherosclerosis One leading cause of heart disease is called atherosclerosis (ah thuh roh skluh ROH sus). In this condition, shown in **Figure 7,** fatty deposits build up on arterial walls. Eating foods high in cholesterol and saturated fats can cause these deposits to form. Atherosclerosis can occur in any artery in the body, but deposits in coronary arteries are especially serious. If a coronary artery is blocked, a heart attack can occur. Open heart surgery may then be needed to correct the problem.

Hypertension Another condition of the cardiovascular system is called hypertension (HI pur TEN chun), or high blood pressure. **Figure 8** shows the instruments used to measure blood pressure. When blood pressure is higher than normal most of the time, extra strain is placed on the heart. The heart must work harder to keep blood flowing. One cause of hypertension is atherosclerosis. A clogged artery can increase pressure within the vessel. The walls become stiff and hard, like a metal pipe. The artery walls no longer contract and dilate easily because they have lost their elasticity.

Heart Failure Heart failure results when the heart cannot pump blood efficiently. It might be caused when heart muscle tissue is weakened by disease or when heart valves do not work properly. When the heart does not pump blood properly, fluids collect in the arms, legs, and lungs. People with heart failure usually are short of breath and tired.

 Reading Check *What is heart failure?*

Figure 8 Blood pressure is measured in large arteries using a blood pressure cuff and stethoscope.

Topic: Cardiovascular Disease

Visit bookd.msscience.com for Web links to recent news or magazine articles about cardiovascular disease.

Activity In your Science Journal, list five steps you can take to lead a healthy life style.

Inquiry Lab

Testing Physical Fitness

Purpose To test physical fitness, have students measure their heart rates before, during, and after exercise, until their heart rates return to normal.

Possible Materials stopwatch, jump rope, or access to steps

Estimated Time 1 class session

Teaching Strategies

• Have students stand for 2 minutes and then measure their heart rate.

• Students can predict their maximum heart rate and level of fitness. Have students measure their heart rate immediately after jumping rope or climbing stairs for 120 s.

• Have students continue exercising an additional 120 s, and then monitor their heart rate and measure the amount of time required for their heart rate to return to normal. During recovery, students should remain standing and relatively still.

• Have students research what their different heart rates indicate about their fitness.

• Allow students to explore other questions that arise.

For additional inquiry activities, see Science Inquiry Labs.

 Reading Check

Answer Heart failure occurs when the heart cannot pump blood efficiently.

LAB DEMONSTRATION

Purpose to compare the flow of liquid through an open tube and a partially blocked tube

Materials two 10-cm pieces of plastic tubing, dropper, mineral oil, modeling clay, tweezers

Preparation Be sure there is enough clay to impede but not stop the flow of oil.

Procedure Insert a dropperful of oil into the tubing. Squeeze the oil through the tubing. Observe the amount of oil that comes out. Compare this to the amount of oil that comes out of a clay-clogged tube.

Expected Outcome Students will observe less oil escaping from the clogged tube.

Assessment

How does this demonstrate what happens in clogged arteries? The clay represents deposits that may collect on the walls of arteries. Blood flow in these tubes is slower, and blocked tubes can carry less blood than unblocked tubes.

Activity

Food Log Have students keep a log of all the foods they eat for a few days. Then have them identify the foods that are high in fat or cholesterol or both. Have them think of low-fat substitutes for those foods.

Discussion

Low Cholesterol Content Why might a food label that proclaims the item has little or no cholesterol be a poor choice for a healthful diet? Foods rated low in cholesterol may be very high in fat and have a negative effect on the cardiovascular system. L2

3 Assess

DAILY INTERVENTION

Check for Understanding

Visual-Spatial Show students a piece of flexible garden hose. Have them explain how the walls of the hose are similar to the walls of an artery. Both have structures that provide strength and flexibility. L1 ELL

Reteach

Heart Action To reinforce the actual position and size of the heart, make a closed fist with your right hand and hold it on your chest above your breastbone. Then ask each student to do the same.

✔ Assessment

Content Have each student make a concept map describing the flow of the blood through the three types of vessels. Use **Performance Assessment in the Science Classroom**, p. 161. L2 P

Figure 9 Nicotine, present in tobacco, contracts blood vessels and causes the body to release hormones that raise blood pressure. **Name** *another substance that raises blood pressure.*

Preventing Cardiovascular Disease Having a healthy lifestyle is important for the health of your cardiovascular system. The choices you make to maintain good health may reduce your risk of future serious illness. Regular checkups, a healthful diet, and exercise are part of a heart-healthy lifestyle.

Many diseases, including cardiovascular disease, can be prevented by following a good diet. Choose foods that are low in salt, sugar, cholesterol, and saturated fats. Being overweight is associated with heart disease and high blood pressure. Large amounts of body fat force the heart to pump faster.

Learning to relax and having a regular program of exercise can help prevent tension and relieve stress. Exercise also strengthens the heart and lungs, helps in controlling cholesterol, tones muscles, and helps lower blood pressure.

Another way to prevent cardiovascular disease is to not smoke. Smoking causes blood vessels to contract, as shown in **Figure 9,** and makes the heart beat faster and harder. Smoking also increases carbon monoxide levels in the blood. Not smoking helps prevent heart disease and a number of respiratory system problems, too.

---

section 1 review

Summary

Cardiovascular System

- Coronary circulation is the flow of blood to and from the tissues of the heart.
- Pulmonary circulation is the flow of blood through the heart, to the lungs, and back to the heart.
- Oxygen-rich blood is moved to all tissues and organs of the body, except the heart and lungs, by systemic circulation.

Blood Vessels

- Arteries carry blood away from the heart.
- Veins carry blood back to the heart.
- Arteries and veins are connected by capillaries.

Blood Pressure

- The force of the blood on the walls of the blood vessels is called blood pressure.

Cardiovascular Disease

- Atherosclerosis occurs when fatty deposits build up on arterial walls.
- High blood pressure is called hypertension.

Self Check

1. **Compare and contrast** the structure of the three types of blood vessels.
2. **Explain** the pathway of blood through the heart.
3. **Contrast** pulmonary and systemic circulation. Identify which vessels carry oxygen-rich blood.
4. **Explain** how exercise can help prevent heart disease.
5. **Think Critically** What waste product builds up in blood and cells when the heart is unable to pump blood efficiently?

Applying Skills

6. **Concept Map** Make an events-chain concept map to show pulmonary circulation beginning at the right atrium and ending at the aorta.
7. **Use a Database** Research diseases of the circulatory system. Make a database showing what part of the circulatory system is affected by each disease. Categories should include the organs and vessels of the circulatory system.

 Science online bookd.msscience.com/self_check_quiz

---

section 1 review

1. Arteries have thick walls. Veins have valves. Capillary walls are only one cell thick.
2. right atrium, right ventricle, lungs, left atrium, left ventricle
3. Pulmonary circulation transports blood through the heart and to the lungs and back to the heart; veins carry oxygen-rich blood. Systemic circulation transports blood to all parts of the body and back to the heart; arteries carry oxygen-rich blood.
4. It strengthens the heart and lungs, helps control cholesterol, and lowers blood pressure.
5. carbon dioxide
6. Map should show blood moving in this order: right atrium, right ventricle, pulmonary artery, lungs, pulmonary vein, left atrium, left ventricle, aorta.
7. Sample entries: atherosclerosis— arteries; myocardial infarction— heart; leukemia—white blood cells

The Heart as a Pump

The heart is a pumping organ. Blood is forced through the arteries as heart muscles contract and then relax. This creates a series of waves in blood as it flows through the arteries. These waves are called the pulse. Try this lab to learn how physical activity affects your pulse.

◉ Real-World Question

What does the pulse rate tell you about the work of the heart?

Goals

■ **Observe** pulse rate.
■ **Compare** pulse rate at rest to rate after jogging.

Materials

watch or clock with a second hand
*stopwatch
*Alternate materials

Pulse Rate

Pulse Rate	Partner's	Yours
At rest	about 70	about 70
After jogging	Answers will vary.	Answers will vary.

◉ Procedure

1. Make a table like the one shown. Use it to record your data.
2. Sit down to take your pulse. Your partner will serve as the recorder.
3. Find your pulse by placing your middle and index fingers over the radial artery in your wrist as shown in the photo. **WARNING:** *Do not press too hard.*
4. **Count** each beat of the radial pulse silently for 15 s. Multiply the number of beats by four to find your pulse rate per minute. Have your partner record the number in the data table.
5. Now jog in place for 1 min and take your pulse again. Count the beats for 15 s.
6. **Calculate** this new pulse rate and have your partner record it in the data table.
7. Reverse roles with your partner and repeat steps 2 through 6.
8. **Collect** and record the new data.

◉ Conclude and Apply

1. **Describe** why the pulse rate changes.
2. **Infer** what causes the pulse rate to change.
3. **Explain** why the heart is a pumping organ.

𝒞ommunicating Your Data

Record the class average for pulse rate at rest and after jogging. Compare the class averages to your data. **For more help, refer to the** Science Skill Handbook.

𝒞ommunicating Your Data

Prepare a graph of the class data and include the class average. Compare the data from your class with those of another class in your school. L2

◉ Real-World Question

Purpose Students measure radial pulse rate and interpret their data. L2 **ELL** COOP LEARN **IS** **Logical-Mathematical**

Process Skills interpret data, communicate, make and use graphs, use numbers, infer

Time Required 30–40 minutes

Safety Precautions Caution students not to press too hard. Students with heart conditions should not jog.

Teaching Strategies

• Encourage all students to perform some activity to increase their heart rate unless medically unadvisable. Suggest that these students be the timekeeper and recorder for a pair of students.
• Students should count their pulses silently and then report results to the recorder.
• Explain that the reason for multiplying by four is to obtain the pulse rate for one minute (15 s × 4 = 60 s or one min).

◉ Conclude and Apply

1. Pulse rate increases as they jog.
2. Greater muscle activity requires the heart to pump more blood (and thus more oxygen) to the muscles.
3. The heart pumps blood to the body to meet all of its needs—both when at rest and when active.

☑ Assessment

Performance Have students design another activity that will result in an increased pulse rate (i.e., dancing or shooting baskets). Have them do the activity and gather and interpret their data. Use **PASC**, p. 95.

1 Motivate

Bellringer

INTERACTIVE CHALKBOARD
PowerPoint® Presentations

Section Focus Transparencies also are available on the Interactive Chalkboard CD-ROM.

L2 ELL

SECTION 2 | Section Focus Transparency | **A Friend in Need**

Do you know someone who has participated in a blood drive? During a blood drive, people are asked to donate blood that will be used to treat sick or injured people. The blood collected by blood banks saves many lives each year.

1. What is the purpose of a blood bank?
2. Who do you think should or should not donate blood?

Circulation

Tie to Prior Knowledge

Blood Volume Fill five 1-L plastic soft drink bottles with red-colored water. Explain to students that this volume of water represents the 5 L of blood in an adult.

Text Question Answer

Blood could be referred to as the tissue of life because it carries oxygen and nutrients to your cells. It also carries waste products to your kidneys to be removed and helps fight infections and heal wounds.

Blood

as you read

What You'll Learn

- **Identify** the parts and functions of blood.
- **Explain** why blood types are checked before a transfusion.
- **Give examples** of diseases of blood.

Why It's Important

Blood plays a part in every major activity of your body.

👁 Review Vocabulary

blood vessels: Structures that include arteries, veins, and capillaries, which transport blood

New Vocabulary
- plasma
- hemoglobin
- platelet

Functions of Blood

You take a last, deep, calming breath before plunging into a dark, vessel-like tube. The water transports you down the slide much like the way blood carries substances to all parts of your body. Blood has four important functions.

1. Blood carries oxygen from your lungs to all your body cells. Carbon dioxide diffuses from your body cells into your blood. Your blood carries carbon dioxide to your lungs to be exhaled.

2. Blood carries waste products from your cells to your kidneys to be removed.

3. Blood transports nutrients and other substances to your body cells.

4. Cells and molecules in blood fight infections and help heal wounds.

Anything that disrupts or changes these functions affects all the tissues of your body. Can you understand why blood is sometimes called the tissue of life?

Parts of Blood

As shown in **Figure 10,** blood is a tissue made of plasma (PLAZ muh), platelets (PLAYT luts), and red and white blood cells. Blood makes up about eight percent of your body's total mass. If you weigh 45 kg, you have about 3.6 kg of blood moving through your body. The amount of blood in an adult would fill five 1-L bottles.

55% — Plasma

White blood cells

45% — Red blood cells

Figure 10 The blood in this graduated cylinder has separated into its parts. Each part plays a key role in body functions.

Plasma The liquid part of blood is mostly water and is called **plasma.** It makes up more than half the volume of blood. Nutrients, minerals, and oxygen are dissolved in plasma and carried to cells. Wastes from cells are also carried in plasma.

Section 2 Resource Manager

Chapter *FAST FILE* Resources

Transparency Activity, p. 47

Directed Reading for Content Mastery, p. 20

MiniLAB, p. 4

Enrichment, p. 31

Reinforcement, p. 28

Mathematics Skill Activities, p. 33

Cultural Diversity, p. 18

Blood Cells A cubic millimeter of blood has about five million red blood cells. These disk-shaped blood cells, shown in **Figure 11,** are different from other cells in your body because they have no nuclei. They contain **hemoglobin** (HEE muh gloh bun), which is a molecule that carries oxygen and carbon dioxide, and made of an iron compound that gives blood its red color. Hemoglobin carries oxygen from your lungs to your body cells. Then it carries some of the carbon dioxide from your body cells back to your lungs. The rest of the carbon dioxide is carried in the cytoplasm of red blood cells and in plasma. Red blood cells have a life span of about 120 days. They are made at a rate of 2 million to 3 million per second in the center of long bones like the femur in your thigh. Red blood cells wear out and are destroyed at about the same rate.

In contrast to red blood cells, a cubic millimeter of blood has about 5,000 to 10,000 white blood cells. White blood cells fight bacteria, viruses, and other invaders of your body. Your body reacts to invaders by increasing the number of white blood cells. These cells leave the blood through capillary walls and go into the tissues that have been invaded. Here, they destroy bacteria and viruses and absorb dead cells. The life span of white blood cells varies from a few days to many months.

Circulating with the red and white blood cells are platelets. **Platelets** are irregularly shaped cell fragments that help clot blood. A cubic millimeter of blood can contain as many as 400,000 platelets. Platelets have a life span of five to nine days.

Sciencenline

Topic: White Blood Cells
Visit bookd.msscience.com for Web links to information about types of human white blood cells and their functions.

Activity Write a brief summary describing how white blood cells destroy bacteria and viruses in your Science Journal.

Figure 11 Red blood cells supply your body with oxygen, and white blood cells and platelets have protective roles.

Platelets

Red blood cells

Nuclei

White blood cells

Color-enhanced SEM
Magnification: 1000×

Platelets help stop bleeding. Platelets not only plug holes in small vessels, they also release chemicals that help form filaments of fibrin.

Several types, sizes, and shapes of white blood cells exist. These cells destroy bacteria, viruses, and foreign substances.

SECTION 2 Blood **D** ◆ **75**

Make a Model

Clay Blood Cells Have students make models of red and white blood cells from modeling clay. Encourage students to make the models to scale in order to reinforce concepts about the relative sizes, shapes, and colors of the cells. [L2] [IS] **Visual-Spatial**

Use an Analogy

Amoebas Have students view a film clip of amoeba activity to draw an analogy to white blood cell movement and ingestion. [L2]

Discussion

Blood Platelets How do blood platelets function in maintaining homeostasis when the skin is cut? Platelets form clots to help prevent further blood loss. [L2]

Quick Demo

Living Blood

Materials students, contained area of space, chairs with wheels

Estimated Time 15 minutes

Procedure Assign student groups to represent red blood cells, white blood cells and platelets. Use chairs with wheels like plasma, to carry cells and platelets. Create a hole in the contained area, allowing some red and white blood cells to escape. Have the platelets try to clog the hole by holding hands. Draw attention to the fact that blood is a living tissue, which must be maintained.

Cultural Diversity

Seaweed Soup It is a tradition for Korean mothers to eat seaweed soup for the first month after giving birth. Koreans believe that seaweed soup cleanses the blood and increases milk production. Seaweeds have generous amounts of calcium and minerals required to maintain healthy bones, which produce blood cells.

Differentiated Instruction

English-Language Learners Have students find out what *CPR* stands for, analyze the parts of the words to determine their meanings, and then describe this technique to their classmates. CPR stands for cardiopulmonary resuscitation. Cardio = heart; pulmonary = lungs; resuscitation = to revive. CPR is an emergency procedure that includes clearing air passages, mouth-to-mouth resuscitation, and heart massage. [L2]

Figure 12 When the skin is damaged, a sticky blood clot seals the leaking blood vessel. Eventually, a scab forms to protect the wound from further damage and allow it to heal.

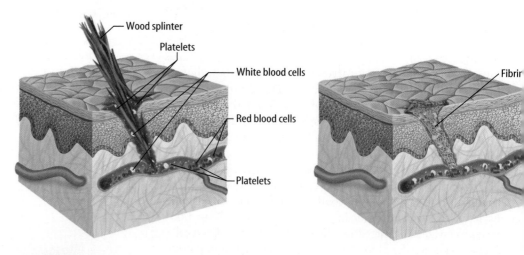

- Wood splinter
- Platelets
- White blood cells
- Red blood cells
- Platelets
- Fibrin

Mini LAB

Modeling Scab Formation

Procedure 🥽 🧤

1. Place a 5-cm × 5-cm square of **gauze** on a piece of **aluminum foil.**
2. Place several drops of a **liquid bandage solution** onto the gauze and let it dry. Keep the liquid bandage away from eyes and mouth.
3. Use a **dropper** to place one drop of **water** onto the area of the liquid bandage. Place another drop of water in another area of the gauze.

Analysis

1. Compare the drops of water in both areas.
2. Describe how the treated area of the gauze is like a scab.

Blood Clotting

You're running with your dog in a park, when all of a sudden you trip and fall down. Your knee starts to bleed, but the bleeding stops quickly. Already the wounded area has begun to heal. Bleeding stops because platelets and clotting factors in your blood make a blood clot that plugs the wounded blood vessels. A blood clot also acts somewhat like a bandage. When you cut yourself, platelets stick to the wound and release chemicals. Then substances called clotting factors carry out a series of chemical reactions. These reactions cause threadlike fibers called fibrin (FI brun) to form a sticky net, as shown in **Figure 12.** This net traps escaping blood cells and plasma and forms a clot. The clot helps stop more blood from escaping. After the clot is in place and becomes hard, skin cells begin the repair process under the scab. Eventually, the scab is lifted off. Bacteria that might get into the wound during the healing process are destroyed by white blood cells.

Reading Check *What blood components help form blood clots?*

Most people will not bleed to death from a minor wound, such as a cut or scrape. However, some people have a genetic condition called hemophilia (hee muh FIH lee uh). Their plasma lacks one of the clotting factors that begins the clotting process. A minor injury can be a life threatening problem for a person with hemophilia.

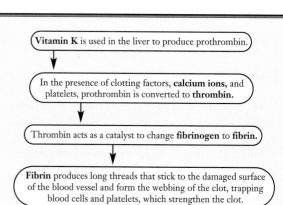

Table 1 Blood Types

Blood Type	Antigen	Antibody
A	A	Anti-B
B	B	Anti-A
AB	A, B	None
O	None	Anti-B Anti-A

Blood Types

Blood clots stop blood loss quickly in a minor wound, but a person with a serious wound might lose a lot of blood and need a blood transfusion. During a blood transfusion, a person receives donated blood or parts of blood. The medical provider must be sure that the right type of blood is given. If the wrong type is given, the red blood cells will clump together. Then, clots form in the blood vessels and the person could die.

The ABO Identification System People can inherit one of four types of blood: A, B, AB, or O, as shown in **Table 1.** Types A, B, and AB have chemical identification tags called antigens (AN tih junz) on their red blood cells. Type O red blood cells have no antigens.

Each blood type also has specific antibodies in its plasma. Antibodies are proteins that destroy or neutralize substances that do not belong in or are not part of your body. Because of these antibodies, certain blood types cannot be mixed. This limits blood transfusion possibilities as shown in **Table 2.** If type A blood is mixed with type B blood, the type A antibodies determine that type B blood does not belong there. The type A antibodies cause the type B red blood cells to clump. In the same way, type B antibodies cause type A blood to clump. Type AB blood has no antibodies, so people with this blood type can receive blood from A, B, AB, and O types. Type O blood has both A and B antibodies.

Reading Check *Why are people with type O blood called universal donors?*

Table 2 Blood Transfusion Options

Type	Can Receive	Can Donate To
A	O, A	A, AB
B	O, B	B, AB
AB	all	AB
O	O	all

Visual Learning

Table 1 and Table 2 After students have studied the information in these tables, have them explain why people with blood type AB are sometimes called universal recipients. These people can receive all blood types. L2

Teacher FYI

Indicator Serums To determine the blood type of an individual, suspensions of the person's red blood cells are mixed separately with different serums. Each serum has a known, particular antibody. When a serum causes agglutination of blood cells, it indicates that the cells contain the antigen with which that specific antibody agglutinates. This reaction identifies the blood type of the individual.

Fun Fact

The first known blood transfusion was conducted in the seventeenth century by French physician Jean Baptiste Denis, who infused sheep's blood into the patient.

Reading Check

Answer People with type O blood are able to give blood to people with all other blood types.

Curriculum Connection

Health Some cultures consider blood to be a necessary part of their diet. Others use it in the preparation of certain foods (blood sausage). Have students find out what nutrients are supplied by blood. usually sodium and iron L2

Research Have students research the pros and cons of artificial blood that scientists are developing. Ask students to find out which areas of the world would most benefit from the use of artificial blood.

✓ Reading Check

Answer If someone with Rh− blood receives a transfusion from someone with Rh+ blood, the results could be fatal.

Applying Science

Answers

1. There would be 54 possible donors. Type B, Rh+ blood can be transfused with Type B, Rh+ (9%); Type B, Rh− (1%); Type O, Rh+ (37%); and Type O, Rh− (7%).

2. Type O, Rh− would be most at risk as this population can receive only Type O, Rh− blood. In an average sample of 100 people, only 7 would match this blood type.

Activity

Blood Transfusions Have students research how blood transfusion experiments started in the early 1800s. The first successful blood transfusion was performed in the seventeenth century by a French physician, Jean Baptiste Denis. He used lamb's blood. His second attempt was unsuccessful and the patient died. [L2]

INTEGRATE
History

Blood Transfusions The first blood transfusions took place in the 1600s and were from animal to animal, and then from animal to human. In 1818, James Blundell, a British obstetrician, performed the first successful transfusion of human blood to a patient for the treatment of hemorrhage.

The Rh Factor Another chemical identification tag in blood is the Rh factor. The Rh factor also is inherited. If the Rh factor is on red blood cells, the person has Rh-positive (Rh+) blood. If it is not present, the person's blood is called Rh-negative (Rh−). If an Rh− person receives a blood transfusion from an Rh+ person, he or she will produce antibodies against the Rh factor. These antibodies can cause Rh+ cells to clump. Clots then form in the blood vessels and the person could die.

When an Rh− mother is pregnant with an Rh+ baby, the mother might make antibodies to the child's Rh factor. Close to the time of birth, Rh antibodies from the mother can pass from her blood into the baby's blood. These antibodies can destroy the baby's red blood cells. If this happens, the baby must receive a blood transfusion before or right after birth. At 28 weeks of pregnancy and immediately after the birth, an Rh− mother can receive an injection that blocks the production of antibodies to the Rh+ factor. These injections prevent this life-threatening situation. To prevent deadly results, blood groups and Rh factor are checked before transfusions and during pregnancies.

✓ Reading Check *Why is it important to check Rh factor?*

Applying Science

Will there be enough blood donors?

Successful human blood transfusions began during World War II. This practice is much safer today due to extensive testing of the donated blood prior to transfusion. Health care professionals have determined that each blood type can receive certain other blood types as illustrated in **Table 2**.

Identifying the Problem

The table on the right lists the average distribution of blood types in the United States. The data are recorded as percents, or a sample of 100 people. By examining these data and the data in **Table 2,** can you determine safe donors for each blood type? Recall that people with Rh− blood cannot receive a transfusion from an Rh+ donor.

Blood Type Distribution		
	Rh+(%)	Rh−(%)
O	37	7
A	36	6
B	9	1
AB	3	1

Solving the Problem

1. If a Type B, Rh+ person needs a blood transfusion, how many possible donors are there?

2. Frequently, the supply of donated blood runs low. Which blood type and Rh factor would be most affected in such a shortage? Explain your answer.

Teacher FYI

Rhesus Monkeys The original research regarding the Rh factor was done with blood cells from rhesus monkeys. The antigen found was named using the first two letters of the word *rhesus*. Treatment for the Rh problem, *erythroblastosis fetalis*, includes blood transfusions and exposure to fluorescent light.

Differentiated Instruction

Challenge Explain to students that if the blood type of the donor and recipient are the same, it is not always true that a blood transfusion is absolutely safe. Have students research reasons for this and write a report. *A number of other blood factors can cause harmful reactions. Also, repeated transfusions of even the same blood type may eventually cause agglutination. This is because there are other antigens on red blood cells besides the A and B antigens.* [L3]

Diseases of Blood

Because blood circulates to all parts of your body and performs so many important functions, any disease of the blood is a cause for concern. One common disease of the blood is anemia (uh NEE mee uh). In this disease of red blood cells, body tissues can't get enough oxygen and are unable to carry on their usual activities. Anemia has many causes. Sometimes, anemia is caused by the loss of large amounts of blood. A diet lacking iron or certain vitamins also might cause anemia. In addition, anemia can be the result of another disease or a side effect of treatment for a disease. Still other types of anemia are inherited problems related to the structure of the red blood cells. Cells from one such type of anemia, sickle-cell anemia, are shown in **Figure 13.**

Leukemia (lew KEE mee uh) is a disease in which one or more types of white blood cells are made in excessive numbers. These cells are immature and do not fight infections well. They fill the bone marrow and crowd out the normal cells. Then not enough red blood cells, normal white blood cells, and platelets can be made. Types of leukemia affect children or adults. Medicines, blood transfusions, and bone marrow transplants are used to treat this disease. If the treatments are not successful, the person eventually will die from related complications.

Color-enhanced TEM Magnification: 7400×

Figure 13 Persons with sickle-cell anemia have misshapened red blood cells. The sickle-shaped cells clog the capillaries of a person with this disease. Oxygen cannot reach tissues served by the capillaries, and wastes cannot be removed. **Describe** how this damages the affected tissues.

Caption Answer
Figure 13 Built-up wastes are toxic to cells. Without oxygen, cell respiration cannot occur.

3 Assess

DAILY INTERVENTION

Check for Understanding
Intrapersonal Survey students to find out whether they know their own blood type. Discuss when it might be important to know this information. If students do not know their blood type, encourage them to ask their parent or guardian.

Reteach
Procedure Divide the class into groups of four. Have each person in each group pick a different blood type. Allow students to decide who can give blood to whom and from whom they can receive blood. L2 IS
Intrapersonal

✔ Assessment

Performance Have students use **Table 1** to determine acceptable donors to those with type AB blood. Individuals with AB blood can receive blood from all the other blood types. Use **Performance Assessment in the Science Classroom**, p. 89. L2

---

section 2 review

Summary

Parts of Blood
- Plasma is made mostly of water, with nutrients, minerals, and oxygen dissolved in it.
- Red blood cells contain hemoglobin, which carries oxygen and carbon dioxide.
- White blood cells control infections and viruses.
- Blood clotting factors and platelets help blood to clot.

Blood Types
- People can inherit one of four types of blood and an Rh factor.
- Type A, B, and AB blood all have antigens. Type O blood has no antigens.

Diseases of Blood
- Anemia is a disease of red blood cells.
- Leukemia is a disease that produces immature white blood cells that don't fight infections.

Self Check

1. **List** the four functions of blood in the body.
2. **Infer** why blood type and Rh factor are checked before a transfusion.
3. **Interpret Data** Look at the data in **Table 2** about blood group interactions. To which group(s) can blood type AB donate blood, and which blood type(s) can AB receive blood from?
4. **Think Critically** Think about the main job of your red blood cells. If red blood cells couldn't deliver oxygen to your cells, what would be the condition of your body tissues?

Applying Math

5. **Use Percentages** Find the total number of red blood cells, white blood cells, and platelets in 1 mm^3 of blood. Calculate what percentage of the total each type is.

line bookd.msscience.com/self_check_quiz

SECTION 2 Blood **D** ◆ 79

---

section 2 review

1. carries oxygen to cells and removes carbon dioxide; carries wastes to kidneys; transports nutrients from the digestive system to cells; has materials to fight infections and heal wounds
2. to prevent blood cells from clumping
3. only to another person with AB blood type; A, B, and O
4. Wastes would build up and become toxic.
5. In a cubic millimeter of blood, there are over 5 million red blood cells, 5,000 to 10,000 white blood cells, and 400,000 platelets. Thus blood is approximately 92.5% red blood cells, 0.09–0.18% white blood cells, and 7.4% platelets.

as you read

What **You'll Learn**

- **Describe** functions of the lymphatic system.
- **Identify** where lymph comes from.
- **Explain** how lymph organs help fight infections.

Why **It's Important**

The lymphatic system helps protect you from infections and diseases.

Review Vocabulary
smooth muscles: muscles found in your internal organs and digestive track

New Vocabulary
- lymph
- lymphatic system
- lymphocyte
- lymph node

Functions of the Lymphatic System

You're thirsty so you turn on the water faucet and fill a glass with water. The excess water runs down the drain. In a similiar way, your body's excess tissue fluid is removed by the lymphatic (lihm FA tihk) system. The nutrient, water, and oxygen molecules in blood diffuse through capillary walls to nearby cells. Water and other substances become part of the tissue fluid that is found between cells. This fluid is collected and returned to the blood by the lymphatic system.

After tissue fluid diffuses into the lymphatic capillaries it is called **lymph** (LIHMF). Your **lymphatic system,** as shown in **Figure 14,** carries lymph through a network of lymph capillaries and larger lymph vessels. Then, the lymph drains into large veins near the heart. No heartlike structure pumps the lymph through the lymphatic system. The movement of lymph depends on the contraction of smooth muscles in lymph vessels and skeletal muscles. Lymphatic vessels, like veins, have valves that keep lymph from flowing backward. If the lymphatic system is not working properly, severe swelling occurs because the tissue fluid cannot get back to the blood.

In addition to water and dissolved substances, lymph also contains **lymphocytes** (LIHM fuh sites), a type of white blood cell. Lymphocytes help your body defend itself against disease-causing organisms.

 Reading Check *What are the differences and similarities between lymph and blood?*

Lymphatic Organs

Before lymph enters the blood, it passes through lymph nodes, which are bean-shaped organs of varying sizes found throughout the body. **Lymph nodes** filter out microorganisms and foreign materials that have been taken up by lymphocytes. When your body fights an infection, lymphocytes fill the lymph nodes. The lymph nodes become warm, reddened, and tender to the touch. After the invaders are destroyed, the redness, warmth, and tenderness in the lymph nodes goes away.

Besides lymph nodes, the tonsils, the thymus, and the spleen are important lymphatic organs. Tonsils are in the back of your throat and protect you from harmful microorganisms that enter through your mouth and nose. Your thymus is a soft mass of tissue located behind the sternum. It makes lymphocytes that travel to other lymph organs. The spleen is the largest lymphatic organ. It is located behind the upper-left part of the stomach and filters the blood by removing worn out and damaged red blood cells. Cells in the spleen take up and destroy bacteria and other substances that invade your body.

A Disease of the Lymphatic System

HIV is a deadly virus. When HIV enters a person's body, it attacks and destroys lymphocytes called helper T cells that help make antibodies to fight infections. This affects a person's immunity to some diseases. Usually, the person dies from these dieseases, not from the HIV infection.

Tonsils
Lymph nodes
Lymph nodes
Lymph nodes
Thymus
Lymphatic duct
Spleen
Thoracic duct
Lymph nodes
Lymph vessels
Lymph nodes

Figure 14 The lymphatic system is connected by a network of vessels.
Describe *how muscles help move lymph.*

section 3 review

Summary

Functions of the Lymphatic System
- Fluid is collected and returned from the body tissues to the blood by the lymphatic system.
- After fluid from tissues diffuses into the lymphatic capillaries it is called lymph.
- Lymphocytes are a type of white blood cell that helps your body defend itself against disease.

Lymphatic Organs
- Lymph nodes filter out microorganisms and foreign materials taken up by lymphocytes.
- The tonsils, thymus, and spleen also protect your body from harmful microorganisms that enter through your mouth and nose.

A Disease of the Lymphatic System
- HIV destroys helper T cells that help make antibodies to fight infections.

Self Check

1. **Describe** where lymph comes from and how it gets into the lymphatic capillaries.
2. **Explain** how lymphatic organs fight infection.
3. **Sequence** the events that occur when HIV enters the body.
4. **Think Critically** When the amount of fluid in the spaces between cells increases, so does the pressure in these spaces. What do you infer will happen?

Applying Skills

5. **Concept Map** The circulatory system and the lymphatic system work together in several ways. Make a concept map comparing the two systems.
6. **Communicate** An infectious microorganism enters your body. In your Science Journal, describe how the lymphatic system protects the body against the microorganism.

Science Online book.msscience.com/self_check_quiz

SECTION 3 The Lymphatic System **D** ◆ 81

---

2 Teach

Caption Answer
Figure 14 As skeletal muscles contract, they force lymph to move within the lymph vessels.

3 Assess

DAILY INTERVENTION

Check for Understanding
Logical-Mathematical Have students construct a table to compare the functions of lymph nodes, the thymus, and the spleen. L2 P

Reteach
Breast Cancer Explain why lymph nodes are sometimes examined to determine the extent of breast cancer. Nodes along the side of the chest and under the arm filter lymph that drains from the breast. The lymph nodes are examined for cancer cells. If present, further treatments are recommended.

✓ Assessment

Performance Ask students to do research and write about the functions of macrophages. Macrophages engulf foreign materials and probably alter them to initiate the immune response. Use **Performance Assessment in the Science Classroom,** p. 159. L2

section 3 review

1. from tissue fluids; by absorption and diffusion
2. Nodes filter out microorganisms and foreign materials; tonsils protect the mouth and throat from germs; thymus makes lymphocytes; spleen removes and recycles old red blood cells and destroys bacteria.
3. It attacks helper T-cells.
4. Diffusion of fluid into the lymphatic capillaries will increase.
5. Cardiovascular: vessels connect heart to body and transport food and gases; Lymphatic: vessels connect lymph nodes to body, transport lymph, return fluid to blood, fight pathogens.
6. Journal entries should reflect the roles of the lymph nodes, lymphocytes, and the spleen in providing protection against microorganisms.

Real-World Question

Purpose Students determine how different blood types react when mixed. L2 ELL
N **Naturalist** P

Process Skills design an experiment, form a hypothesis, observe and infer, communicate, recognize cause and effect, separate and control variables, interpret data

Time Required 50 minutes

Materials For simulated blood, mix 10 mL of lowfat milk with 10 mL of water and add 2 or 3 drops of red food coloring. The lemon juice and water are used as antigens. Also needed are droppers, small paper cups, a marking pen, and a graduated cylinder.

Form a Hypothesis

Possible Hypothesis Most students' hypotheses will reflect that there will be clumping when some blood types are mixed.

Test Your Hypothesis

Possible Procedures

- Mark four paper cups with blood type names A, B, AB, and O.
- Add 5 mL simulated blood to each cup.
- Use the lemon juice as antigen A for blood types B and O. Add 2 to 3 drops of lemon juice to cups B and O. Clumping occurs.
- Use water as antigen A for blood types A and AB. Add 2 to 3 drops to cups A and AB. No clumping occurs.

Blood Type Reactions

Real-World Question

Human blood can be classified into four main blood types—A, B, AB, and O. These types are determined by the presence or absence of antigens on the red blood cells. After blood is collected into a transfusion bag, it is tested to determine the blood type. The type is labeled clearly on the bag. Blood is refrigerated to keep it fresh and available for transfusion. What happens when two different blood types are mixed?

Form a Hypothesis

Based on your reading and observations, state a hypothesis about how different blood types will react to each other.

Goals

- **Design** an experiment that simulates the reactions between different blood types.
- **Identify** which blood types can donate to which other blood types.

Possible Materials

simulated blood (10 mL low-fat milk and 10 mL water plus red food coloring)
lemon juice as antigen A (for blood types B and O)
water as antigen A (for blood types A and AB)
droppers
small paper cups
marking pen
10-mL graduated cylinder

Safety Precautions

WARNING: *Do not taste, eat, or drink any materials used in the lab.*

Alternative Inquiry Lab

Extend the Activity Make this lab an Inquiry Lab by building on the experience. Encourage your students to use what they have learned to brainstorm questions about easing the ongoing problem of blood supply shortages. Have student groups each choose one question to explore. Ask them to list the materials and do the research they need to explore their questions. Unsafe or impractical questions should be eliminated. Students could develop a marketing plan or education program to recruit more blood donors. Conduct the experiments after all of the necessary materials and research have been gathered.

Test Your Hypothesis

Make a Plan

1. As a group, agree upon the hypothesis and decide how you will test it. Identify the results that will confirm the hypothesis.

2. **List** the steps you must take and the materials you will need to test your hypothesis. Be specific. Describe exactly what you will do in each step.

3. **Prepare** a data table like the one at the right in your Science Journal to record your observations.

4. Reread the entire experiment to make sure all steps are in logical order.

5. **Identify** constants and variables. Blood type O will be the control.

Blood Type Reactions	
Blood Type	**Clumping (Yes or No)**
A	No
B	Yes
AB	No
O	Yes

Follow Your Plan

1. While doing the experiment, record your observations and complete the data table in your Science Journal.

Analyze Your Data

1. **Compare** the reactions of each blood type (A, B, AB, and O) when antigen A was added to the blood.

2. **Observe** where clumping took place.

3. **Compare** your results with those of other groups.

4. What was the control factor in this experiment?

5. What were your variables?

Conclude and Apply

1. Did the results support your hypothesis? Explain.

2. **Predict** what might happen to a person if other antigens are not matched properly.

3. What would happen in an investigation with antigen B added to each blood type?

Communicating Your Data

Write a brief report on how blood is tested to determine blood type. **Describe** why this is important to know before receiving a blood transfusion. **For more help, refer to the** Science Skill Handbook.

SECTION 3 The Lymphatic System **D ◆ 83**

Teaching Strategy Instruct students to look for curdling of the milk in the simulated blood as it reacts with the acidic lemon juice. This represents the "clumping" of blood cells.

Analyze Your Data

Expected Outcomes Clumping will occur when the lemon juice antigen is mixed with blood types B and O. No clumping will occur when the water antigen is mixed with blood types A and AB.

Answers to Questions

1. Blood types B and O clumped when lemon juice antigen A was added. Blood types A and AB did not clump when water antigen A was added.

2. Clumping took place in cups with B and O blood types.

3. Students' results should be similar to those of other groups.

4. The control in this experiment was the blood solution and the amount of each antigen added to the blood.

5. The variable was the type of antigen solution used.

Error Analysis Have students compare their results with their hypotheses and explain any differences that might have occurred.

Conclude and Apply

1. Answers will be determined by student hypotheses.

2. Clumping of blood cells could result.

3. Clumping would occur with blood types A and O and not with blood types B and AB.

✓ Assessment

Oral Have students explain why persons with blood type O can donate to anyone but can receive only from a person with blood type O. Type O has no A or B antigens and has antibodies A and B. L2

Communicating Your Data

Have students do online or library research to find information on how blood is checked before a transfusion is given.

TIME

SCIENCE AND HISTORY

SCIENCE CAN CHANGE THE COURSE OF HISTORY!

Content Background

Medieval and early Renaissance medicine in Europe was dominated by the theories of Galen, a Roman physician. Galen taught that there were two types of blood and separate circulatory systems, venous and arterial. It was believed that blood was manufactured in the liver and delivered to veins. The blood received air from the lungs and was carried to the heart by the pulmonary vein, which also took "sooty vapours" back to be expelled by the lungs. Oxygenated blood supposedly seeped from the right to the left side of the heart and became arterial blood that was then consumed by the body.

Renaissance doctors began to question this theory when Arab medical texts became available in the West. Pulmonary circulation and the function of the lungs were described in the 1200s.

Harvey correctly described the circulatory system in 1628. Harvey also discovered that the volume of blood exiting the heart could not be replaced by the daily intake of food and water.

Discussion

Theory of Circulation What did Harvey do to develop his theory of circulation that is still done in medical research today? Possible answer: He used animals for his early observations and applied his findings to humans.

Historical Significance

Harvey's discovery and theory were based on the observations of his predecessors and measurable phenomenon to construct a result that others could reproduce. He had developed a scientific method. Investigation, as opposed to traditional authority, was a defining aspect of the Renaissance that led to modern scientific practices.

Have a Heart

Dr. Daniel Hale Williams was a pioneer in open-heart surgery.

People didn't always know where blood came from or how it moved through the body

"Ouch!" You prick your finger, and when blood starts to flow out of the cut, you put on a bandage. But if you were a scientist living long ago, you might have also asked yourself some questions: How did your blood get to the tip of your finger? And why and how does it flow through (and sometimes out of!) your body?

As early as the 1500s, a Spanish scientist named Miguel Serveto (mee GEL • ser VE toh) asked that question. His studies led him to the theory that blood circulated throughout the human body, but he didn't know how or why.

About 100 years later, William Harvey, an English doctor, explored Serveto's idea. Harvey studied animals to develop a theory about how the heart and the circulatory system work.

Harvey hypothesized, from his observations of animals, that blood was pumped from the heart throughout the body, and that it returned to the heart and recirculated. He published his ideas in 1628 in his famous book, *On the Motion of the Heart and Blood in Animals*. His theories were correct, but many of Harvey's patients left him. His patients thought his ideas were ridiculous. His theories were correct, and over time, Harvey's book became the basis for all modern research on heart and blood vessels.

Medical Pioneer

More than two centuries later, another pioneer stepped forward and used Harvey's ideas to change the science frontier again. His name was Dr. Daniel Hale Williams. In 1893, Williams used what he knew about heart and blood circulation to become a new medical pioneer. He performed the first open-heart surgery by removing a knife from the heart of a stabbing victim. He stitched the wound to the fluid-filled sac surrounding the heart, and the patient lived several more years. In 1970, the U.S. recognized Williams by issuing a stamp in his honor.

Report Identify a pioneer in science or medicine who has changed our lives for the better. Find out how this person started in the field, and how they came to make an important discovery. Give a presentation to the class.

Science online

For more information, visit bookd.msscience.com/time

Report Divide students into teams and assign each an organ of the body. Each team will research that organ and prepare a presentation that compares its functions as they were known before the Renaissance with what is known today. The results can be presented as individual team reports or compiled into a pamphlet or bulletin board presentation. L2

Resources for Teachers and Students

The Greatest Benefit to Mankind: A Medical History of Humanity by Roy Porter. New York: W. W. Norton, 1998

Medicine: An Illustrated History by Albert S. Lyons and R. Joseph Petrucelli, II. New York: Harry N. Abrams, Inc., 1978

"William Harvey" by Frederick G. Kilgour, *Scientific American*, June 1952

Reviewing Main Ideas

Section 1 The Circulatory System

1. Arteries carry blood away from the heart. Capillaries allow the exchange of nutrients, oxygen, and wastes in cells. Veins return blood to the heart.

2. Carbon-dioxide-rich blood enters the right atrium, moves to the right ventricle, and then goes to the lungs through the pulmonary artery. Oxygen-rich blood returns to the left atrium, moves to the left ventricle, and then leaves through the aorta.

3. Pulmonary circulation is the path of blood between the heart and lungs. Circulation through the rest of the body is called systemic circulation. Coronary circulation is the flow of blood to tissues of the heart.

Section 2 Blood

1. Plasma carries nutrients, blood cells, and other substances.

2. Red blood cells carry oxygen and carbon dioxide, platelets form clots, and white blood cells fight infection.

3. A, B, AB, and O blood types are determined by the presence or absence of antigens on red blood cells.

4. Anemia is a disease of red blood cells, in which not enough oxygen is carried to the body's cells.

5. Leukemia is a disease where one or more types of white blood cells are present in excessive numbers. These cells are immature and do not fight infection well.

Section 3 The Lymphatic System

1. Lymph structures filter blood, produce white blood cells that destroy bacteria and viruses, and destroy worn out blood cells.

2. HIV attacks helper T cells, which are a type of lymphocyte. The person is unable to fight infections well.

Visualizing Main Ideas

Copy and complete this concept map on the functions of the parts of the blood.

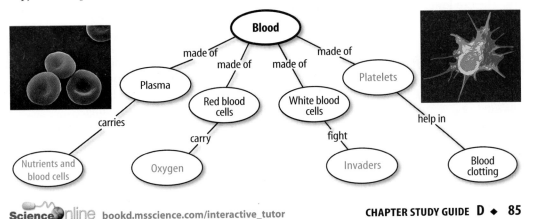

Blood — made of — Plasma — carries — Nutrients and blood cells

Blood — made of — Red blood cells — carry — Oxygen

Blood — made of — White blood cells — fight — Invaders

Blood — made of — Platelets — help in — Blood clotting

Reviewing Main Ideas

Summary statements can be used by students to review the major concepts of the chapter.

Visualizing Main Ideas

See student page.

Science Online

Visit bookd.msscience.com
/self_check_quiz
/interactive_tutor
/vocabulary_puzzlemaker
/chapter_review
/standardized_test

Assessment Transparency

For additional assessment questions, use the *Assessment Transparency* located in the transparency book.

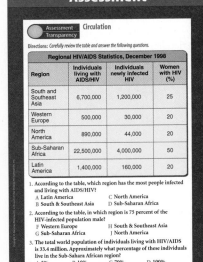

Assessment

Assessment Transparency — Circulation

Directions: Carefully review the table and answer the following questions.

Regional HIV/AIDS Statistics, December 1998

Region	Individuals living with AIDS/HIV	Individuals newly infected HIV	Women with HIV (%)
South and Southeast Asia	6,700,000	1,200,000	25
Western Europe	500,000	30,000	20
North America	890,000	44,000	20
Sub-Saharan Africa	22,500,000	4,000,000	50
Latin America	1,400,000	160,000	20

1. According to the table, which region has the most people infected and living with AIDS/HIV?
   A Latin America   C North America
   B South & Southeast Asia   D Sub-Saharan Africa
2. According to the table, in which region is 75 percent of the HIV-infected population male?
   F Western Europe   H South & Southeast Asia
   G Sub-Saharan Africa   J North America
3. The total world population of individuals living with HIV/AIDS is 33.4 million. Approximately what percentage of these individuals live in the Sub-Sahara African region?
   A 5%   B 10%   C 70%   D 100%

Using Vocabulary

1. coronary circulation (or veins)
2. lymphatic system
3. Hemoglobin
4. Platelets
5. capillaries
6. pulmonary circulation
7. Lymphatic system or Lymphocytes
8. systemic circulation
9. Arteries
10. ventricles

Checking Concepts

11. B   16. C
12. C   17. D
13. A   18. D
14. C   19. A
15. A

Thinking Critically

20. Oxygen-rich blood: aorta, coronary arteries, left atrium, left ventricle; carbon dioxide-filled blood: coronary veins, inferior vena cava, right atrium, right ventricle, superior vena cava

21. All three blood vessels transport blood. Capillaries are only one cell thick; arteries have three layers; veins have valves. Veins carry blood to the heart; arteries carry blood away from the heart; capillaries link veins to arteries.

Using Vocabulary

artery p.68	lymphocyte p.80
atrium p.65	plasma p.74
capillary p.69	platelet p.75
coronary circulation p.65	pulmonary circulation p.66
hemoglobin p.75	
lymph p.80	systemic circulation p.67
lymph node p.80	vein p.68
lymphatic system p.80	ventricle p.65

Fill in the blanks with the correct vocabulary word(s).

1. The _____ carries blood to the heart.
2. The _____ transports tissue fluid through a network of vessels.
3. _____ is the chemical in red blood cells.
4. _____ are cell fragments.
5. The smallest blood vessels are called the _____.
6. The flow of blood to and from the lungs is called _____.
7. _____ helps protect your body against infections.
8. The largest section of the circulatory system is the _____.
9. _____ are blood vessels that carry blood away from the heart.
10. The two lower chambers of the heart are called the right and left _____.

Checking Concepts

Choose the word or phrase that best answers the question.

11. Where does the exchange of food, oxygen, and wastes occur?
    A) arteries   C) veins
    B) capillaries   D) lymph vessels

12. What is circulation to all body organs called?
    A) coronary   C) systemic
    B) pulmonary   D) organic

13. Where is blood under greatest pressure?
    A) arteries   C) veins
    B) capillaries   D) lymph vessels

14. Which cells fight off infection?
    A) red blood   C) white blood
    B) bone   D) nerve

15. Of the following, which carries oxygen in blood?
    A) red blood cells   C) white blood cells
    B) platelets   D) lymph

16. What is required to clot blood?
    A) plasma   C) platelets
    B) oxygen   D) carbon dioxide

17. What kind of antigen does type O blood have?
    A) A   C) A and B
    B) B   D) no antigen

Use the figure below to answer question 18.

Lymphocytes

18. What is the bean-shaped organ above that filters out microorganisms and foreign materials taken up by lymphocytes?
    A) kidney   C) lung
    B) lymph   D) lymph node

19. What is the largest filtering lymph organ?
    A) spleen   C) tonsil
    B) thymus   D) node

 Science online bookd.msscience.com/vocabulary_puzzlemaker

Use the ExamView® Pro Testmaker CD-ROM to:

- create multiple versions of tests
- create modified tests with one mouse click for inclusion students
- edit existing questions and add your own questions
- build tests aligned with state standards using built-in State Curriculum Tags
- change English tests to Spanish with one mouse click and vice versa

Thinking Critically

20. Identify the following as having oxygen-rich or carbon dioxide-filled blood: *aorta, coronary arteries, coronary veins, inferior vena cava, left atrium, left ventricle, right atrium, right ventricle,* and *superior vena cava.*

21. Compare and **contrast** the three types of blood vessels.

22. Compare and **contrast** the life spans of the red blood cells, white blood cells, and platelets.

23. Describe the sequence of blood clotting from the wound to forming a scab.

24. Compare and **contrast** the functions of arteries, veins, and capillaries.

25. Concept Map Copy and complete the events-chain concept map showing how lymph moves in your body.

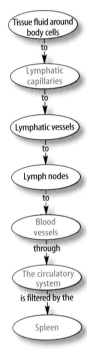

26. Explain how the lymphatic system works with the cardiovascular system.

27. Infer why cancer of the blood cells or lymph nodes is hard to control.

28. Explain why a pulse is usually taken at the neck or wrist, when arteries are distributed throughout the body.

Performance Activities

29. Poster Prepare a poster illustrating heart transplants. Include an explanation of why the patient is given drugs that suppress the immune system and describe the patient's life after the operation.

30. Scientific Illustrations Prepare a drawing of the human heart and label its parts.

Applying Math

Use the table below to answer question 31.

Gender and Heart Rate	
Sex	**Pulse/Minute**
Male 1	72
Male 2	64
Male 3	65
Female 1	67
Female 2	84
Female 3	74

31. Heart Rates Using the table above, find the average heart rate of the three males and the three females. Compare the two averages.

32. Blood Mass Calculate how many kilograms of blood is moving through your body, if blood makes up about eight percent of your body's total mass and you weigh 38 kg.

 Science Online book.msscience.com/chapter_review

Thinking Critically

22. red blood cells—120 days; white blood cells—a few days to several months; platelets—5 to 9 days

23. Student responses should match **Figure 12.**

24. All transport blood. Arteries carry blood away from the heart. Veins carry blood to the heart. Capillaries connect arteries and veins.

25. See student page.

26. The lymphatic system, much like the cardiovascular system, carries fluid away from body tissues and returns it to your circulatory system through veins. The lymphatic system collects tissue fluid and returns it to the blood.

27. Blood and lymph move throughout the entire body.

28. The arteries there are close to the skin, so the pulse can be easily felt.

Performance Activities

29. Drugs are given to prevent the body from rejecting the transplant (an antigen). Patients must avoid conditions that will bring them into contact with germs while their immune systems are suppressed. Use **Performance Assessment in the Science Classroom,** p. 145.

30. Compare student drawings to the illustration of the heart in **Figure 2.** Use **Performance Assessment in the Science Classroom,** p. 127.

Applying Math

National Math Standards
1, 5, 9

31. males = 67; females = 75; In general, males' heart rates are lower than females'.

32. 3 Kg

---

chapter ③ Standardized Test Practice

FAST FILE

Answer Sheet A practice answer sheet can be found at bookd.msscience.com/answer_sheet.

SAMPLE

Part 1 | Multiple Choice

1. C	**6.** B
2. A	**7.** C
3. D	**8.** A
4. A	**9.** B
5. A	**10.** D

Part 2 | Short Response

11. 2,000,000/sec × 60 sec/min × 60 min/hr = 7,200,000,000

12. 400,000 ÷ 10,000 = 40; 40 times more platelets than white blood cells

13. If type A blood is given to a type O person, the antibodies in type A blood would cause type O red blood cells to clump.

14. A is the pulmonary artery. Blood in the pulmonary artery could not get to the lungs to get rid of carbon dioxide and wastes and take on oxygen. The body would not be supplied with enough oxygen and waste gas would not be completely removed.

Part 1 | Multiple Choice

Record your answers on the answer sheet provided by your teacher or on a sheet of paper.

1. Which of the following is a function of blood?
- **A.** carry saliva to the mouth
- **B.** excrete salts from the body
- **C.** transport nutrients and other substances to cells
- **D.** remove lymph from around cells

Use the table below to answer questions 2 and 3.

Results from Ashley's Activities

Activity	Pulse Rate (beats/min)	Body Temperature	Degree of Sweating
1	80	98.6°F	None
2	90	98.8°F	Minimal
3	100	98.9°F	Little
4	120	99.1°F	Moderate
5	150	99.5°F	Considerable

2. Which of the following activities caused Ashley's pulse to be less than 100 beats per minute?
- **A.** Activity 2　　**C.** Activity 4
- **B.** Activity 3　　**D.** Activity 5

3. A reasonable hypothesis based on these data, is that during Activity 2, Ashley was probably
- **A.** sprinting　　**C.** sitting down
- **B.** marching　　**D.** walking slowly

4. Which of the following activities contributes to cardiovascular disease?
- **A.** smoking　　**C.** sleeping
- **B.** jogging　　**D.** balanced diet

5. Where does blood low in oxygen enter first?
- **A.** right atrium　　**C.** left ventricle
- **B.** left atrium　　**D.** right ventricle

6. Which of the following is an artery?
- **A.** left ventricle　　**C.** superior vena cava
- **B.** aorta　　**D.** inferior vena cava

7. Which of the following is NOT a part of the lymphatic system?
- **A.** lymph nodes　　**C.** heartlike structure
- **B.** valves　　**D.** lymph capillaries

Use the table below to answer questions 8 and 9.

Blood Cell Counts (per 1 mm³)

Patient	Red Blood Cells	White Blood Cells	Platelets
Normal	3.58–4.99 million	3,400–9,600	162,000–380,000
Mrs. Stein	3 million	8,000	400,000
Mr. Chavez	5 million	7,500	50,000

8. What problem might Mrs. Stein have?
- **A.** low oxygen levels in tissues
- **B.** inability to fight disease
- **C.** poor blood clotting
- **D.** irregular heart beat

9. If Mr. Chavez cut himself, what might happen?
- **A.** minimal bleeding
- **B.** prolonged bleeding
- **C.** infection
- **D.** quick healing

10. Which lymphatic organ protects your body from harmful microorganisms that enter through your mouth?
- **A.** spleen　　**C.** node
- **B.** thymus　　**D.** tonsils

Test-Taking Tip

Don't Stray During the test, keep your eyes on your own paper. If you need to rest them, close them or look up at the ceiling.

---

15. B is the coronary circulation. If the coronary circulation is blocked, oxygen and nutrients cannot reach all the cells in the heart. This can result in a heart attack.

16. Capillaries have thin walls—one cell layer thick—so that nutrients and oxygen can diffuse into body cells from capillaries and waste materials and carbon dioxide can diffuse from body cells into capillaries. If capillaries were thick walled, then diffusion could not take place through their walls.

17. A person with hemophilia lacks one of the clotting factors that begin the clotting process. Bleeding in a cut would not stop quickly. If the cut was severe, the bleeding might become life threatening.

18. In leukemia, immature white blood cells crowd out the normal cells in the bone marrow. Thus not enough red blood cells, normal white blood cells and platelets can be made. The counts of these cells in the blood could be decreased.

Part 2 | **Short Response/Grid In**

Record your answers on the answer sheet provided by your teacher or on a sheet of paper.

11. If red blood cells are made at the rate of 2 million per second in the center of long bones, how many red blood cells are made in one hour?

12. If a cubic milliliter of blood has 10,000 white blood cells and 400,000 platelets, how many times more platelets than white blood cells are present in a cubic milliliter of blood?

13. What would happen if type A blood was given to a person with type O blood?

Use the illustration below to answer questions 14 and 15.

14. What might happen if there was a blood clot blocking vessel "A"?

15. What might happen if there was a blood clot blocking vessel "B"?

16. Why don't capillaries have thick, elastic walls?

17. Why would a cut be dangerous for a person with hemophilia?

18. Why would a person with leukemia have low numbers of red blood cells, normal white blood cells, and platelets in the blood?

Part 3 | **Open Ended**

Record your answers on a sheet of paper.

Use the illustration below to answer questions 19 and 20.

19. What is wrong with this heart? How do you know?

20. The left ventricle pumps blood under higher pressure than the right ventricle does. In which direction would you predict blood would flow through the hole in the heart? Compare the circulation in this heart with that of a normal heart.

21. What are some ways to prevent cardiovascular disease?

22. Compare and contrast diffusion and active transport.

23. Describe the role of the brain in blood pressure homeostasis. Why is this important?

24. Thrombocytopenia is a condition in which the number of platelets in the blood is decreased. Hemophilia is a genetic condition where blood plasma lacks one of the clotting factors. Compare how a small cut would affect a person with thrombocytopenia and someone with hemophilia.

the other way around. The oxygen level in the blood in the right ventricle would be higher than normal.

21. Some ways to prevent cardiovascular disease include having a healthy lifestyle, regular checkups, a healthful diet, and exercise. Not smoking is an important way to prevent cardiovascular disease.

22. Both processes move materials into and out of cells. Diffusion occurs when a material moves from an area where there is more of it to an area where there is less of it. Active transport moves a material from an area where there is less of it to an area where there is more of it. Active transport requires energy, but diffusion does not.

23. Special nerve cells in the walls of some arteries sense changes in blood pressure. When blood pressure is higher or lower than normal, messages are sent to your brain by these nerve cells. Then messages are sent by your brain to raise or lower blood pressure—by speeding up or slowing the heart rate. This keeps blood pressure constant in the arteries. Constant blood pressure ensures that enough blood reaches all organs and tissues in the body and nutrients are delivered to every cell.

24. Platelets help clot blood. They are the first step in the clotting process. They stick to the wound and release chemicals. If platelets were decreased, blood would not clot as quickly. The person might have bleeding that did not stop quickly. In hemophilia, one of the clotting factors is absent which begins the clotting process. Bleeding will not stop quickly; a minor injury could be a life-threatening problem.

Part 3 | **Open Ended**

19. There is a hole in the heart where there should not be one, between the two ventricles. Normally there is a wall between the two ventricles without a hole, as can be seen in the illustration of the heart and lungs in this chapter.

20. In a normal heart, blood returning from the body enters the right side of the heart. This blood contains wastes—carbon dioxide and other substances. The blood is pumped through the right atrium into the right ventricle and then to the lungs through the pulmonary artery. Then blood rich in oxygen returns from the lungs to the left atrium and into the left ventricle.

Oxygen-rich blood then leaves the heart to go the body. In this heart, there is a hole between the ventricles which allows the blood in both ventricles to mix. Because the left ventricle is under more pressure than the right ventricle, blood will flow through the hole from the left ventricle to the right ventricle, not

Rubrics

For more help evaluating open-ended assessment questions, see the rubric on p. 10T.

Section/Objectives	Standards		Labs/Features
Chapter Opener	**National**	**State/Local**	**Launch Lab:** Effect of Activity on Breathing, p. 91 **Foldables,** p. 91
	See pp. 16T–17T for a Key to Standards.		A data-collection lab using Probeware technology can be found in the **Probeware Lab Manual,** pp. 13–15
Section 1 The Respiratory System 🕐 2 sessions 📦 1 block 1. **Describe** the functions of the respiratory system. 2. **Explain** how oxygen and carbon dioxide are exchanged in the lungs and in tissues. 3. **Identify** the pathway of air in and out of the lungs. 4. **Explain** the effects of smoking on the respiratory system.	National Content Standards: UCP.1–UCP.3, UCP.5, A.1, A.2, C.1, C.3		**Integrate Earth Science,** p. 93 **Science Online,** p. 95 **MiniLAB:** Comparing Surface Area, p. 96 **Visualizing Abdominal Thrusts,** p. 97 **Science Online,** p. 98
Section 2 The Excretory System 🕐 3 sessions 📦 1.5 blocks 5. **Distinguish** between the excretory and urinary systems. 6. **Describe** how the kidneys work. 7. **Explain** what happens when urinary organs don't work.	National Content Standards: UCP.1–UCP.3, UCP.5, A.1, A.2, C.1, C.3, G.3		**MiniLAB:** Modeling Kidney Function, p. 103 **Applying Science:** How does your body gain and lose water?, p. 104 **Integrate Social Studies,** p. 105 **Lab:** Kidney Structure, p. 107 **Lab:** Simulating the Abdominal Thrust Maneuver, p. 108 **Science and History:** Overcoming the Odds, p. 111

Lab Materials	Reproducible Resources	Section Assessment	Technology
Launch Lab: stopwatch or clock with second hand, calculator	**Chapter *FAST FILE* Resources** Foldables Worksheet, p. 15 Directed Reading Overview, p. 17 Note-taking Worksheets, pp. 29–31	GLENCOE'S ASSESSMENT ADVANTAGE	**Teacher*Works* includes:** • Interactive Teacher Edition • Lesson Planner with calendar • Access to all program blacklines • Correlations to standards • Web links
MiniLAB: bathroom-tissue cardboard tube, bowl, marbles, calculator	**Chapter *FAST FILE* Resources** Transparency Activity, p. 40 MiniLAB, p. 3 Enrichment, p. 27 Reinforcement, p. 25 Directed Reading, p. 18 Lab Activity, pp. 9–12, 13–14 **Performance Assessment in the Science Classroom,** p. 48 **Reading and Writing Skill Activities,** p. 39 **Life Science Critical Thinking/ Problem Solving,** p. 17	**Portfolio** Activity, p. 95 **Performance** MiniLAB, p. 96 Applying Skills, p. 100 **Content** Section Review, p. 100	Section Focus Transparency Virtual Labs CD-ROM Guided Reading Audio Program Interactive Chalkboard CD-ROM
MiniLAB: 3 cups, soil, fine gravel, water, funnel, small piece of wire screen, filter paper **Lab:** large animal kidney, scalpel, magnifying lens, disposable gloves **Lab:** cardboard tube, paper, clay, bicycle pump, sports bottle, scissors *Need materials?* Contact Science Kit at 1-800-828-7777 or www.sciencekit.com on the Internet.	**Chapter *FAST FILE* Resources** Transparency Activity, p. 41 MiniLAB, p. 4 Enrichment, p. 28 Reinforcement, p. 26 Directed Reading, pp. 19, 20 Lab Worksheet, pp. 5–6, 7–8 Transparency Activity, pp. 43–44 **Lab Management and Safety,** p. 77 **Mathematics Skill Activities,** p. 1 **Home and Community Involvement,** p. 40	**Portfolio** MiniLAB Assessment, p. 103 **Performance** MiniLAB, p. 103 Applying Science, p. 104 Applying Math, p. 106 **Content** Section Review, p. 106	Section Focus Transparency Teaching Transparency Virtual Labs CD-ROM Guided Reading Audio Program Interactive Chalkboard CD-ROM Video Lab Probeware Lab

End of Chapter Assessment

GLENCOE'S ASSESSMENT ADVANTAGE

Blackline Masters	Technology	Professional Series
Chapter *FAST FILE* Resources Chapter Review, pp. 33–34 Chapter Tests, pp. 35–38 **Standardized Test Practice,** pp. 19–22	MindJogger Videoquiz Virtual Labs CD-ROM Exam*View*® Pro Testmaker TeacherWorks CD-ROM Interactive Chalkboard CD-ROM	**Performance Assessment in the Science Classroom (PASC)**

Transparencies

Section Focus

This is a representation of key blackline masters available in the Teacher Classroom Resources. See Resource Manager boxes within the chapter for additional information.

Key to Teaching Strategies

The following designations will help you decide which activities are appropriate for your students.

L1 Level 1 activities should be appropriate for students with learning difficulties.

L2 Level 2 activities should be within the ability range of all students.

L3 Level 3 activities are designed for above-average students.

ELL ELL activities should be within the ability range of English-Language Learners.

COOP LEARN Cooperative Learning activities are designed for small group work.

LS Multiple Learning Styles logos, as described on page 12T, are used throughout to indicate strategies that address different learning styles.

P These strategies represent student products that can be placed into a best-work portfolio.

PBL Problem-Based Learning activities apply real-world situations to learning.

Assessment

Teaching

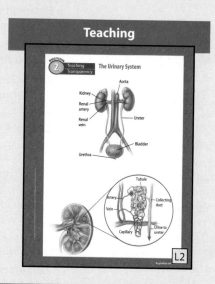

Hands-on Activities

Student Text Lab Worksheet

Laboratory Activities

Meeting Different Ability Levels

Content Outline

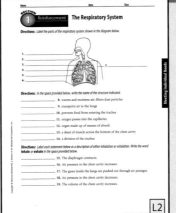

L2

Reinforcement

L2

Enrichment

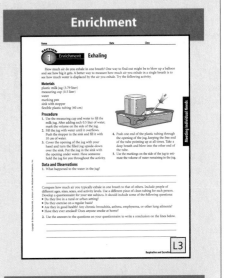

L3

Directed Reading (English/Spanish)

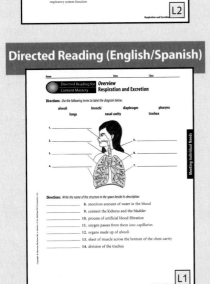

L1

Study Guide

Study Guide

Features
• Contains a study guide page for each section of the chapter
• Reviews key concepts
• Includes answer pages

L2

Reading Essentials

Reading Essentials for Glencoe Science
An Interactive Student Workbook

Features
• Condensed core content
• Actively involves students in reading
• Reinforces key vocabulary

L1

Assessment

Test Practice Workbook

GO ON L2

Glencoe Life Science

Chapter Review

L2

Chapter Tests

L2

Science Content Background

section 1

The Respiratory System

Functions of the Respiratory System

In order to function, cells need nutrients, which must be oxidized in order to release energy. The process of obtaining energy from nutrients is called cellular respiration. In respiration the most commonly used carbohydrate is glucose. The oxidation of glucose produces water and carbon dioxide, and releases energy.

$$C_6H_{12}O_6 + 6O_2 \rightarrow 6H_2O + 6CO_2 + energy$$

Obtaining oxygen and removing carbon dioxide are the major functions of the respiratory system. These processes occur in two successive phases of functioning—breathing and transporting gases. In order to effectively exchange the gases involved in respiration, a large surface area is required. There are 300 million to 400 million alveoli in each lung. The air sacs of both lungs have a total surface area of about 93 m², nearly 50 times the total surface area of the skin.

The Lungs

Lungs are pink at birth, but as a person ages, they become gray and mottled from tiny particles breathed in with the air. Usually people who live in cities and industrial areas have darker lungs than those who live in the country.

In the adult human, the left lung is divided into two sections, or lobes—the superior and the inferior. The right lung is somewhat larger than the left lung and is divided into three lobes—the superior, middle, and inferior. The two lungs are separated by an area which contains the heart, trachea, esophagus, and blood vessels.

The movement of air in and out of the lungs is possible due to three factors: the ability of the thoracic cavity to change size, the elasticity of the lung tissue, and the difference in pressure between the lungs and chest.

Diseases and Disorders of the Respiratory System

Many diseases and disorders affect the health of the human respiratory system and interfere with its effectiveness. Allergies affect so many people that pollen counts of the atmosphere are reported in the media. The worst allergens include the pollen of wind-pollinated trees, grasses, and ragweed, and air pollutants.

Pneumonia is the term used to describe any condition that results in alveoli filling up with fluid. It can be caused by a number of different factors, including chemicals, bacteria, viruses, or fungi. Blood infections, chronic alcoholism, inhalation of fluids into the lungs, or even prolonged bed rest can predispose a person to infection of the lungs by microorganisms. Chronic smoking has the potential to promote emphysema and lung cancer.

---

chapter content resources

Internet Resources

For additional content background, visit
bookd.msscience.com to:
- access your book online
- find references to related articles in popular science magazines
- access Web links with related content background
- access current events with science journal topics

Print Resources

Biology (6th Edition), by Neil A. Campbell, Jane B. Reece, Pearson Benjamin Cummings Publishing, 2001

Human Anatomy & Physiology (5th Edition), by Elaine N. Marieb, Pearson Benjamin Cummings Publishing Company, 2000

Principles of Human Physiology, by William J. Germann, Cindy L. Stanfield; Pearson Benjamin Cummings Publishing, 2001

The Excretory System

The Urinary System

The metabolic processes of the body produce waste products. The respiratory system rids the body of carbon dioxide and other waste gases. The digestive system eliminates solid wastes. The urinary system removes a variety of dissolved salts and nitrogenous wastes from the blood and lymph systems.

The major organs of the urinary system are a pair of bean-shaped structures called kidneys, each of which is approximately 10 cm long and 5 cm wide. They weigh about 170 g each. The functioning unit of the kidney is the nephron. All of the blood in the body flows through the kidneys about once every five minutes.

Urine

Urea and uric acid are wastes from the metabolism of proteins. The straw color of fresh urine is due to a pigment called urochrome. The average pH of urine is approximately 6.0, making it slightly acidic.

The urinary system also functions in maintaining the homeostasis of body fluids and electrolytes and keeps the levels of acids and bases in proper balance. All of this provides for the uniform composition of the blood components.

Urinary Disease and Disorders

Urinary tract infections are common, second only to respiratory infections. Normally urine is sterile. An infection occurs when microbes, usually bacteria from the digestive tract, adhere to the opening of the urethra and begin to multiply. Most urinary tract infections can be traced to one type of colon bacteria, *Escherichia coli* (*E. coli*). Often the bacteria move from the urethra to the bladder causing a bladder infection. Such infections are usually treated with specific antibacterial drugs.

> **Teacher to Teacher**
> Jeff Remington
> Palmyra Middle School
> Palmyra, PA
>
> "To show students that water vapor is released in the cellular respiration equation, I invert a dry glass beaker for a few seconds over a lit Bunsen burner. The inside of the beaker instantly fogs and becomes wet from the flame. It is a discrepant event but shows students when you burn an organic compound such as sugar or methane, water vapor is produced. Jet fuel is a carbon compound as well. Hence, you see water vapor trails behind jets in the sky as they respire."
>
> *Jeff Remington*

Greg Vaughn/Tom Stack & Associates

Chapter Vocabulary

Science Journal Student responses may vary, but may include questions about breathing harder or faster, and questions about perspiring.

INTERACTIVE CHALKBOARD with Image Bank

PowerPoint® Presentations

This CD-ROM is an editable Microsoft® PowerPoint® presentation that includes:
- a pre-made presentation for every chapter
- interactive graphics
- animations
- audio clips
- image bank
- all new section and chapter questions
- Standardized Test Practice
- transparencies
- pre-lab questions for all labs
- Foldables directions
- links to bookd.msscience.com

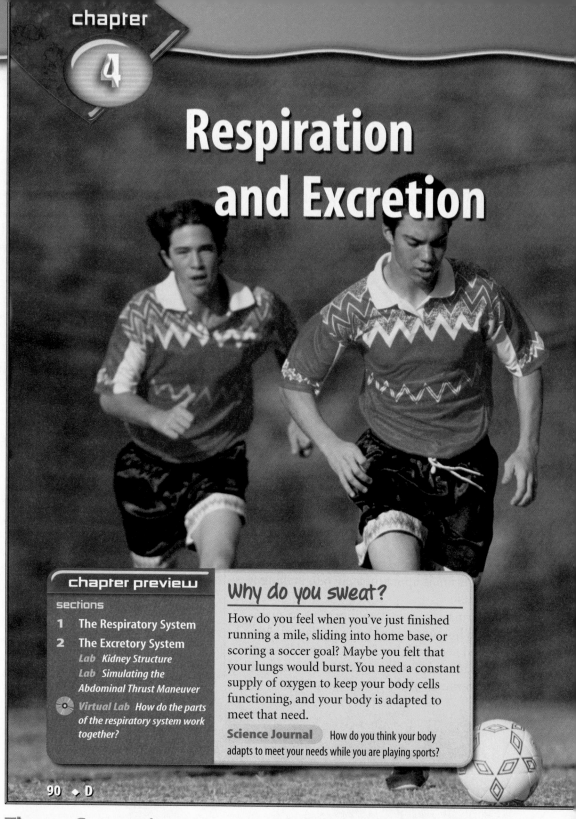

Respiration and Excretion

chapter preview

sections

1 The Respiratory System

2 The Excretory System
Lab Kidney Structure
Lab Simulating the Abdominal Thrust Maneuver
Virtual Lab How do the parts of the respiratory system work together?

Why do you sweat?

How do you feel when you've just finished running a mile, sliding into home base, or scoring a soccer goal? Maybe you felt that your lungs would burst. You need a constant supply of oxygen to keep your body cells functioning, and your body is adapted to meet that need.

Science Journal How do you think your body adapts to meet your needs while you are playing sports?

Theme Connection

Energy Energy transformation is a central theme in this text. Human cells require oxygen in order to utilize nutrients and provide energy for cellular activities. Chemical energy is transformed into thermal and mechanical energy.

About the Photo

Increased Respiration During heavy exercise, respiration increases about 20 times. Rapid delivery of oxygen and fast removal of waste and heat is required. The cardiovascular and respiratory systems deliver oxygen and fuel, and remove waste and heat. More heat can be removed by the skin through evaporation.

Start-Up Activities

Effect of Activity on Breathing

Your body can store food and water, but it cannot store much oxygen. Breathing brings oxygen into your body. In the following lab, find out about one factor that can change your breathing rate.

1. Put your hand on the side of your rib cage. Take a deep breath. Notice how your rib cage moves out and upward when you inhale.

2. Count the number of breaths you take for 15 s. Multiply this number by four to calculate your normal breathing rate for 1 min.

3. Repeat step 2 two more times, then calculate your average breathing rate.

4. Do a physical activity described by your teacher for 1 min and repeat step 2 to determine your breathing rate now.

5. Time how long it takes for your breathing rate to return to normal.

6. **Think Critically** Explain how breathing rate appears to be related to physical activity.

 Preview this chapter's content and activities at bookd.msscience.com

---

FOLDABLES Study Organizer

Respiration and Excretion
Make the following Foldable to help you identify what you already know, what you want to know, and what you learned about respiration.

STEP 1 Fold a vertical sheet of paper from side to side. Make the front edge about 1.25 cm shorter than the back edge.

STEP 2 Turn lengthwise and fold into thirds.

STEP 3 Unfold and cut only the top layer along both folds to make three tabs.

STEP 4 Label each tab.

| Know | Want | Learned |

Read and Write Before you read the chapter, write what you already know about respiration under the left tab of your Foldable, and write questions about what you'd like to know under the center tab. After you read the chapter, list what you learned under the right tab.

Launch LAB

Purpose Use the Launch Lab to introduce students to respiration. Students will discover how the respiratory system responds to physical activity. L2 ELL LS
Kinesthetic

Preparation Check with the school nurse to determine whether any students should not jog or engage in activities that stress the heart and respiratory system.

Materials watch or clock with second hand, calculator

Teaching Strategies
• Any students not able to participate in the physical part of this activity can be designated as timekeepers or recorders.
• Review the reason for multiplying by four to obtain the breathing rate for one minute.

Think Critically

Breathing rates increase after physical activity.

Assessment

Performance Have students design another activity that will result in an increase in breathing rate, do the activity, and gather the data. Use **Performance Assessment in the Science Classroom,** pp. 95, 98.

FOLDABLES Study Organizer **Dinah Zike Study Fold**

Student preparation materials for this Foldable are available in the Chapter *FAST FILE* Resources.

Probeware Labs

This chapter's data-collection lab using Probeware technology can be found in the *Probeware Lab Manual* pages 13–15.

1 Motivate

Bellringer

Section Focus Transparencies also are available on the Interactive Chalkboard CD-ROM.

 ELL

Tie to Prior Knowledge

Oxygen Movement Students are aware that they need oxygen to live. Ask students how they get oxygen into their bodies. Most will say breathing. Point out that oxygen taken in by the respiratory system is transported to the body's cells by the circulatory system. **L2**

The Respiratory System

as you read

What **You'll Learn**

- **Describe** the functions of the respiratory system.
- **Explain** how oxygen and carbon dioxide are exchanged in the lungs and in tissues.
- **Identify** the pathway of air in and out of the lungs.
- **Explain** the effects of smoking on the respiratory system.

Why **It's Important**

Your body's cells depend on your respiratory system to supply oxygen and remove carbon dioxide.

⊙ **Review Vocabulary**

lungs: saclike respiratory organs that function with the heart to remove carbon dioxide from blood and provide it with oxygen

New Vocabulary

- pharynx
- larynx
- trachea
- bronchi
- alveoli
- diaphragm
- emphysema
- asthma

Figure 1 Air, which is needed by most organisms, is only 21 percent oxygen.

Functions of the Respiratory System

Can you imagine an astronaut walking on the Moon without a space suit or a diver exploring the ocean without scuba gear? Of course not. You couldn't survive in either location under those conditions because you need to breathe air. Earth is surrounded by a layer of gases called the atmosphere (AT muh sfihr). You breathe atmospheric gases that are closest to Earth. As shown in **Figure 1,** oxygen is one of those gases.

For thousands of years people have known that air, food, and water are needed for life. However, the gas in the air that is necessary for life was not identified as oxygen until the late 1700s. At that time, a French scientist experimented and discovered that an animal breathed in oxygen and breathed out carbon dioxide. He measured the amount of oxygen that the animal used and the amount of carbon dioxide produced by its bodily processes. After his work with animals, the French scientist used this knowledge to study the way that humans use oxygen. He measured the amount of oxygen that a person uses when resting and when exercising. These measurements were compared, and he discovered that more oxygen is used by the body during exercise.

Oxygen 21%
Argon 0.9%
Carbon dioxide 0.04%
Other gases 0.06%
Nitrogen 78%

Section 1 Resource Manager

Chapter *FAST FILE* Resources
- Transparency Activity, p. 40
- Note-taking Worksheets, pp. 29–31
- MiniLAB, p. 3
- Enrichment, p. 27
- Reinforcement, p. 25
- Directed Reading for Content Mastery, pp. 17, 18

- Lab Activity, pp. 9–12, 13–14
- **Performance Assessment in the Science Classroom,** p. 48
- **Reading and Writing Skill Activities,** p. 39
- **Life Science Critical Thinking/Problem Solving,** p. 17

Figure 2 Several processes are involved in how the body obtains, transports, and uses oxygen.

$$C_6H_{12}O_6 \ + \ 6O_2 \ \longrightarrow \ 6CO_2 \ + \ 6H_2O \ + \ \text{Energy}$$

Glucose + Oxygen ⟶ Carbon + Water + Energy
                        dioxide

Respiration

Oxygen supplied to body

Oxygen carried to body cells

Carbon dioxide removed from cells to lungs

Carbon dioxide waste expelled

Circulation

Breathing
(Inhale)

Breathing
(Exhale)

Breathing and Respiration People often confuse the terms *breathing* and *respiration*. Breathing is the movement of the chest that brings air into the lungs and removes waste gases. The air entering the lungs contains oxygen. It passes from the lungs into the circulatory system because there is less oxygen in the blood than in cells of the lungs. Blood carries oxygen to individual cells. At the same time, the digestive system supplies glucose from digested food to the same cells. The oxygen delivered to the cells is used to release energy from glucose. This chemical reaction, shown in the equation in **Figure 2,** is called cellular respiration. Without oxygen, this reaction would not take place. Carbon dioxide and water molecules are waste products of cellular respiration. They are carried back to the lungs in the blood. Exhaling, or breathing out, eliminates waste carbon dioxide and some water molecules.

Reading Check *What is respiration?*

INTEGRATE Earth Science

Water Vapor The amount of water vapor in the atmosphere varies from almost none over deserts to nearly four percent in tropical rain forest areas. This means that every 100 molecules that make up air include only four molecules of water. In your Science Journal, infer how breathing dry air can stress your respiratory system.

INTEGRATE Earth Science

Water Vapor Breathing dry air can irritate nasal and throat passages.

Reading Check

Answer A cellular chemical reaction in which glucose and oxygen combine and produce CO_2 and H_2O with the release of energy.

Quick Demo
Pig Lungs
Materials pig lungs
Estimated Time 10 minutes
Procedure Obtain pig lungs from a meat-packing house or biological supply company for students to examine. Lead a discussion on why lungs aren't heavy. Lungs are composed of alveoli, which are hollow. L2

Activity
Carbon Dioxide Reaction Limewater is made by mixing 1.5 g calcium hydroxide with 1 L of distilled water. Allow it to stand overnight and filter it before using. Have students blow through a straw into a test tube one-fourth full of limewater. Note the change from a clear liquid to a cloudy liquid. This indicates the presence of carbon dioxide. L1 IS **Kinesthetic**

Teacher FYI

Nasal Cavities Sinuses are air-filled cavities in the cranial bones that open into the nasal cavity. The cavities act as resonant chambers and affect the sound of our speech.

Differentiated Instruction

Challenge An opera singer's ability to be heard over an orchestra in a large auditorium for an extended period of time is a result of breath control. Breath control enables singers to sustain a long musical phrase, and change volume for dramatic effect. Invite students who have studied voice or a wind instrument to perform for the class and demonstrate their breathing techniques. L3 ELL IS
Auditory-Musical

Text Question Answer

The food or drink has gotten into your airway.

Caption Answer

Figure 3 It can be cleaned, warmed, and moistened before moving to the pharynx.

Make a Model

Balloon Music Blow up a balloon and stretch the opening into a narrow slit. Explain to students that the balloon represents a lung and its neck is the trachea. Stretch the slit to make it longer and release a bit to make it shorter, noting the changes in pitch. Correlate the higher-pitched sounds and tighter stretch with the shorter vocal cords of females and the lower-pitched sounds and looser stretch with the longer vocal cords of males.

Use an Analogy

Trapping Dust The nasal cavity traps air particles just as a dust mask traps dust and pollen from the air.

Virtual Labs

Respiratory System *How do parts of the respiratory system work together?*

Organs of the Respiratory System

The respiratory system, shown in **Figure 3,** is made up of structures and organs that help move oxygen into the body and waste gases out of the body. Air enters your body through two openings in your nose called nostrils or through the mouth. Fine hairs inside the nostrils trap dust from the air. Air then passes through the nasal cavity, where it gets moistened and warmed by the body's heat. Glands that produce sticky mucus line the nasal cavity. The mucus traps dust, pollen, and other materials that were not trapped by nasal hairs. This process helps filter and clean the air you breathe. Tiny, hairlike structures, called cilia (SIH lee uh), sweep mucus and trapped material to the back of the throat where it can be swallowed.

Pharynx Warmed, moist air then enters a tubelike passageway used by food, liquid, and air called the **pharynx** (FER ingks). At the lower end of the pharynx is a flap of tissue called the epiglottis (eh puh GLAH tus). When you swallow, your epiglottis folds down to prevent food or liquid from entering your airway. The food enters your esophagus instead. If you began to choke, what do you think has happened?

Figure 3 Air can enter the body through the nostrils and the mouth.
Explain *the advantages of having air enter through the nostrils.*

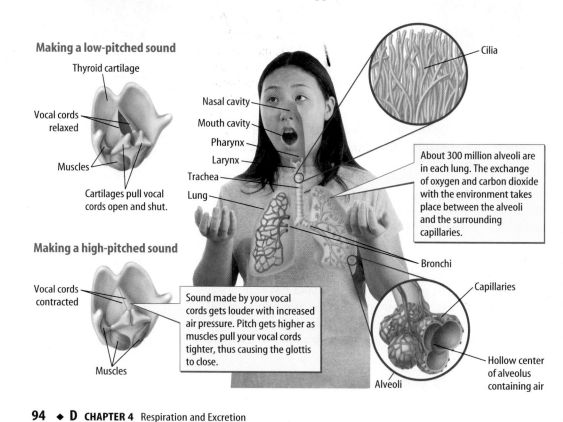

Making a low-pitched sound

Thyroid cartilage

Vocal cords relaxed

Muscles

Cartilages pull vocal cords open and shut.

Making a high-pitched sound

Vocal cords contracted

Muscles

Sound made by your vocal cords gets louder with increased air pressure. Pitch gets higher as muscles pull your vocal cords tighter, thus causing the glottis to close.

Nasal cavity
Mouth cavity
Pharynx
Larynx
Trachea
Lung

Cilia

About 300 million alveoli are in each lung. The exchange of oxygen and carbon dioxide with the environment takes place between the alveoli and the surrounding capillaries.

Bronchi

Capillaries

Hollow center of alveolus containing air

Alveoli

Curriculum Connection

Health The pharynx serves as the passageway of food into the esophagus and air into the trachea. The epiglottis is a small flap of tissue that normally closes over the tracheal opening when food is swallowed. Sometimes food or liquid gets past the epiglottis and goes into the trachea, triggering the choking reflex. Ask students to discuss ways to prevent choking. [L2] [LS] **Logical-Mathematical**

Differentiated Instruction

Challenge A person can experience oxygen deficiency in carbon monoxide poisoning. Have students research how carbon monoxide impairs the delivery of oxygen to tissues. Prepare a chart to show how to avoid carbon monoxide poisoning in the home. [L3]

Larynx and Trachea Next, the air moves into your larynx (LER ingks). The **larynx** is the airway to which two pairs of horizontal folds of tissue, called vocal cords, are attached as shown in **Figure 3.** Forcing air between the cords causes them to vibrate and produce sounds. When you speak, muscles tighten or loosen your vocal cords, resulting in different sounds. Your brain coordinates the movement of the muscles in your throat, tongue, cheeks, and lips when you talk, sing, or just make noise. Your teeth also are involved in forming letter sounds and words.

From the larynx, air moves into the **trachea** (TRAY kee uh), which is a tube about 12 cm in length. Strong, C-shaped rings of cartilage prevent the trachea from collapsing. The trachea is lined with mucous membranes and cilia, as shown in **Figure 3,** that trap dust, bacteria, and pollen. Why must the trachea stay open all the time?

Bronchi and the Lungs Air is carried into your lungs by two short tubes called **bronchi** (BRAHN ki) (singular, *bronchus*) at the lower end of the trachea. Within the lungs, the bronchi branch into smaller and smaller tubes. The smallest tubes are called bronchioles (BRAHN kee ohlz). At the end of each bronchiole are clusters of tiny, thin-walled sacs called **alveoli** (al VEE uh li). Air passes into the bronchi, then into the bronchioles, and finally into the alveoli. Lungs are masses of alveoli arranged in grapelike clusters. The capillaries surround the alveoli like a net, as shown in **Figure 3.**

The exchange of oxygen and carbon dioxide takes place between the alveoli and capillaries. This easily happens because the walls of the alveoli (singular, *alveolus*) and the walls of the capillaries are each only one cell thick, as shown in **Figure 4.** Oxygen moves through the cell membranes of the alveoli and then through the cell membranes of the capillaries into the blood. There the oxygen is picked up by hemoglobin (HEE muh gloh bun), a molecule in red blood cells, and carried to all body cells. At the same time, carbon dioxide and other cellular wastes leave the body cells. The wastes move through the cell membranes of the capillaries. Then they are carried by the blood. In the lungs, waste gases move through the cell membranes of the capillaries and through the cell membranes of the alveoli. Then waste gases leave the body during exhalation.

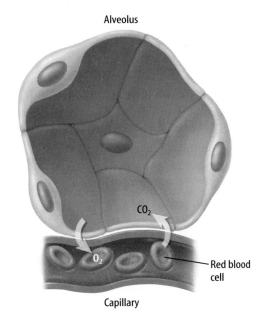

Alveolus

CO_2

O_2

Red blood cell

Capillary

Figure 4 The thin capillary walls allow gases to be exchanged easily between the alveoli and the capillaries.

Science Online

Topic: Speech

Visit bookd.msscience.com for Web links to information about how speech sounds are made.

Activity In your Science Journal, describe the changes in the position of your lips and tongue when you say each letter of the alphabet.

Purpose Students observe the increased surface area provided by alveoli. L2 ELL

LS **Logical-Mathematical**

Materials bathroom-tissue cardboard tube, marbles, bowl, calculator

Teaching Strategy Gently shake the tube when half-full of marbles to settle them and avoid gaps.

Analysis

1. Answers will vary depending on stacking techniques, but will usually indicate a more than twofold increase in the surface area when using marbles.

2. The marbles represent the alveoli.

3. More gas can be exchanged because there is greater surface area within the same space.

Assessment

Performance Have students calculate the surface area of a cube that is 10 cm × 5 cm × 2 cm and compare this with the surface area of one hundred 1-cm × 1-cm × 1-cm cubes that have the same volume as the larger cube. Use **Performance Assessment in the Science Classroom**, p. 101.

✔ Reading Check

Answer It helps move gases into and out of the body.

Comparing Surface Area

Procedure 🗈

1. Stand a **bathroom-tissue cardboard tube** in an **empty bowl.**

2. Drop **marbles** into the tube, filling it to the top.

3. Count the number of marbles used.

4. Repeat steps 2 and 3 two more times. Calculate the average number of marbles needed to fill the tube.

5. The tube's inside surface area is approximately 161.29 cm^2. Each marble has a surface area of approximately 8.06 cm^2. Calculate the surface area of the average number of marbles.

Analysis

1. Compare the inside surface area of the tube with the surface area of the average number of marbles needed to fill the tube.

2. If the tube represents a bronchus, what do the marbles represent?

3. Using this model, explain what makes gas exchange in the lungs efficient.

Figure 5 Your lungs inhale and exhale about 500 mL of air with an average breath. This increases to 2,000 mL of air per breath when you do strenuous activity.

Why do you breathe?

Signals from your brain tell the muscles in your chest and abdomen to contract and relax. You don't have to think about breathing to breathe, just like your heart beats without you telling it to beat. Your brain can change your breathing rate depending on the amount of carbon dioxide present in your blood. As carbon dioxide increases, your breathing rate increases. When there is less carbon dioxide in your blood, your breathing rate decreases. You do have some control over your breathing—you can hold your breath if you want to. Eventually, though, your brain will respond to the buildup of carbon dioxide in your blood. The brain's response will tell your chest and abdomen muscles to work automatically, and you will breathe whether you want to or not.

Inhaling and Exhaling Breathing is partly the result of changes in air pressure. Under normal conditions, a gas moves from an area of high pressure to an area of low pressure. When you squeeze an empty, soft-plastic bottle, air is pushed out. This happens because air pressure outside the top of the bottle is less than the pressure you create inside the bottle when you squeeze it. As you release your grip on the bottle, the air pressure inside the bottle becomes less than it is outside the bottle. Air rushes back in, and the bottle returns to its original shape.

Your lungs work in a similar way to the squeezed bottle. Your **diaphragm** (DI uh fram) is a muscle beneath your lungs that contracts and relaxes to help move gases into and out of your lungs. **Figure 5** illustrates breathing.

✔ Reading Check *How does your diaphragm help you breathe?*

When a person is choking, a rescuer can use abdominal thrusts, as shown in **Figure 6,** to save the life of the choking victim.

Inhale   **Exhale**

Visual Learning

Figure 5 The position of the diaphragm during the process of inhaling and expanding is shown. Compare this process with the squeezing of the plastic bottle discussed in the text.

Teacher **FYI**

Hiccups Hiccups are caused by spasmodic contractions of the diaphragm. The result is a sudden inhaling of air. Choking could result if a reflex action did not automatically cause the epiglottis to close over the trachea and prevent any food from entering.

NATIONAL GEOGRAPHIC VISUALIZING ABDOMINAL THRUSTS

Figure 6

When food or other objects become lodged in the trachea, airflow between the lungs and the mouth and nasal cavity is blocked. Death can occur in minutes. However, prompt action by someone can save the life of a choking victim. The rescuer uses abdominal thrusts to force the victim's diaphragm up. This decreases the volume of the chest cavity and forces air up in the trachea. The result is a rush of air that dislodges and expels the food or other object. The victim can breathe again. This technique is shown at right and should only be performed in emergency situations.

Food is lodged in the victim's trachea.

The rescuer places her fist against the victim's stomach.

The rescuer's second hand adds force to the fist.

A The rescuer stands behind the choking victim and wraps her arms around the victim's upper abdomen. She places a fist (thumb side in) against the victim's stomach. The fist should be below the ribs and above the navel.

An upward thrust dislodges the food from the victim's trachea.

B With a violent, sharp movement, the rescuer thrusts her fist up into the area below the ribs. This action should be repeated as many times as necessary.

SECTION 1 The Respiratory System **D** ◆ **97**

Visualizing Abdominal Thrusts

Have students examine the pictures and read the captions. Then ask the following questions.

Why should abdominal thrusts only be performed in emergencies, and never performed on other people for practice or for fun? Abdominal thrusts could cause injury if performed on a person who is not choking.

Why is it important that the rescuer's fist be located below the ribs of the choking victim? The fist must be below the diaphragm in order for an upward force to be applied to the diaphragm. A fist located on the rib cage or breastbone could cause injury to the victim.

Activity

Memory Device Have students work in small groups to develop a mnemonic, or memory, device that will allow them to quickly and accurately remember the steps of proper abdominal thrusts to save a choking victim. L2

Visual Learning

Figure 6 Review the theory of how abdominal thrusts work. This maneuver is often called the Heimlich maneuver. Abdominal thrusts lift the diaphragm and force enough air from the lungs to create an artificial cough. The cough is intended to move and expel an obstructing foreign body from an airway.

Differentiated Instruction

English-Language Learners Have students practice their communication skills by pretending to call the emergency number to contact the local rescue squad. Students can take turns being the operator who asks vital questions and the bystander who reports the choking incident. L1

Curriculum Connection

Health Arrange a visit to a Red Cross center or have a health specialist come to school and demonstrate how to use abdominal thrusts and cardiopulmonary resuscitation (CPR) to revive a person who is not breathing. Ask students to find out where CPR training is available in their area. L2

Attack of Viral Particles

Purpose to compare the effect of different quantities of inhaled virus or bacteria particles on the cells of the respiratory system

Possible Materials dominoes, large marbles

Estimated Time 1 class session

Teaching Strategies

• Students can set up the dominoes, which represent respiratory cells, so that when the dominoes fall, a cascade of events is triggered.

• Students can designate specific areas of dominoes to represent different areas of the respiratory system. Designate the large marbles as bacteria or virus particles.

• Students can drop one or two marbles on the dominoes to demonstrate what happens when you breathe in a small quantity of particles, acquired from dirty hands or contaminated surface areas.

• Students can drop several marbles on the dominoes to demonstrate what happens when you breathe in large quantities of particles, acquired from a sneeze or cough.

• Allow students to explore other questions that arise.

For additional inquiry activities, see *Science Inquiry Labs.*

✓ Reading Check

Answer all parts, but usually the upper part, from the nose to the pharynx

---

Science Online

Topic: Second-Hand Smoke
Visit bookd.msscience.com for Web links to information about the health concerns of second-hand smoke.

Activity Make a poster to teach younger students about the dangers of second-hand smoke.

Table 1 Smokers' Risk of Death from Disease	
Disease	**Smokers' Risk Compared to Nonsmokers' Risk**
Lung cancer	23 times higher for males, 11 times higher for females
Chronic bronchitis and emphysema	5 times higher
Heart disease	2 times higher

Diseases and Disorders of the Respiratory System

INTEGRATE Environment   If you were asked to list some of the things that can harm your respiratory system, you probably would put smoking at the top. As you can see in **Table 1,** many serious diseases are related to smoking. The chemical substances in tobacco—nicotine and tars—are poisons and can destroy cells. The high temperatures, smoke, and carbon monoxide produced when tobacco burns also can injure a smoker's cells. Even if you are a nonsmoker, inhaling smoke from tobacco products—called secondhand smoke—is unhealthy and has the potential to harm your respiratory system. Smoking, polluted air, coal dust, and asbestos (as BES tus) have been related to respiratory problems such as bronchitis (brahn KI tus), emphysema (em fuh SEE muh), asthma (AZ muh), and cancer.

Respiratory Infections   Bacteria, viruses, and other microorganisms can cause infections that affect any of the organs of the respiratory system. The common cold usually affects the upper part of the respiratory system—from the nose to the pharynx. The cold virus also can cause irritation and swelling in the larynx, trachea, and bronchi. The cilia that line the trachea and bronchi can be damaged. However, cilia usually heal rapidly. A virus that causes influenza, or flu, can affect many of the body's systems. The virus multiplies in the cells lining the alveoli and damages them. Pneumonia is an infection in the alveoli that can be caused by bacteria, viruses, or other microorganisms. Before antibiotics were available to treat these infections, many people died from pneumonia.

✓ Reading Check   *What parts of the respiratory system are affected by the cold virus?*

🔲 LAB DEMONSTRATION

Purpose to compare how tar affects cilia function

Materials toothbrush, water, black pepper, molasses, newspaper

Preparation Cover work area with newspaper.

Procedure Wet the toothbrush bristles (cilia) and sprinkle them with pepper (dust). Run a finger over the bristles five times. Wash the toothbrush and repeat the process using molasses (tar) instead of water.

Expected Outcome Students will see how tar prevents cilia from moving.

Assessment

Why do foreign particles need to be removed from the bronchial tubes? Particles can irritate tissues, and bacteria can cause infections. In addition to preventing normal cilia action, why are tars dangerous? They are poisonous. [L2]

Chronic Bronchitis When bronchial tubes are irritated and swell, and too much mucus is produced, a disease called bronchitis develops. Sometimes, bacterial infections occur in the bronchial tubes because the mucus there provides nearly ideal conditions for bacteria to grow. Antibiotics are effective treatments for this type of bronchitis.

Many cases of bronchitis clear up within a few weeks, but the disease sometimes lasts for a long time. When this happens, it is called chronic (KRAH nihk) bronchitis. A person who has chronic bronchitis must cough often to try to clear the excess mucus from the airway. However, the more a person coughs, the more the cilia and bronchial tubes can be harmed. When cilia are damaged, they cannot move mucus, bacteria, and dirt particles out of the lungs effectively. Then harmful substances, such as sticky tar from burning tobacco, build up in the airways. Sometimes, scar tissue forms and the respiratory system cannot function properly.

Emphysema A disease in which the alveoli in the lungs enlarge is called **emphysema** (em fuh SEE muh). When cells in the alveoli are reddened and swollen, an enzyme is released that causes the walls of the alveoli to break down. As a result, alveoli can't push air out of the lungs, so less oxygen moves into the bloodstream from the alveoli. When blood becomes low in oxygen and high in carbon dioxide, shortness of breath occurs. Some people with emphysema require extra oxygen as shown in **Figure 7.** Because the heart works harder to supply oxygen to body cells, people who have emphysema often develop heart problems, as well.

Figure 7 Lung diseases can have major effects on breathing.

A normal, healthy lung can exchange oxygen and carbon dioxide effectively.

A diseased lung carries less oxygen to body cells.

Emphysema may take 20 to 30 years to develop.

SECTION 1 The Respiratory System **D** ◆ **99**

Teacher FYI

Nicotine The chemical nicotine has been widely used by farmers and gardeners since the seventeenth century in sprays and dusts as an insecticide. Its use is now more carefully regulated to prevent accidental poisonings.

Curriculum Connection

Health To test for healthy lungs, a doctor may thump the back or chest of the patient. If there is a hollow sound, the lungs are filled with air. If there is a dull sound, it is evidence of fluid in the lungs. Have students find out which respiratory infections can cause fluid buildup in the lungs. L2

IDENTIFYING Misconceptions

Viruses Cause Colds Many people believe that being exposed to cold drafts or cold rain will cause a cold. Colds are caused by viruses and not by exposure to cold and wet conditions. People already infected by cold germs who get cold and wet and then develop the full symptoms may thereby associate the two events.

Teacher FYI

Irritating Cells Inhaling tobacco smoke or other chemical irritants stimulates an increase in goblet cells and the enlargement of mucous cells in the lining of the bronchial tubes. This is the cause of the increased mucus in the bronchi of bronchitis sufferers.

Use Science Words

Word Origin The word *emphysema* comes from two Greek words: *em-*, meaning *"in,"* and *physan*, meaning *"blow."* How does the origin of the word relate to the symptoms of the disease? Persons with the disease have difficulty "blowing" air in and out of their lungs.

Use an Analogy

Stretched Balloons The alveoli of persons with emphysema are like balloons that have been blown up too many times and with too much air. In both cases the walls have been stretched, become thin, and can rupture.

Reading Check

Answer The air passages will become irritated, and cancer cells may develop and destroy healthy lung tissue.

3 Assess

DAILY INTERVENTION

Check for Understanding

Linguistic Have students write a paragraph describing why air moves into the lungs when the ribs move upward and the diaphragm moves downward. This action reduces air pressure within the chest cavity, and the higher external air pressure causes air to rush into the lungs. L2

Reteach

Pressure Use a lung demonstration apparatus to illustrate how the downward movement of the diaphragm causes reduced pressure within the chest cavity. L2

✓ Assessment

Process Have students use a chart of the respiratory system to describe the passage of air into and out of the lungs. Use **Performance Assessment in the Science Classroom,** p. 143. L2

Figure 8 More than 85 percent of all lung cancer is related to smoking. Smoking also can play a part in the development of cancer in other body organs indicated above.

Lung Cancer The third leading cause of death in men and women in the United States is lung cancer. Inhaling the tar in cigarette smoke is the greatest contributing factor to lung cancer. Tar and other ingredients found in smoke act as carcinogens (kar SIH nuh junz) in the body. Carcinogens are substances that can cause an uncontrolled growth of cells. In the lungs, this is called lung cancer. As represented in **Figure 8,** smoking also has been linked to the development of cancers of the esophagus, mouth, larynx, pancreas, kidney, and bladder.

✓ **Reading Check** *What happens to the lungs of people who begin smoking?*

Asthma Shortness of breath, wheezing, or coughing can occur in a lung disorder called **asthma.** When a person has an asthma attack, the bronchial tubes contract quickly. Inhaling medicine that relaxes the bronchial tubes is the usual treatment for an asthma attack. Asthma is often an allergic reaction. An allergic reaction occurs when the body overreacts to a foreign substance. An asthma attack can result from breathing certain substances such as cigarette smoke or certain plant pollen, eating certain foods, or stress in a person's life.

 section **1** review

Summary

Functions of the Respiratory System

- Breathing brings air into the lungs and removes waste gases.
- Cellular respiration converts oxygen and glucose to carbon dioxide, water, and energy.

Organs of the Respiratory System

- Air is carried into the lungs by bronchi.
- Bronchioles are smaller branches of bronchi, and at the ends of these are alveoli.

Diseases and Disorders of the Respiratory System

- Emphysema is a disease that causes the alveoli to enlarge.
- Lung cancer occurs when carcinogens cause an uncontrolled growth of cells.

Self Check

1. **Describe** the main function of the respiratory system.
2. **Explain** how oxygen, carbon dioxide, and other waste gases are exchanged in the lungs and body tissues.
3. **Identify** how air moves into and out of the lungs.
4. **Think Critically** How is the work of the digestive and circulatory systems related to the respiratory system?

Applying Skills

5. **Research Information** Nicotine in tobacco is a poison. Using library references, find out how nicotine affects the body.
6. **Communicate** Use references to find out about lung disease common among coal miners, stonecutters, and sandblasters. Find out what safety measures are required now for these trades. In your Science Journal, write a paragraph about these safety measures.

section **1** review

1. supply oxygen and remove carbon dioxide
2. Oxygen, carbon dioxide, and waste gases are exchanged by diffusion into and out of the blood.
3. movement of the diaphragm and rib cage; differences in pressure

4. digestive system—provides food for cell respiration; circulatory system—transports oxygen for food breakdown and carries respiration waste products to the lungs for expulsion

5. Nicotine causes blood vessels to constrict, resulting in increased blood pressure. It also causes nausea, headaches, and gastric upset.
6. Students answers will vary.

The Excretory System

Functions of the Excretory System

It's your turn to take out the trash. You carry the bag outside and put it in the trash can. The next day, you bring out another bag of trash, but the trash can is full. When trash isn't collected, it piles up. Just as trash needs to be removed from your home to keep it livable, your body must eliminate wastes to remain healthy. Undigested material is eliminated by your large intestine. Waste gases are eliminated through the combined efforts of your circulatory and respiratory systems. Some salts are eliminated when you sweat. These systems function together as parts of your excretory system. If wastes aren't eliminated, toxic substances build up and damage organs. If not corrected, serious illness or death occurs.

The Urinary System

The **urinary system** rids the blood of wastes produced by the cells. **Figure 9** shows how the urinary system functions as a part of the excretory system. The urinary system also controls blood volume by removing excess water produced by body cells during respiration.

as you read

What You'll Learn
- **Distinguish** between the excretory and urinary systems.
- **Describe** how the kidneys work.
- **Explain** what happens when urinary organs don't work.

Why It's Important
The urinary system helps clean your blood of cellular wastes.

Review Vocabulary
blood: tissue that transports oxygen, nutrients, and waste materials throughout your body

New Vocabulary
- urinary system
- urine
- kidney
- nephron
- ureter
- bladder
- urethra

Figure 9 The excretory system includes other body systems.

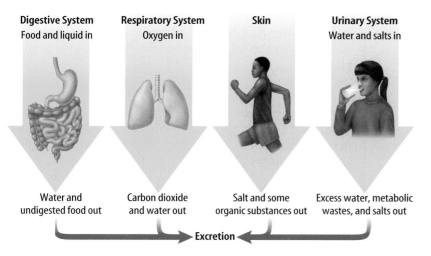

Digestive System Food and liquid in — Water and undigested food out

Respiratory System Oxygen in — Carbon dioxide and water out

Skin — Salt and some organic substances out

Urinary System Water and salts in — Excess water, metabolic wastes, and salts out

Excretion

Bellringer

INTERACTIVE CHALKBOARD PowerPoint® Presentations

Section Focus Transparencies also are available on the Interactive Chalkboard CD-ROM.

L2 ELL

Section Focus Transparency — Liquid Wastes

Have you ever thought of your skin as an organ that rids your body of waste? You probably perspire most heavily when you exercise. Perspiration is a liquid waste given off by the body.

1. How is perspiring helpful to the body?
2. Why is it important to drink plenty of fluids before, during, and after periods of intense physical activity?
3. What other body system is involved with the removal of liquid wastes?

Tie to Prior Knowledge

Filters Remind students of how the filter on a coffeemaker works. Only liquid is allowed to flow through. Explain that, in a similar way, the urinary system acts as a filter.

SECTION 2 The Excretory System **D** ◆ **101**

Section 2 Resource Manager

Chapter FAST FILE Resources
Transparency Activity, pp. 41, 43–44
MiniLAB, p. 4
Enrichment, p. 28
Reinforcement, p. 26
Directed Reading for Content Mastery, pp. 19, 20

Lab Worksheet, pp. 5–6, 7–8
Lab Management and Safety, p. 77
Mathematics Skill Activities, p. 1
Home and Community Involvement, p. 40

Activity

Urine Composition Have students do research and construct a circle graph to illustrate the composition of urine. water = 95%, urea = 2%, sodium chloride = 1%, other substances = 2% L3 **[LS] Visual-Spatial**

Visual Learning

Figure 10 Have students study this figure and make a sequencing concept map. Student maps should outline each step in the process by which the human body determines how much urine to excrete. L2

✔ Reading Check

Answer by increasing and decreasing the amount of wastewater excreted

Quick Demo

Diffusion

Materials cellophane bags, container of water, colored sugar solution, container of sugar solution, colored pure water

Estimated Time 15 minutes

Procedure Set up a diffusion experiment using a cellophane bag with a colored sugar solution placed in a container of water. To demonstrate diffusion in the other direction, place a cellophane bag of colored pure water into a container of sugar solution.

Your brain detects too little water in your blood. Your hypothalamus then releases a larger amount of hormone.

Figure 10 The amount of urine that you eliminate each day is determined by the level of a hormone that is produced by your hypothalamus.

This release signals the kidneys to return more water to your blood and decrease the amount of urine excreted.

Regulating Fluid Levels To stay in good health, the fluid levels within the body must be balanced and normal blood pressure must be maintained. An area in the brain, the hypothalamus (hi poh THA luh mus), constantly monitors the amount of water in the blood. When the brain detects too much water in the blood, the hypothalamus releases a lesser amount of a specific hormone. This signals the kidneys to return less water to the blood and increase the amount of wastewater, called **urine,** that is excreted. **Figure 10** indicates how the body reacts when too little water is in the blood.

✔ Reading Check
How does the urinary system control the volume of water in the blood?

A specific amount of water in the blood is also important for the movement of gases and excretion of solid wastes from the body. The urinary system also balances the amounts of certain salts and water that must be present for all cell activities to take place.

Organs of the Urinary System Excretory organs is another name for the organs of the urinary system. The main organs of the urinary system are two bean-shaped **kidneys.** Kidneys are located on the back wall of the abdomen at about waist level. The kidneys filter blood that contains wastes collected from cells. In approximately 5 min, all of the blood in your body passes through the kidneys. The red-brown color of the kidneys is due to their enormous blood supply. In **Figure 11,** you can see that blood enters the kidneys through a large artery and leaves through a large vein.

102 ◆ D CHAPTER 4 Respiration and Excretion

Curriculum Connection

Math Calculate the ratio of body weight to amount of urine excreted. If an 11-kg child excretes 600 mL, what would you expect a 45-kg adult to excrete? 2,455 mL The amount is actually only about 1500 mL. The amount excreted by children is greater in proportion to their weight. L2 **[LS] Logical-Mathematical**

Teacher FYI

Body Homeostasis Filtering waste from the circulatory system is essential to maintaining life. The urinary system regulates the concentration and volume of blood by removing and restoring selected amounts of water and chemicals. Any change in the normal functioning of the urinary system represents a health threat.

Filtration in the Kidney The kidney, as shown in **Figure 11A,** is a two-stage filtration system. It is made up of about 1 million tiny filtering units called **nephrons** (NEF rahnz), which are shown in **Figure 11B.** Each nephron has a cuplike structure and a tube-like structure called a duct. Blood moves from a renal artery to capillaries in the cuplike structure. The first filtration occurs when water, sugar, salt, and wastes from the blood pass into the cuplike structure. Left behind in the blood are red blood cells and proteins. Next, liquid in the cuplike structure is squeezed into a narrow tubule. Capillaries that surround the tubule perform the second filtration. Most of the water, sugar, and salt are reabsorbed and returned to the blood. These collection capillaries merge to form small veins, which merge to form a renal vein in each kidney. Purified blood is returned to the main circulatory system. The liquid left behind flows into collecting tubules in each kidney. This wastewater, or urine, contains excess water, salts, and other wastes that are not reabsorbed by the body. An average-sized person produces about 1 L of urine per day.

Figure 11 The urinary system removes wastes from the blood and includes the kidneys, the bladder, and the connecting tubes.

A Kidneys are made up of many nephrons.

B A single nephron is shown in detail. **Describe** *the main function of the nephron.*

Mini LAB

Modeling Kidney Function

Procedure 🥽🧤🔬🧫

1. Mix a small amount of **soil** and **fine gravel** with **water** in a **clean cup.**
2. Place the **funnel** into a **second cup.**
3. Place a small piece of **wire screen** in the funnel.
4. Carefully pour the mud-water-gravel mixture into the funnel. Let it drain.
5. Remove the screen and replace it with a piece of **filter paper.**
6. Place the funnel in **another clean cup.**
7. Repeat step 4.

Analysis

1. What part of the blood does the gravel represent?
2. How does this experiment model the function of a person's kidneys?

Mini LAB

Purpose Students model and observe the function of a kidney. L2 [IS] **Kinesthetic**

Materials soil (2 T), fine gravel (1 T), 8-ounce plastic cups (3), funnel, wire screen, filter paper, tap water

Teaching Strategy Students may work in pairs to cut down on the amount of materials needed.

Troubleshooting Moisten the filter paper before filtering the dirty water so that the paper adheres to the funnel.

Analysis

1. the blood cells and proteins
2. This experiment modeled the two-stage filtration process of the kidneys. The filter removes dirt and particles, like a nephron, which filters wastes from the blood.

Assessment

Portfolio Have students make a labeled drawing of the urinary system. Have them place arrows on the diagrams to show the flow of fluids through the nephrons to the bladder and then out of the body. Use **Performance Assessment in the Science Classroom,** p. 127. L2 [P]

Caption Answer
Figure 11B to filter blood

Active Reading

Synthesis Journal In this strategy, students reflect on a project, a paper, or a performance in light of their own experiences and plan for personal application. Have each student divide a piece of paper into three sections. Have them record *What I did, What I learned,* and *How I can use it.* Have students write a Synthesis Journal entry for the MiniLAB. L2

Fun Fact

Protozoans are complete organisms (most are one-celled) that ingest food, digest food, expel waste, and breathe without the benefit of separate organs such as those that humans have.

Urine Collection and Release The urine in each collecting tubule drains into a funnel-shaped area of each kidney that leads to the ureter (YOO ruh tur). **Ureters** are tubes that lead from each kidney to the bladder. The **bladder** is an elastic, muscular organ that holds urine until it leaves the body. The elastic walls of the bladder can stretch to hold up to 0.5 L of urine. When empty, the bladder looks wrinkled and the cells lining the bladder are thick. When full, the bladder looks like an inflated balloon and the cells lining the bladder are stretched and thin. A tube called the **urethra** (yoo REE thruh) carries urine from the bladder to the outside of the body.

Applying Science

How does your body gain and lose water?

Your body depends on water. Without water, your cells could not carry out their activities and body systems could not function. Water is so important to your body that your brain and other body systems are involved in balancing water gain and water loss.

Identifying the Problem

Table A shows the major sources by which your body gains water. Oxidation of nutrients occurs when energy is released from nutrients by your body's cells. Water is a waste product of these reactions. **Table B** lists the major sources by which your body loses water. The data show you how daily gain and loss of water are related.

Solving the Problem

1. What is the greatest source of water gained by your body?
2. Explain how the percentages of water gained and lost would change in a person who was working in extremely warm temperatures. In this case, what organ of the body would be the greatest contributor to water loss?

Table A

Major Sources by Which Body Water is Gained		
Source	Amount (mL)	Percent
Oxidation of nutrients	250	10
Foods	750	30
Liquids	1,500	60
Total	2,500	100

Table B

Major Sources by Which Body Water is Lost		
Source	Amount (mL)	Percent
Urine	1,500	60
Skin	500	20
Lungs	350	14
Feces	150	6
Total	2,500	100

Differentiated Instruction

Challenge Adult kidneys weigh only about 170 g each. The kidneys of an average adult process about 1,600 L of liquid per day, most of which is recycled. Have students calculate how many liters an adult's kidneys process in a year, in a decade, and in 75 years. 584,000 L; 5,840,000 L; 43,800,000 L [L3] [IS] **Logical-Mathematical**

Curriculum Connection

Health Small stones made up of precipitated minerals such as uric acid or calcium salts may form in the kidneys. These kidney stones may move into the ureter and can cause severe pain. Drinking large quantities of water can help prevent the formation of the stones. Ask students to investigate what foods may contribute to the formation of kidney stones. [L2]

Other Organs of Excretion

Large amounts of liquid wastes are lost every day by your body in other ways, as shown in **Figure 12**. The liver also filters the blood to remove wastes. Certain wastes are converted to other substances. For example, excess amino acids are changed to a chemical called urea (yoo REE uh) that is excreted in urine. Hemoglobin from broken-down red blood cells becomes part of bile, which is the digestive fluid from the liver.

Urinary Diseases and Disorders

What happens when someone's kidneys don't work properly or stop working? Waste products that are not removed build up and act as poisons in body cells. Water that normally is removed from body tissues accumulates and causes swelling of the ankles and feet. Sometimes these fluids also build up around the heart, causing it to work harder to move blood to the lungs.

Without excretion, an imbalance of salts occurs. The body responds by trying to restore this balance. If the balance isn't restored, the kidneys and other organs can be damaged. Kidney failure occurs when the kidneys don't work as they should. This is always a serious problem because the kidneys' job is so important to the rest of the body.

Infections caused by microorganisms can affect the urinary system. Usually, the infection begins in the bladder. However, it can spread and involve the kidneys. Most of the time, these infections can be cured with antibiotics.

Because the ureters and urethra are narrow tubes, they can be blocked easily in some disorders. A blockage of one of these tubes can cause serious problems because urine cannot flow out of the body properly. If the blockage is not corrected, the kidneys can be damaged.

 Reading Check **Why is a blocked ureter or urethra a serious problem?**

Detecting Urinary Diseases Urine can be tested for any signs of a urinary tract disease. A change in the urine's color can suggest kidney or liver problems. High levels of glucose can be a sign of diabetes. Increased amounts of a protein called albumin (al BYOO mun) indicate kidney disease or heart failure. When the kidneys are damaged, albumin can get into the urine, just as a leaky water pipe allows water to drip.

Figure 12 On average, the volume of water lost daily by exhaling is a little more than the volume of a soft-drink can. The volume of water lost by your skin each day is about the volume of a 20-ounce soft-drink bottle.

 INTEGRATE Social Studies

Desalination Nearly 80 percent of Earth's surface is covered by water. Ninety-seven percent of this water is salt water. Humans cannot drink salt water. Desalination is a process that removes salt from salt water making it safe for human consumption. Research to learn which countries use desalination as a source of drinking water. Mark the countries' locations on a world map.

Figure 13 A dialysis machine can replace or help with some of the activities of the kidneys in a person with kidney failure. Like the kidney, the dialysis machine removes wastes from the blood.

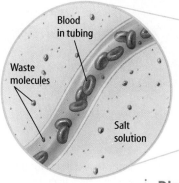

Blood in tubing

Waste molecules

Salt solution

Dialysis A person who has only one kidney still can live normally. The remaining kidney increases in size and works harder to make up for the loss of the other kidney. However, if both kidneys fail, the person will need to have his or her blood filtered by an artificial kidney machine in a process called dialysis (di AH luh sus), as shown in **Figure 13.**

section 2 review

Summary

The Urinary System

- The urinary system rids the blood of wastes produced by your cells.
- The hypothalamus monitors and regulates the amount of water in the blood.
- Nephrons are tiny filtering units in the kidneys that remove water, sugar, salt, and wastes from blood.
- Urine from the kidneys drains into the ureter, then into the bladder, and is carried outside the body by the urethra.

Urinary Diseases and Disorders

- Waste products that are not removed build up and act as poisons in your cells.
- If both kidneys fail, your blood will need to be filtered using a process called dialysis.
- Urine can be tested for kidney and liver problems, heart failure, and diabetes.

Self Check

1. **Explain** how the kidneys remove wastes and keep fluids and salts in balance.
2. **Describe** what happens when the urinary system does not function properly.
3. **Compare** the excretory system and urinary system.
4. **Concept Map** Using a network-tree concept map, compare the excretory functions of the kidneys and the lungs.
5. **Think Critically** Explain why reabsorption of certain materials in the kidneys is important to your health.

Applying Math

6. **Solve One-Step Equations** In approximately 5 min, all 5 L of blood in the body pass through the kidneys. Calculate the average rate of flow through the kidneys in liters per minute.

section 2 review

1. Kidneys filter the blood to remove wastes, sugar, water, and salt. Necessary amounts of water, sugar, and salt are returned to the blood.
2. Waste products not removed cause the destruction of cells. Fluids not removed from body tissues cause swellings in the extremities and buildup of fluids around the heart. Salts are in imbalance in body fluids, which can lead to organ damage.
3. excretory system—includes all systems that rid the body of wastes; urinary system—consists of organs that produce urine as waste
4. Many of the substances are needed by the body to maintain homeostasis.
5. Wastes in blood are carried to the lungs, which remove water and carbon dioxide, and to the kidneys, which remove water and excess salts, and other wastes.
6. 1 liter per minute rate of flow

Kidney Structure

As your body uses nutrients, wastes are created. One role of the kidneys is to filter waste products out of the bloodstream and excrete this waste outside the body. How can these small structures filter all the blood in the body in 5 min?

Real-World Question

How does the structure of the kidney relate to the function of a kidney?

Goals
■ **Observe** the external and internal structures of a kidney.

Materials
large animal kidney
*model of a kidney
scalpel
magnifying lens
disposable gloves
dissecting tray
*Alternate materials

Safety Precautions

WARNING: *Use extreme care when using sharp instruments. Wear disposable gloves. Wash your hands with soap after completing this lab.*

Procedure

1. **Examine** the outside of the kidney supplied by your teacher.

2. If the kidney still is encased in fat, peel off the fat carefully.

3. Using a scalpel, carefully cut the tissue in half lengthwise around the outline of the kidney. This cut should result in a section similar to the illustration on this page.

4. **Observe** the internal features of the kidney using a magnifying lens, or view these features in a model.

5. **Compare** the specimen or model with the kidney in the illustration.

6. **Draw** the kidney in your Science Journal and label its structures.

Conclude and Apply

1. What part makes up the cortex of the kidney? Why is this part red?

2. **Describe** the main function of nephrons.

3. The medulla of the kidney is made up of a network of tubules that come together to form the ureter. What is the function of this network of tubules?

4. How can the kidney be compared to a portable water-purifying system?

Communicating
Your Data

Compare your conclusions with those of other students in your class. **For more help, refer to the** Science Skill Handbook.

Communicating
Your Data

Students should discuss why their conclusions did or did not agree. They can prepare a listing of references that support their findings. L2

Real-World Question

Purpose Students examine the structures in a kidney and relate each structure to its function. L2 IS **Kinesthetic**

Process Skills observe and infer, interpret scientific illustrations, compare and contrast

Time Required 50 minutes

Safety Precautions Caution students about using sharp objects.

Teaching Strategies
• You may wish to have some kidneys remain intact.
• Other kidneys may be already sliced longitudinally.
• Kidneys can be reused.

Troubleshooting Demonstrate proper techniques for scalpel usage.

Conclude and Apply

1. Nephrons; the color is caused by the blood in the nephrons.
2. to filter blood within the kidneys
3. The network of tubules moves the fluid from the kidney to the bladder so it can be excreted.
4. Both are filtering mechanisms.

✓ Assessment

Oral Have students describe the evidence that two kidneys are more than enough to take care of excretory functions. Possible answer: people who have only one kidney are still able to function normally. L2

Model and Invent

▶ Real-World Question

Purpose Students model a blocked trachea and demonstrate how the abdominal thrust maneuver is used to remove the blockage. L2 IS **Kinesthetic**

Process Skills record observations, make models, analyze results, recognize cause and effect, draw conclusions

Time Required 40 minutes

▶ Make a Model

Discussion Tell students that the trachea is a tube that carries air from the mouth to the lungs. This passageway is the only normal path for air to flow into the lungs. What might happen if this passage were blocked? The oxygen supply would be cut off, and the person would die within a few minutes. Explain that the abdominal thrust maneuver is a simple method of removing a blockage from this passageway.

Possible Materials paper towel roll tube or other tube, paper, clay, bellows, bicycle pump, sports bottle, scissors

Safety Precautions Caution students to use care with scissors.

Simulating the Abdominal Thrust Maneuver

Goals
- **Construct** a model of the trachea with a piece of food stuck in it.
- **Demonstrate** what happens when the abdominal thrust maneuver is performed on someone.
- **Predict** another way that air could get into the lungs if the food could not be dislodged with an abdominal thrust maneuver.

Possible Materials
paper towel roll or other tube
paper (wadded into a ball)
clay
bicycle pump
sports bottle
scissors

Safety Precautions
🔥🧤⚠️🚫🔧
Always be careful when you use scissors.

▶ Real-World Question

Have you ever taken a class in CPR or learned about how to help a choking victim? Using the abdominal thrust maneuver, or Heimlich maneuver, is one way to remove food or another object that is blocking someone's airway. What happens internally when the maneuver is used? What can you use to make a model of the trachea? How can you simulate what happens during an abdominal thrust maneuver using your model?

▶ Make a Model

1. **List** the materials that you will need to construct your model. What will represent the trachea and a piece of food or other object blocking the airway?

2. How can you use your model to simulate the effects of an abdominal thrust maneuver?

3. Suggest a way to get air into the lungs if the food could not be dislodged. How would you simulate this method in your model?

Alternative Inquiry Lab

Extend the Activity Make this Lab an Inquiry Lab by building on the experience. Encourage your students to use what they have learned to brainstorm questions about what to do if the airway is blocked by water, in the case of a drowning victim. Have student groups each choose 1 question to explore. Ask them to list the materials they need to explore their questions. Unsafe or impractical questions should be eliminated. Students should have their plans for their additional experiments approved before continuing. Conduct the experiments after all of the necessary materials have been gathered. L2

4. **Compare** your plans for the model and the abdominal thrust maneuver simulation with those of other students in your class. Discuss why each of you chose the plans and materials that you did.

5. Make sure your teacher approves your plan and materials for your model before you start.

● Test the Model

1. **Construct** your model of a trachea with an object stuck in it. Make sure that air cannot get through the trachea if you try blowing softly through it.

2. Simulate what happens when an abdominal thrust maneuver is used. Record your observations. Was the object dislodged? How hard was it to dislodge the object?

3. Replace the object in the trachea. Use your model to simulate how you could get air into the lungs if an abdominal thrust maneuver did not remove the object. Is it easy to blow air through your model now?

4. Model a crushed trachea. Is it easy to blow air through the trachea in this case?

● Analyze Your Data

1. **Describe** how easy it was to get air through the trachea in each step in the Make the Model section above. Include any other observations that you made as you worked with your model.

2. Think about what you did to get air into the trachea when the object could not be dislodged with an abdominal thrust maneuver. How could this be done to a person? Do you know what this procedure is called?

● Conclude and Apply

Explain why the trachea has cartilage around it to protect it. What might happen if it did not?

𝒞ommunicating
Your Data

Explain to your family or friends what you have learned about how the abdominal thrust maneuver can help choking victims.

Teaching Strategies

- A model or anatomy wall chart showing the mouth, trachea, and lungs will help students conceptualize the problems caused by a blocked trachea.

- Encourage students to make a checklist of items they need to include in their models.

● Test the Model

Expected Outcome Students will build a model that simulates a trachea. They will simulate food blockage and the abdominal thrust maneuver and brainstorm ways to get oxygen to the lungs if the blockage cannot be dislodged.

● Analyze Your Data

1. Students should find that the abdominal thrust maneuver successfully dislodges most obstructions.

2. Students will likely suggest that a small incision could be cut below the blockage to allow air into the lungs. This procedure is called tracheostomy or tracheotomy.

● Conclude and Apply

Cartilage protects the trachea from being punctured and keeps it from collapsing.

☑ Assessment

Oral Ask students to name other instances in which the trachea might become blocked and a tracheostomy or tracheotomy would need to be performed. Possible answers: an accident that causes severe damage to the mouth or neck, cancerous or tumorous growths that block the trachea Use **Performance Assessment in the Science Classroom**, p. 87. L2

𝒞ommunicating
Your Data

Encourage students to use drawings showing that the trachea is the only pathway to the lungs. Then they can better describe the importance of the abdominal thrust maneuver.

TIME SCIENCE AND HISTORY

SCIENCE CAN CHANGE THE COURSE OF HISTORY!

Content Background

Samuel Kountz was born in extreme poverty in an all-black town in Arkansas in 1930. His grandmother was born a slave. He became the first African American to be accepted to the University of Arkansas Medical School.

While interning at Stanford, Kountz discovered that large amounts of the steroid methylprednisolone given to the patient after the transplant operation helped to reverse the rejection of the new organ. Kountz was a man of many achievements, and received several awards during his career.

Discussion

Kidney Rejection What did Kountz discover was the reason kidneys were being rejected after transplant surgeries? Possible answer: The patient's cells attacked and destroyed the small blood vessels of the transplanted kidney, thus, the kidney would die from lack of blood-supplied oxygen.

Historical Significance

Kountz's work also had a significant impact on other transplant surgeries, because other transplant procedures were associated with similar rejection problems.

The first successful kidney transplant without the use of immunosuppressive drugs was performed in 1954, because the donor was the recipient's twin. Organ rejection can be lessened when the donor is a sibling or other family member.

As a prelude to the Research activity, have students create a time line of transplant history starting from the early 1900s. Have students use poster board and ask them to include photographs and illustrations that illustrate transplant history. L2

LS Visual-Spatial

Overcoming the Odds

Guts and determination helped one pioneering doctor to save the lives of thousands

O vercoming the odds is a challenge that many people face. Dr. Samuel Lee Kountz, Jr. had the odds stacked against him. Thanks to his determination he beat them.

Dr. Kountz was interested in kidney transplants, a process that was still brand new in the 1950s. For many patients, a kidney transplant added months or a year to one's life. But then a patient's body would reject the kidney, and the patient would die. Dr. Kountz was determined to see that kidney transplants saved lives and kept patients healthy for years.

A donated organ is on its way to save a life.

Fixing the Problem

Kountz discovered the root of the problem—why and how a patient's body rejected the transplanted kidney. He discovered that the patient's cells attacked and destroyed the small blood vessels of the transplanted kidney. So the new kidney would die from lack of blood-supplied oxygen. From this, doctors knew when to give patients the right kinds of drugs, so that their bodies could overcome the rejection process.

In 1959, Kountz performed the first successful kidney transplant. He went on to develop a procedure to keep body organs healthy for up to 60 hours after being taken from a donor. He also set up a system of organ donor cards through the National Kidney Foundation. And in his career, Dr. Kountz transplanted more than 1,000 kidneys himself—and paved the way for thousands more.

Research What kinds of medical breakthroughs has the last century brought? Locate an article that explains either a recent advance in medicine or the work that doctors and medical researchers are doing. Share your findings with your class.

Science Online

For more information, visit bookd.msscience.com/time

Research First, ask students to focus on one part of medicine or one specialization in medicine that interests them. If a student is interested in the brain, suggest a search for an article about neurological advancements in medicine. Suggest avenues that are available for your students to successfully fulfill research in whatever interests they present for this project.

Resources for Teachers and Students

"The Black Surgeon in the Twentieth Century: A Tribute to Samuel L. Kountz," by Claude Organ. *Journal of the National Medical Association,* (September, 1978)

Understanding Kidney Transplantation by Edith T. Oberley and Neal R. Glass. Thomas; Springfield, Ill. 1987

Reviewing Main Ideas

Section 1 The Respiratory System

1. The respiratory system brings oxygen into the body and removes carbon dioxide.

2. Inhaled air passes through the nasal cavity, pharynx, larynx, trachea, bronchi, and into the alveoli of the lungs.

3. Breathing brings air into the lungs and removes waste gases.

4. The chemical reaction in the cells that needs oxygen to release energy from glucose is called cellular respiration.

5. The exchange of oxygen and carbon dioxide between aveoli and capillaries, and between capillaries and body cells, happens by the process of diffusion.

6. Smoking causes many problems throughout the respiratory system, including chronic bronchitis, emphysema, and lung cancer.

Section 2 The Excretory System

1. The kidneys are the major organs of the urinary system. They filter wastes from all of the blood in the body.

2. The first stage of kidney filtration occurs when water, sugar, salt, and wastes from the blood pass into the cuplike part of the nephron. The capillaries surrounding the tubule part of the nephron perform the second filtration, returning most of the water, sugar, and salt to the blood.

3. The urinary system is part of the excretory system. The skin, lungs, liver, and large intestine are also excretory organs.

4. Urine can be tested for signs of urinary tract disease and other diseases.

5. A person who has only one kidney still can live normally. When kidneys fail to work, an artificial kidney can be used to filter the blood in a process called dialysis.

Visualizing Main Ideas

Copy and complete the following table on the respiratory and excretory systems.

Human Body Systems

	Respiratory System	Excretory System
Major Organs	lungs	kidneys, lungs, large intestine, skin, liver
Wastes Eliminated	carbon dioxide, water vapor	water, salts, toxins
Disorders	chronic bronchitis, emphysema, lung cancer, asthma	builldup of waste, infections

Science Online bookd.msscience.com/interactive_tutor

Reviewing Main Ideas

Summary statements can be used by students to review the major concepts of the chapter.

Visualizing Main Ideas

See student page.

Science Online

Visit **bookd.msscience.com**
/self_check_quiz
/interactive_tutor
/vocabulary_puzzlemaker
/chapter_review
/standardized_test

Assessment Transparency

For additional assessment questions, use the *Assessment Transparency* located in the transparency book.

Using Vocabulary

1. Both are structures of the respiratory system.

2. Urine is stored in the bladder until it can be eliminated from the body.

3. Both are structures in the passageway leading to the esophagus.

4. The ureter carries urine to the bladder, and the urethra carries urine away from the bladder.

5. Alveoli are structures in the lungs that are damaged by the disease emphysema.

6. A nephron is the filtering unit of the kidney.

7. The urethra is a tube that carries urine away from the bladder.

8. Asthma is a disorder that causes the bronchi to contract.

9. The kidney filters blood and discharges liquid wastes, called urine.

10. Both are structures of the respiratory system.

Checking Concepts

11. B	16. D
12. C	17. B
13. A	18. A
14. A	19. C
15. B	20. C

Thinking Critically

21. Small objects can be sucked into and block their small windpipes, causing the child to choke.

22. Having many air sacs increases the surface area for gas exchange.

23. Tars coat cilia, making them less flexible and unable to move particles out of the lungs; alveoli lose elasticity, decreasing the total surface area of the lungs available for gas exchange; carcinogens cause the growth of cancerous cells in lung tissue.

Using Vocabulary

alveoli p. 95	nephron p. 103
asthma p. 100	pharynx p. 94
bladder p. 104	trachea p. 95
bronchi p. 95	ureter p. 104
diaphragm p. 96	urethra p. 104
emphysema p. 99	urinary system p. 101
kidney p. 102	urine p. 102
larynx p. 95	

For each set of vocabulary words below, explain the relationship that exists.

1. alveoli—bronchi

2. bladder—urine

3. larynx—pharynx

4. ureter—urethra

5. alveoli—emphysema

6. nephron—kidney

7. urethra—bladder

8. asthma—bronchi

9. kidney—urine

10. diaphragm—alveoli

Checking Concepts

Choose the word or phrase that best answers the question.

11. When you inhale, which of the following contracts and moves down?
    A) bronchioles   C) nephrons
    B) diaphragm   D) kidneys

12. Air is moistened, filtered, and warmed in which of the following structures?
    A) larynx   C) nasal cavity
    B) pharynx   D) trachea

Science Online bookd.msscience.com/vocabulary_puzzlemaker

13. Exchange of gases occurs between capillaries and which of the following structures?
    A) alveoli   C) bronchioles
    B) bronchi   D) trachea

14. Which of the following is a lung disorder that can occur as an allergic reaction?
    A) asthma   C) atherosclerosis
    B) cancer   D) emphysema

15. When you exhale, which way does the rib cage move?
    A) up   C) out
    B) down   D) stays the same

16. Which of the following conditions does smoking worsen?
    A) arthritis   C) excretion
    B) respiration   D) emphysema

17. In the illustration to the right, what is the name of the organ labeled A?
    A) kidneys
    B) bladder
    C) ureter
    D) urethra

18. What are the filtering units of the kidneys?
    A) nephrons   C) neurons
    B) ureters   D) alveoli

19. Approximately 1 L of water is lost per day through which of the following?
    A) sweat   C) urine
    B) lungs   D) large intestine

20. Which of the following substances is not reabsorbed by blood after it passes through the kidneys?
    A) salt   C) wastes
    B) sugar   D) water

Use the Exam*View*® Pro Testmaker CD-ROM to:
- create multiple versions of tests
- create modified tests with one mouse click for inclusion students
- edit existing questions and add your own questions
- build tests aligned with state standards using built-in State Curriculum Tags
- change English tests to Spanish with one mouse click and vice versa

Thinking Critically

21. Explain why certain foods, such as peanuts, can cause choking in small children.

22. Infer why it is an advantage to have lungs with many smaller air sacs instead of having just two large sacs, like balloons.

23. Explain the damage to cilia, alveoli, and lungs from smoking.

24. Describe what happens to the blood if the kidneys stop working.

25. Explain why it is often painful when small, solid particles called kidney stones, pass into the ureter.

Use the table below to answer question 26.

Materials Filtered by the Kidneys

Substance Filtered in Urine	Amount Moving Through Kidney	Amount Excreted
Water	125 L	1 L
Salt	350 g	10 g
Urea	1 g	1 g
Glucose	50 g	0 g

26. Interpret Data Study the data above. How much of each substance is reabsorbed into the blood in the kidneys? What substance is excreted completely in the urine?

27. Recognize Cause and Effect Discuss how lack of oxygen is related to lack of energy.

28. Form a hypothesis about the number of breaths a person might take per minute in each of these situations: sleeping, exercising, and standing on top of Mount Everest. Give a reason for each hypothesis.

Performance Activities

29. Questionnaire and Interview Prepare a questionnaire that can be used to interview a health specialist who works with lung cancer patients.

Applying Math

30. Lung Capacity Make a circle graph of total lung capacity using the following data:

- volume of air in a normal inhalation or exhalation = 500 mL
- volume of additional air that can be inhaled forcefully after a normal inhalation = 3,000 mL
- volume of additional air that can be exhaled forcefully after a normal expiration = 1,100 mL
- volume of air still left in the lungs after all the air that can be exhaled has been forcefully exhaled = 1,200 mL

Use the table below to answer question 31.

Death Rates in Industry

Industry	Number of Deaths (1999)	Current Smokers (2000)
Construction	3336	37.4%
Eating and drinking places	907	39.7%
Engineering and science	55	18.7%
Mining	327	32.6%
Railroads	385	24.8%
Trucking service	1004	33.2%

31. Lung Cancer Deaths The table above shows the number of lung cancer deaths and the percentage of smokers for specified industries. How many times higher are the death rates for the construction industry than for the eating-and-drinking-places industry?

 Science Online bookd.msscience.com/chapter_review

Thinking Critically

24. If the kidneys stopped working, blood would accumulate waste products from the body's organs. These wastes would act as poisons, and the person would need immediate medical care.

25. Kidney stones in the ureter extend and block the tube and cause severe pain. Infections may also occur.

26. Water: 124 L; salt: 340 g; glucose: 50 g; all urea is excreted.

27. Cells need oxygen to break down food and release energy.

28. Possible answers: Sleeping—breathing rate is low because less respiration is occurring; exercising—breathing rate would increase to get oxygen to the muscles; on Mount Everest—breathing rate would increase because less oxygen is present.

Performance Activities

29. Students should prepare questionnaires and conduct interviews. Use **Performance Assessment in the Science Classroom,** p. 91.

Applying Math

National Math Standards
5

30. Check student graphs for accuracy: 500 mL = 9% of circle (32°); 3,000 mL = 52% (187°); 1,100 mL = 19% (68°); 1,200 mL = 21% (76°).

31. 3.7 times; Construction workers breathe in a lot of particulate matter.

✓ Assessment Resources

📁 Reproducible Masters

Chapter *Fast File* Resources
Chapter Review, pp. 33–34
Chapter Tests, pp. 35–38
Assessment Transparency Activity, p. 45

Glencoe Science Web site
Chapter Review Test
Standardized Test Practice

Glencoe Technology

- Assessment Transparency
- Exam*View*® Pro Testmaker
- MindJogger Videoquiz
- Interactive Chalkboard

Answer Sheet A practice answer sheet can be found at bookd.msscience.com/answer_sheet.

S A M P L E

Invertebrates **169**

Part 1 Multiple Choice

1. A
2. C
3. D
4. B
5. C
6. C
7. A

Part 1 Multiple Choice

Record your answers on the answer sheet provided by your teacher or on a sheet of paper.

1. Which of the following diseases is caused by smoking?
   A. lung cancer   C. dialysis
   B. diabetes   D. bladder infection

Use the table below to answer questions 2 and 3.

Major Sources by Which Body Water is Lost		
Source	Amount per day (mL)	Percent
Urine	1,500	60
Skin	500	20
Lungs	350	14
Feces	150	6
Total	2,500	100

2. If the amount of body water lost in the urine increased by 500 mL, what percent of the total body water lost would now be lost in the urine?
   A. 60%   C. 67%
   B. 75%   D. 66%

3. If a person had diarrhea, which source of body water loss would increase?
   A. urine   C. skin
   B. lungs   D. feces

4. The movement of the chest that brings air into the lungs and removes waste gases is called
   A. oxidation.   C. respiration.
   B. breathing.   D. expiration.

5. What traps dust, pollen, and other materials in your nose?
   A. glands
   B. vocal cords
   C. nasal hairs and mucus
   D. epiglottis

Use the illustration below to answer question 6.

6. What is the structure shown above and to what body system does it belong?
   A. capillary—circulatory
   B. alveolus—respiratory
   C. nephron—urinary
   D. ureter—excretory

7. What is the correct order of steps in the abdominal thrust maneuver?
   A. Rescuer stands behind victim and wraps arms around victim's upper abdomen; rescuer places fist against victim's stomach; rescuer thrusts fist up into area below ribs; rescuer repeats action as many times as necessary.
   B. Rescuer places fist against victim's stomach; rescuer thrusts fist up into area below ribs; rescuer stands behind victim and wraps arms around victim's upper abdomen; rescuer repeats action as many times as necessary.
   C. Rescuer places fist against victim's stomach; rescuer thrusts fist up into area below ribs; rescuer repeats action as many times as necessary.
   D. Rescuer stands in front of victim; rescuer places fist against victim's stomach; rescuer thrusts fist up into area below ribs; rescuer repeats action as needed.

114 ◆ D STANDARDIZED TEST PRACTICE

Part 2 Short Response/Grid In

8. $0.50 + 0.50 + 0.55 + 0.32 = 1.87$; $1.87 \div 4 = 0.47$ L
9. Mr. Stoler
10. Day 3
11. Mr. Stoler
12. nicotine and tars
13. In some people, plant pollen can cause asthma. Because asthma can

be an allergic reaction, people who are allergic to certain plant pollen can have an asthma attack.

14. It allows oxygen to diffuse out of alveoli and carbon dioxide to diffuse into alveoli. If the alveoli were thick walled, diffusion could not take place as easily.

15. Energy is released from glucose through respiration. The oxygen delivered to the cells is used to release energy from glucose. Water and carbon dioxide also are produced.

Record your answers on the answer sheet provided by your teacher or on a sheet of paper.

Use the paragraph and table below to answer questions 8–11.

For one week, research scientists collected and accurately measured the amount of body water lost and gained per day for four different patients. The following table lists results from their investigation.

Body Water Gained (+) and Lost (−)				
Person	Day 1 (L)	Day 2 (L)	Day 3 (L)	Day 4 (L)
Mr. Stoler	+0.15	+0.15	−0.35	+0.12
Mr. Jemma	−0.01	0.00	−0.20	−0.01
Mr. Lowe	0.00	+0.20	−0.28	+0.01
Mr. Cheng	−0.50	−0.50	−0.55	−0.32

8. What was Mr. Cheng's average daily body water loss for the 4 days shown in the table?

9. Which patient had the greatest amount of body water gained on days 1 and 2?

10. According to the data in the table, on which day was the temperature in each patient's hospital room probably the hottest?

11. Which patient had the highest total gain in body water over the 4-day period?

12. What chemical substances in tobacco can destroy cells?

13. What effect can plant pollen have on the respiratory system?

14. Why do alveoli have thin walls?

15. How is energy released from glucose? What also is produced?

Record your answers on a sheet of paper.

16. Explain the role of cilia in the respiratory system. Give an example of a disease in which cilia are damaged. What effects does this damage have on the respiratory system?

Use the table below to answer questions 17–19.

Urine Test Results				
Test Items	Normal Results	Mrs. Beebe	Mrs. Chavez	Mrs. Jelton
Glucose	Absent	High	Absent	Absent
Albumin	Absent	Absent	Absent	Absent
Urine volume per 24 hours	1 L	1 L	1 L	0.5 L

17. Mrs. Jelton's urine tests were done when outside temperatures had been higher than 35°C for several days. When Mrs. Jelton came to Dr. Marks' office after the urine test, he asked her about the amount of liquid that she had been drinking. Infer why Dr. Marks asked this question.

18. Assuming that Mrs. Jelton is healthy, form a hypothesis that would explain what had happened.

19. Dr. Marks called another patient to come in for more testing. Who was it? How do you know?

signals the kidneys to return more water to the blood and decrease the amount of urine excreted. If Mrs. Jelton was taking in a normal amount of water, then she might be losing more water from perspiration. She should drink more water to replace the extra water lost by sweating.

18. Dr. Marks called Mrs. Beebe. Mrs. Beebe had glucose in the urine. Glucose normally is not excreted in the urine in large amounts. Dr. Marks wanted to find out if Mrs. Beebe had diabetes.

19. The liver filters the blood to remove wastes. Some wastes are converted to other substances. Excess amino acids are changed to urea (which is excreted by the kidneys). Hemoglobin from broken down red blood cells becomes part of bile, the digestive fluid from the liver. The skin removes some salts and organic substances from the body through perspiration. The skin also removes water.

Rubrics

For more help evaluating open-ended assessment questions, see the rubric on p. 10T.

16. Cilia remove mucus, bacteria, and dirt particles from the respiratory system. Chronic bronchitis is a disease in which the cilia are damaged. (Although cilia are damaged in the common cold, cilia damage usually heals quickly in this disease.) If the cilia do not remove these materials, they build up in the airways and the airways cannot work properly.

17. Mrs. Jelton produced less urine in one day than an average-sized person usually does. Dr. Marks wanted to find out why. Since Mrs. Jelton did not have any dis- ease that might affect the amount of urine produced, the decrease in the amount of urine was a response of her body to a decrease in body water. When the brain detects too little water in the blood, the hypothalamus releases a larger amount of hormone. This

Section/Objectives	Standards		Labs/Features
	National	State/Local	
Chapter Opener	See pp. 16T–17T for a Key to Standards.		**Launch Lab:** How quick are your responses?, p. 117 **Foldables,** p. 117
Section 1 **The Nervous System** 🕐 2 sessions 📦 1 block 1. **Describe** the basic structure of a neuron and how an impulse moves across a synapse. 2. **Compare** the central and peripheral nervous systems. 3. **Explain** how drugs affect the body.	National Content Standards: UCP.1, UCP.2, UCP.3, UCP.5, A.1, A.2, C.1, C.3, C.5, F.1, G.3		**Integrate History,** p. 119 **Visualizing Nerve Impulse Pathways,** p. 120 **Integrate Chemistry,** p. 122 **Science Online,** p. 123 **Science Online,** p. 125 **Lab:** Improving Reaction Time, p. 127
Section 2 **The Senses** 🕐 3 sessions 📦 1.5 blocks 4. **List** the sensory receptors in each sense organ. 5. **Explain** what type of stimulus each sense organ responds to and how. 6. **Explain** why healthy senses are needed.	National Content Standards: UCP.1, UCP.2, UCP.3, UCP.5, A.1, A.2, C.1, C.3, C.5		**Integrate Astronomy,** p. 130 **MiniLAB:** Observing Balance Control, p. 132 **Science Online,** p. 133 **Applying Math:** Speed of Sound, p. 133 **MiniLAB:** Comparing Sense of Smell, p. 134 **Lab:** Skin Sensitivity, p. 136 **Science and Language Arts:** Sula, p. 138

Lab Materials	Reproducible Resources	Section Assessment	Technology
Launch Lab: safety goggles, chair, sheet of discarded paper	**Chapter FAST FILE Resources** Foldables Worksheet, p. 17 Directed Reading Overview, p. 19 Note-taking Worksheets, pp. 31–33	**GLENCOE'S ASSESSMENT ADVANTAGE**	**TeacherWorks** includes: • Interactive Teacher Edition • Lesson Planner with calendar • Access to all program blacklines • Correlations to standards • Web links
Lab: metric ruler	**Chapter FAST FILE Resources** Transparency Activity, p. 42 Lab Worksheet, pp. 5–6 Enrichment, p. 29 Reinforcement, p. 27 Directed Reading, p. 20 Transparency Activity, pp. 45–46 Lab Activity, pp. 9–12 **Reading and Writing Skill Activities,** p. 17 **Life Science Critical Thinking/ Problem Solving,** pp. 2, 18 **Mathematics Skill Activities,** p. 9	**Portfolio** Science Journal, p. 119 Assessment, p. 126 **Performance** Applying Skills, p. 126 **Content** Section Review, p. 126	Section Focus Transparency Teaching Transparency Virtual Labs CD-ROM Guided Reading Audio Program Interactive Chalkboard CD-ROM Video Lab
MiniLAB: 2 narrow strips of paper, tape **MiniLAB:** samples of different foods, colognes, or household products; cotton balls; blindfold **Lab:** 3-in × 5-in index card, toothpicks, tape, metric ruler *Need materials?* Contact Science Kit at 1-800-828-7777 or www.sciencekit.com on the Internet.	**Chapter FAST FILE Resources** Lab Worksheet, pp. 7–8 Enrichment, p. 30 Reinforcement, p. 28 Directed Reading, pp. 21, 22 Transparency Activity, p. 43 Lab Activity, pp. 13–16 MiniLAB, pp. 3, 4 **Home and Community Involvement,** p. 28 **Performance Assessment in the Science Classroom,** p. 66 **Lab Management and Safety,** p. 65	**Portfolio** Reteach, p. 135 **Performance** MiniLAB, p. 132 Applying Math, p. 133 MiniLAB, p. 134 Applying Skills, p. 135 **Content** Section Review, p. 135	Section Focus Transparency Virtual Labs CD-ROM Guided Reading Audio Program Interactive Chalkboard CD-ROM

End of Chapter Assessment

GLENCOE'S ASSESSMENT ADVANTAGE

Blackline Masters	Technology	Professional Series
Chapter FAST FILE Resources Chapter Review, pp. 35–36 Chapter Tests, pp. 37–40 **Standardized Test Practice,** pp. 23–26	MindJogger Videoquiz Virtual Labs CD-ROM ExamView® Pro Testmaker TeacherWorks CD-ROM Interactive Chalkboard CD-ROM	**Performance Assessment in the Science Classroom (PASC)**

Transparencies

Section Focus

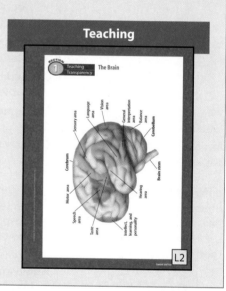

Assessment

Teaching

This is a representation of key blackline masters available in the Teacher Classroom Resources. See Resource Manager boxes within the chapter for additional information.

Key to Teaching Strategies

The following designations will help you decide which activities are appropriate for your students.

L1   Level 1 activities should be appropriate for students with learning difficulties.

L2   Level 2 activities should be within the ability range of all students.

L3   Level 3 activities are designed for above-average students.

ELL   ELL activities should be within the ability range of English-Language Learners.

COOP LEARN   Cooperative Learning activities are designed for small group work.

LS   Multiple Learning Styles logos, as described on page 12T, are used throughout to indicate strategies that address different learning styles.

P   These strategies represent student products that can be placed into a best-work portfolio.

PBL   Problem-Based Learning activities apply real-world situations to learning.

Hands-on Activities

Student Text Lab Worksheet

Laboratory Activities

Meeting Different Ability Levels

Content Outline

Note-taking Worksheet
Control and Coordination

Section 1   The Nervous System

A. Your nervous system helps your body make adjustments to changes in your _____
   1. Stimulus—any change inside or outside your body that brings about a(n) _____
   2. _____—the regulation of steady conditions inside an organism
B. Neurons are made up of a cell body and _____ called dendrites and axons.
   1. _____ receive messages and send them to the cell body.
   2. _____ carry messages away from the cell body.
   3. Messages carried by nerve cells are called _____
   4. You have three kinds of nerve cells.
      a. _____ nerve cells receive information and send impulses to the brain or spinal cord.
      b. _____ relay the impulses from sensory nerve cells to motor nerve cells.
      c. Motor nerve cells conduct impulses from the brain to _____ and _____
   5. Nerve cells do not touch each other, yet still pass _____ to each other.
      a. A **synapse** is a(n) _____ between nerve cells.
      b. When an impulse reaches the end of an axon, the axon releases a(n) _____
      c. This chemical flows across the synapse and relays the impulse to the _____ of the next neuron.
C. The **central nervous system** is made up of the brain and _____
   1. The _____ coordinates all of your body activities.
   2. **Cerebrum**—the part of the brain that interprets impulses from the senses, stores _____ and controls movements
      a. _____ takes place here.
      b. _____ part of the brain
      c. Outer layer is called the _____, which allows more complex thoughts to be processed.
   3. _____—the part of the brain located behind and under the cerebrum
      a. Interprets _____ from the eyes, ears, muscles, and tendons
      b. Coordinates _____ muscle movements, maintains muscle tone, and helps maintain _____

L2

Reinforcement

Reinforcement 1
The Nervous System

Directions: *Define each term. Use the terms to label the diagram below.*

1. neuron _____
2. dendrite _____
3. axon _____
4. synapse _____

Directions: *Name the three kinds of neurons and describe the function of each.*

10. _____

11. _____

12. _____

Directions: *In the space below, make a simple drawing of the brain and label its three main parts.*

L2

Enrichment

Enrichment 1
I Can't Hear What I'm Seeing

Many people have a hard time reading simple words on a page. People with this problem are usually very intelligent but have a nervous system problem called dyslexia [dis-lex-ee-ah]. Dyslexia is a word that is used to describe many different types of reading problems. One of the main problems for people with dyslexia is that they cannot see the letters and words on the page correctly. They appear backwards or out of order.

Doctors and scientists once thought the problem started in the brain itself. They incorrectly thought the problem was due to brain damage. Some thought that certain brain cells did not work as well as they should. Now, new research is helping us understand what really causes some types of dyslexia.

Stimuli
   When stimuli enter the brain they are sent by signals that we recognize, like the sound of a dog barking or the sight of a ball. New information about people with dyslexia shows that, for them, certain kinds of stimuli do not get translated properly by the brain.

Genetic Trait
   Almost 98% of the people with this disorder are male. This leads researchers to believe that this form of dyslexia is a genetic trait.

Many of the boys and men with dyslexia suffered numerous ear infections as children.

The Inner Ear and Dyslexia
   Using these observations, researchers and doctors are looking at a possible connection between the inner ear and dyslexia. It is thought that the inner ear may have been damaged or does not properly interpret stimuli. You may already know that the inner ear is important for balance and coordination. A problem with the inner ear may prevent some people from unscrambling the signals that come into a particular part of the brain.
   One of the leading scientists in this area of research is Nobel Laureate Sir Robert Barany. He has designed a test to measure inner ear dysfunction. His data, along with the fact that people with dyslexia are usually very intelligent and do not have brain damage, gives hope to millions of people with the disorder. This research has led to this particular kind of dyslexia being called Cerebellar Vestibular dysfunction. (Cerebellar refers to the cerebellum of the brain, and vestibular refers to the vestibule of the inner ear.) New ways of teaching people to read and to adjust to their reading problems may be near.

1. What are people with certain types of dyslexia unable to do very well? _____

2. What did doctors and scientists think caused dyslexia? _____

3. Some scientists think there is a genetic cause for dyslexia. Why do they think this? _____

4. The most common type of dyslexia is the brain's inability to sort out visual stimuli of letters and words on a page. Where does this inability seem to start? _____

L3

Directed Reading (English/Spanish)

Directed Reading for Content Mastery
Overview   Control and Coordination

Directions: *Complete the concept map using the terms in the list below.*

brain   brain stem   cerebellum   cerebrum

Directions: *Answer the following questions on the lines provided.*

1. Which sense organ has rods and cones that help you see light and color? _____

2. Which sense organ has olfactory cells that let you detect an odor? _____

L1

Study Guide

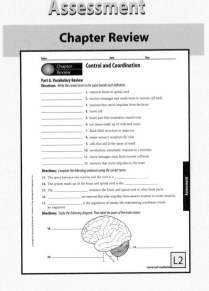

Study Guide

Features
• Contains a study guide page for each section of the chapter
• Reviews key concepts
• Includes answer pages

L2

Reading Essentials

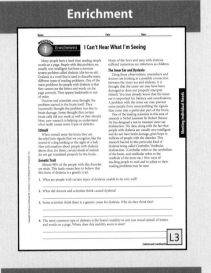

Reading Essentials for Glencoe Science
An Interactive Student Workbook

Features
• Condensed core content
• Actively involves students in reading
• Reinforces key vocabulary

L1

Assessment

Test Practice Workbook

Chapter 21 *Control and Coordination*   **Standardized Test Practice**

DIRECTIONS:
Read each question. Then, on your answer sheet, mark the answer choice that you think is best.

1 How does shivering best help the human body?
   A It exercises our muscles.
   B It helps us keep cold.
   C It exercises our bones.
   D It helps us keep warm.

2 Why is earwax so important?
   F It traps germs.
   G It lets germs enter the body.
   H It breaks down food.
   J It aids in breathing.

3 Which of the following statements is accurate?
   A Reflexes are voluntary actions.
   B Reflexes are caused by muscle contractions.
   C Reflexes are involuntary actions.
   D Reflexes are not reactions to stimuli.

4 Which of the statements below provides the best description of how alcohol and caffeine affect your body?
   F Alcohol and caffeine directly affect the nervous system.
   G Alcohol and caffeine have minimal effects upon your body.
   H Alcohol and caffeine have no effect upon the nervous system.
   J Both alcohol and caffeine speed up the central nervous system.

5 Lawrence's teacher is describing a certain part of the eye. He says it is a tissue at the back of the eye that is sensitive to light. The tissue contains two types of cells called rods and cones. Lawrence correctly identifies the part as the
   A pupil
   B retina
   C optic nerve
   D lens

GO ON   **L2**

Glencoe Life Science

Chapter Review

Chapter Review
Control and Coordination

Part A. Vocabulary Review
Directions: *Write the correct term in the space beside each definition.*

_____ 1. connects brain to spinal cord
_____ 2. receives messages and sends them to neuron cell body
_____ 3. neurons that move impulses from the brain
_____ 4. nerve cell
_____ 5. brain part that maintains muscle tone
_____ 6. eye tissue made up of rods and cones
_____ 7. fluid-filled structure in inner ear
_____ 8. major sensory receptors for taste
_____ 9. cells that aid in the sense of smell
_____ 10. involuntary, automatic response to a stimulus
_____ 11. move messages away from neuron cell body
_____ 12. neurons that move impulses to the brain

Directions: *Complete the following sentences using the correct terms.*

13. The space between one neuron and the next is a _____
14. The system made up of the brain and spinal cord is the _____
15. The _____ connects the brain and spinal cord to other body parts.
16. _____ are neurons that relay impulses from sensory neurons to motor neurons.
17. _____ is the regulation of steady, life-maintaining conditions inside an organism.

Directions: *Study the following diagram. Then label the parts of the brain shown.*

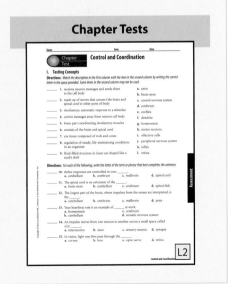

18. _____
19. _____
20. _____

L2

Chapter Tests

Chapter Test
Control and Coordination

I. Testing Concepts

Directions: *Match the description in the first column with the item in the second column by writing the correct letter in the space provided. Some items in the second column may not be used.*

_____ 1. receives neuron messages and sends them to the cell body
_____ 2. made up of nerves that connect the brain and spinal cord to other parts of body
_____ 3. involuntary, automatic response to a stimulus
_____ 4. carries messages away from neuron cell body
_____ 5. brain part coordinating involuntary muscles
_____ 6. consists of the brain and spinal cord
_____ 7. eye tissue composed of rods and cones
_____ 8. regulation of steady, life-maintaining conditions in an organism
_____ 9. fluid-filled structure in inner ear shaped like a snail's shell

a. axon
b. brain stem
c. central nervous system
d. cerebrum
e. cochlea
f. dendrite
g. homeostasis
h. motor neurons
i. olfactory cells
j. peripheral nervous system
k. reflex
l. retina

Directions: *For each of the following, write the letter of the term or phrase that best completes the sentence.*

_____ 10. Reflex responses are controlled in your _____
   a. cerebellum   b. cerebrum   c. midbrain   d. spinal cord

_____ 11. The spinal cord is an extension of the _____
   a. brain stem   b. cerebellum   c. spinal disk   d. cerebrum

_____ 12. The largest part of the brain, where impulses from the senses are interpreted, is the _____
   a. cerebellum   b. cerebrum   c. midbrain   d. pons

_____ 13. Your heartbeat rate is an example of _____ at work.
   a. homeostasis   b. cerebrum   c. peripheral nervous system   d. somatic nervous system

_____ 14. An impulse moves from one neuron to another across a small space called a(n) _____
   a. interneuron   b. axon   c. sensory neuron   d. synapse

_____ 15. In vision, light rays first pass through the _____
   a. cornea   b. lens   c. optic nerve   d. retina

L2

Science Content Background

section 1 The Nervous System

Nerve Cells

Specialized receptor cells respond to specific stimuli from various parts of the body. These stimuli produce a self-propagating wave of negative charges that is transmitted to the central nervous system via peripheral nerves. The nerve impulse travels at a rate of approximately 120 m/s. The brain and spinal cord of the central nervous system interpret the stimuli information. Appropriate responses are sent via nerves to the various body parts, which react to the stimulus. The response is a coordinated, integrated action that maintains homeostasis within the body.

section 2 The Senses

Hearing and Taste

The sensory receptors for the senses of hearing, equilibrium, and taste are specialized. Each type is found in only one place, or pair of places, in the body. Vibrations in the air with frequencies between about 16,000 and 20,000 cycles-per-second can be detected as a sound by your ears. Hair cells within the inner ear are found in the organ of Corti. The hair cells' responses to the vibrations are converted to electrical signals. Sensory hair cells help maintain balance by responding to movements of liquids and of the tiny bits of calcium carbonate called otoliths in the labyrinth canals. Taste buds, located on small projections called papillae on the tongue, the soft palate, and the walls of the pharynx, are sensitive to substances dissolved in liquids. Specialized taste cells within the taste buds function as receptors.

Understanding the Eye

At the back of the human eye is a layer called the retina that contains photosensitive cells. These cells contain pigments that, when exposed to sufficient light, change their shape and break into two parts. This stimulates the nerve cell attached to the photoreceptor, which sends a signal down the optic nerve and into the back of the brain. For humans to see an object, therefore, light must strike the object and be reflected toward the eye. The light energy must have a wavelength between 380 nm and 760 nm in order to stimulate the photoreceptive pigments in the retina.

chapter content resources

Internet Resources
For additional content background, visit bookd.msscience.com to:
- access your book online
- find references to related articles in popular science magazines
- access Web links with related content background
- access current events with science journal topics

Print Resources
Biology (6th Edition), by Neil A. Campbell, Jane B. Reece, Pearson Benjamin Cummings Publishing, 2001

Human Anatomy & Physiology (5th Edition), by Elaine N. Marieb, Pearson Benjamin Cummings Publishing, 2000

Principles of Human Physiology, by William J. Germann, Cindy L. Stanfield; Pearson Benjamin Cummings Publishing, 2001

IDENTIFYING ▷ Misconceptions

Find Out What Students Think

Students may think that . . .

Human eyes "see" by sending rays toward an object.

Students seldom understand the link between light and sight. Light is often viewed as a substance that fills a space, as in "the room was filled with light." Students' everyday experiences with light do not reveal the nature of light as wave energy. Student models of how vision works range from no connection between the eye and the object it sees to believing that the eyes themselves send out beams of light or some other energy to illuminate the object and allow sight. Some students may even conclude that it is possible to see in total darkness if they think that the eye provides its own source of illumination. The experience of seeing animal eyes "glow" at night may support this. Very few students have experienced total darkness, so they are confident in their abilities to see in the dark. They know their eyes "get used" to, or adapt to, semidarkness, allowing limited vision. Even if students are exposed to total darkness, the conclusion they draw may be that they will be able to see once their eyes "get used" to the dark.

Activity

After identifying the parts of the eye, sketch a diagram of an eye on one end of the board and an object at the other end. Ask students to draw a diagram that explains how the eye is able to "see" the object. Students should label all parts of their diagram to make their explanations clear. L2

Promote Understanding

Demonstration

Materials shoe box, sharp knife, cardboard tube (about 5 cm long), black electrician's tape, flashlight, black spray paint, small object
Preparation Cut a hole in the box top. Tape a flashlight over the hole. Seal the edges with tape. Cut a peephole in one box end. Tape the cardboard tube over the hole. Paint the inside of the box black. Place an object inside and replace the lid.

Procedure

- Have students look in the box with the light off and describe what they can see. They should see nothing. Have students turn the flashlight on and look in the box again. The object is now visible.

- On the board, sketch a picture of the box with the object inside. Show how light comes from the flashlight and illuminates the object. Light reflected from the object reaches the eye and stimulates the retina, allowing the viewer to see the object. L2

The sight box, as it should be assembled

Inner view of the sight box

Assess

After completing the chapter, see *Identifying Misconceptions* in the Study Guide at the end of the chapter.

Control and Coordination

Chapter Vocabulary

Science Journal Student responses may vary, but may include questions about hearing and reaction time.

INTERACTIVE CHALKBOARD with Image Bank

PowerPoint® Presentations

This CD-ROM is an editable Microsoft® PowerPoint® presentation that includes:
- a pre-made presentation for every chapter
- interactive graphics
- animations
- audio clips
- image bank
- all new section and chapter questions
- Standardized Test Practice
- transparencies
- pre-lab questions for all labs
- Foldables directions
- links to bookd.msscience.com

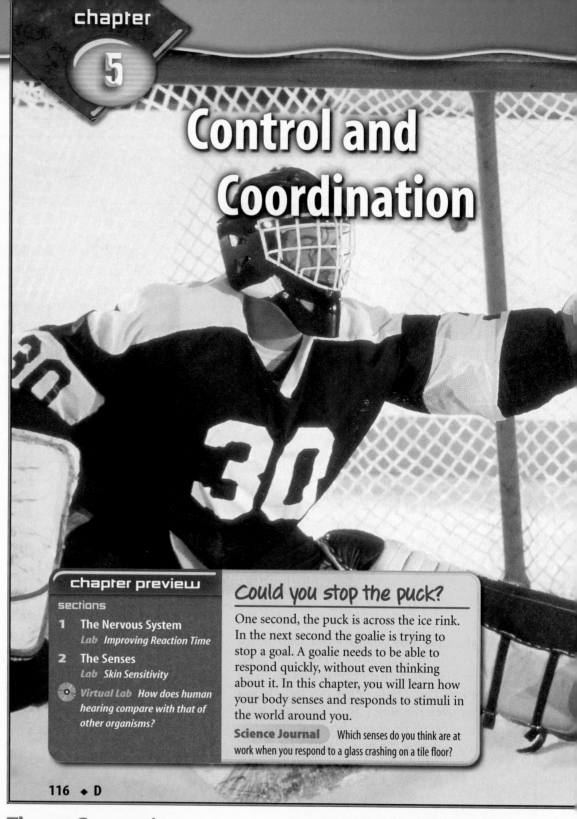

chapter preview

sections

1 **The Nervous System**
   Lab Improving Reaction Time

2 **The Senses**
   Lab Skin Sensitivity

Virtual Lab How does human hearing compare with that of other organisms?

Could you stop the puck?

One second, the puck is across the ice rink. In the next second the goalie is trying to stop a goal. A goalie needs to be able to respond quickly, without even thinking about it. In this chapter, you will learn how your body senses and responds to stimuli in the world around you.

Science Journal Which senses do you think are at work when you respond to a glass crashing on a tile floor?

116 ◆ D

Theme Connection

Stability and Change The stimulus-response action of the nervous system helps maintain the stable environment necessary for the healthy functioning of the body.

About the Photo

Don't Blink It takes 0.3 seconds for a single blink of the eye, with an average of 2.8 seconds between blinks. There are 100 billion neurons in the human brain, and the typical neuron has 1,000 to 10,000 synapses. Your hand has 1,300 nerve endings per square inch. A hockey goalie's senses must be finely tuned to stop his opponent from scoring.

Start-Up Activities

How quick are your responses?

If the weather is cool, you might put on a jacket. If you see friends, you might call out to them. You also might pick up a crying baby. Every second of the day you react to different sights, sounds, and smells in your environment. You control some of these reactions, but others take place in your body without thought. Some reactions protect you from harm.

1. Wearing safety goggles, sit on a chair 1 m away from a partner.

2. Ask your partner to toss a wadded-up piece of paper at your face without warning you.

3. Switch positions and repeat the activity.

4. **Think Critically** Describe in your Science Journal how you reacted to the ball of paper being thrown at you. Explain how your anticipation of being hit altered your body's response.

Preview this chapter's content and activities at bookd.msscience.com

FOLDABLES™ Study Organizer

Senses Your body is constantly responding to stimuli around you. Make the following Foldable to help you understand your five senses.

STEP 1 Collect three sheets of paper and layer them about 1.25 cm apart vertically. Keep the edges level.

STEP 2 Fold up the bottom edges of the paper to form six equal tabs.

STEP 3 Crease the fold, and then staple along the fold. **Label** the tabs *Five Senses, Vision, Hearing, Smell, Taste,* and *Touch.*

Read and Write As you read the chapter, write what you learn about each of your senses under the appropriate tab.

D ◆ 117

Section Focus Transparencies also are available on the Interactive Chalkboard CD-ROM.

L2 ELL

SECTION 1 Section Focus Transparency | **Jump Start**

In track competitions, time is critical. Sometimes, only a fraction of a second is the difference between winning a race and coming in second. Adjustable starting blocks, as seen below, help sprinters get their best starts. It takes a lot of training and practice to coordinate nerves and muscles for competition.

1. What happens when the sprinters hear the starter's pistol?
2. How do you think nerves are involved in this reponse?

Control and Coordination

Tie to Prior Knowledge

Muscle Actions Have students brainstorm a list of muscle actions that are out of their conscious control. Lists might include blinking or heartbeat. Explain that these actions occur as the body responds to stimuli.
L1

Caption Answer

Figure 1 Sights, sounds, odors, tastes; accept reasonable answers.

The Nervous System

as you read

What **You'll Learn**
- **Describe** the basic structure of a neuron and how an impulse moves across a synapse.
- **Compare** the central and peripheral nervous systems.
- **Explain** how drugs affect the body.

Why **It's Important**
Your body is able to react to your environment because of your nervous system.

Review Vocabulary
response: a reaction to a specific stimulus

New Vocabulary
- homeostasis
- neuron
- dendrite
- axon
- synapse
- central nervous system
- peripheral nervous system
- cerebrum
- cerebellum
- brain stem
- reflex

How the Nervous System Works

After doing the dishes and finishing your homework, you settle down in your favorite chair and pick up that mystery novel you've been trying to finish. Only three pages to go . . . Who did it? Why did she do it? Crash! You scream. What made that unearthly noise? You turn around to find that your dog's wagging tail has just swept the lamp off the table. Suddenly, you're aware that your heart is racing and your hands are shaking. After a few minutes though, your breathing returns to normal and your heartbeat is back to its regular rate. What's going on?

Responding to Stimuli The scene described above is an example of how your body responds to changes in its environment. Any internal or external change that brings about a response is called a stimulus (STIHM yuh lus). Each day, you're bombarded by thousands of stimuli, as shown in **Figure 1.** Noise, light, the smell of food, and the temperature of the air are all stimuli from outside your body. Chemical substances such as hormones are examples of stimuli from inside your body. Your body adjusts to changing stimuli with the help of your nervous system.

Figure 1 Stimuli are everywhere and all the time, even when you're with your friends.
List *the types of stimuli present at this party.*

Section 1 Resource Manager

Chapter *FAST FILE* Resources
Transparency Activity, pp. 42, 45–46
Directed Reading for Content Mastery, pp. 19, 20
Note-taking Worksheets, pp. 31–33
Lab Worksheet, pp. 5–6
Enrichment, p. 29

Lab Activity, pp. 9–12
Reinforcement, p. 27
Reading and Writing Skill Activities, p. 17
Life Science Critical Thinking/Problem Solving, pp. 2, 18
Mathematics Skill Activities, p. 9

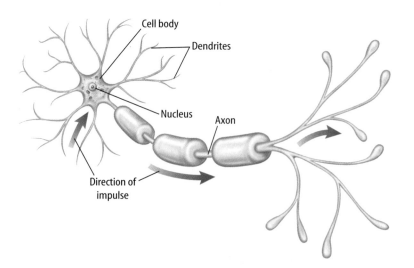

Cell body

Dendrites

Nucleus

Axon

Direction of impulse

Homeostasis

It's amazing how your body handles all these stimuli. Control systems maintain steady internal conditions. The regulation of steady, life-maintaining conditions inside an organism, despite changes in its environment, is called **homeostasis.** Examples of homeostasis are the regulation of your breathing, heartbeat, and digestion. Your nervous system is one of several control systems used by your body to maintain homeostasis.

Nerve Cells

The basic functioning units of the nervous system are nerve cells, or **neurons** (NOOR ahnz). As shown in **Figure 2,** a neuron is made up of a cell body and branches called dendrites and axons. Any message carried by a neuron is called an impulse. **Dendrites** receive impulses from other neurons and send them to the cell body. **Axons** (AK sahns) carry impulses away from the cell body. Notice the branching at the end of the axon. This allows the impulses to move to many other muscles, neurons, or glands.

Types of Nerve Cells

Your body has sensory receptors that produce electrical impulses and respond to stimuli, such as changes in temperature, sound, pressure, and taste. Three types of neurons—sensory neurons, motor neurons, and interneurons—transport impulses. Sensory neurons receive information and send impulses to the brain or spinal cord, where interneurons relay these impulses to motor neurons. Motor neurons then conduct impulses from the brain or spinal cord to muscles or glands throughout your body.

INTEGRATE
History

Multiple Sclerosis In 1868, Jean Martin Charcot, a neurology professor in Paris, was the first to scientifically describe, document, and name the disease multiple sclerosis. It was named because of the many scars found widely dispersed throughout the central nervous system. Research to find out the symptoms of multiple sclerosis.

Fun Fact

The structure of an axon of a neuron can change when used. More and better connections with other neurons result from learning. Schoolwork helps neurons make connections.

Science Journal

Nerve Analogy Have students write a paragraph in their Science Journals that explains how a nerve is similar to a wire going from a controlling switch (stimulus) to a light bulb (response). Possible response: The switch receives a stimulus, which travels along the wire. The bulb responds to the stimulus by lighting up. L2 LS
Linguistic P

Visualizing Nerve Impulse Pathways

Have students examine the pictures and read the captions. Then ask the following questions.

What would happen if an interneuron could not perform its function? Possible answer: There would be no connection between the sensory neuron and the motor neuron. The nerve impulse may not be passed on.

What are the differences between a sensory neuron and a motor neuron? Possible answer: Sensory neurons detect internal or external stimuli and transfer impulses to the spinal cord or brain. Motor neurons respond to stimuli from the spinal cord or brain and carry impulses back out to muscles.

Activity

Model Neurons Have students make a model of a neuron. Students can use yarn and markers on construction paper to model and label the different parts of a neuron including the dendrites, the cell body, and the axon. Students can also show the direction of impulse transmission. Dendrites receive an impulse from another neuron and pass it on to the cell body. The axon carries the impulse to the next neuron. L2

NATIONAL GEOGRAPHIC **VISUALIZING NERVE IMPULSE PATHWAYS**

Figure 3

Millions of nerve impulses are moving throughout your body as you read this page. In response to stimuli, many impulses follow a specific pathway —from sensory neuron to interneuron to motor neuron— to bring about a response. Like a relay team, these three types of neurons work together. The illustration on this page shows how the sound of a breaking window might startle you and cause you to drop a glass of water.

SENSORY NEURONS When you hear a loud noise, receptors in your ears—the specialized endings of sensory neurons—are stimulated. These sensory neurons produce nerve impulses that travel to your brain.

INTERNEURONS Interneurons in your brain receive the impulses from sensory neurons and pass them along to motor neurons.

MOTOR NEURONS Impulses travel down the axons of motor neurons to muscles—in this case, your biceps— which contract to jerk your arms in response to the loud noise.

Sensory neuron

Interneuron

Motor neuron

120 ◆ D **CHAPTER 5** Control and Coordination

Differentiated Instruction

Challenge Have students research the differences between myelinated neurons and unmyelinated neurons. Students should determine which type of nerve impulse conduction each has. They can present their results on a poster. L3

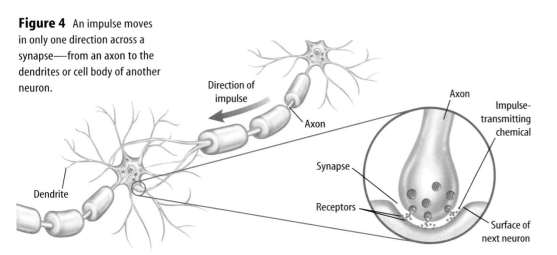

Figure 4 An impulse moves in only one direction across a synapse—from an axon to the dendrites or cell body of another neuron.

Synapses In a relay race, the first runner sprints down the track with a baton in his or her hand. As the runner rounds the track, he or she hands the baton off to the next runner. The two runners never physically touch each other. The transfer of the baton signals the second runner to continue the race.

As shown in **Figure 3,** your nervous system works in a similar way. Like the runners in a relay race, neurons don't touch each other. How does an impulse move from one neuron to another? To move from one neuron to the next, an impulse crosses a small space called a **synapse** (SIH naps). In **Figure 4,** note that when an impulse reaches the end of an axon, the axon releases a chemical. This chemical flows across the synapse and stimulates the impulse in the dendrite of the next neuron. Your neurons are adapted in such a way that impulses move in only one direction. An impulse moves from neuron to neuron just like a baton moves from runner to runner in a relay race. The baton represents the chemical at the synapse.

The Central Nervous System

Figure 5 shows the organs of the central nervous system (CNS) and the peripheral (puh RIH fuh rul) nervous system (PNS). The **central nervous system** is made up of the brain and spinal cord. The **peripheral nervous system** is made up of all the nerves outside the CNS. These nerves include those in your head, called cranial nerves, and the nerves that come from your spinal cord, called spinal nerves. The peripheral nervous system connects the brain and spinal cord to other body parts. Sensory neurons send impulses to the brain or spinal cord.

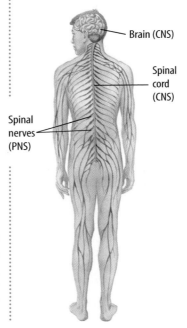

Figure 5 The brain and spinal cord (yellow) form the central nervous system (CNS). All other nerves (green) are part of the peripheral nervous system (PNS).

SECTION 1 The Nervous System **D** ◆ **121**

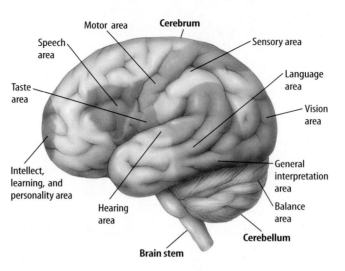

Motor area Cerebrum Sensory area Speech area Language area Taste area Vision area Intellect, learning, and personality area General interpretation area Hearing area Balance area Cerebellum Brain stem

Figure 6 Different areas of the brain control specific body activities.
Describe *the three major parts of the brain, and their functions.*

INTEGRATE Chemistry

Impulses Acetylcholine (uh see tul KOH leen) is a chemical produced by neurons, which carries an impulse across a synapse to the next neuron. After the impulse is started, the acetylcholine breaks down rapidly. In your Science Journal, hypothesize why the breakdown of acetylcholine is important.

The Brain The brain coordinates all of your body activities. If someone tickles your feet, why does your whole body seem to react? The brain is made up of approximately 100 billion neurons, which is nearly ten percent of all the neurons in the human body. Surrounding and protecting the brain are a bony skull, three membranes, and a layer of fluid. As shown in **Figure 6,** the brain is divided into three major parts—the brain stem, the cerebellum (ser uh BE lum), and the cerebrum (suh REE brum).

Cerebrum Thinking takes place in the **cerebrum,** which is the largest part of the brain. This also is where impulses from the senses are interpreted, memory is stored, and movements are controlled. The outer layer of the cerebrum, called the cortex, is marked by many ridges and grooves. These structures increase the surface area of the cortex, allowing more complex thoughts to be processed. **Figure 6** shows some of the motor and sensory tasks that the cortex controls.

Reading Check *What major activity takes place within the cerebrum?*

Cerebellum Stimuli from the eyes and ears and from muscles and tendons, which are the tissues that connect muscles to bones, are interpreted in the **cerebellum.** With this information, the cerebellum is able to coordinate voluntary muscle movements, maintain muscle tone, and help maintain balance. A complex activity, such as riding a bike, requires a lot of coordination and control of your muscles. The cerebellum coordinates your muscle movements so that you can maintain your balance.

Brain Stem At the base of the brain is the **brain stem.** It extends from the cerebrum and connects the brain to the spinal cord. The brain stem is made up of the midbrain, the pons, and the medulla (muh DUH luh). The midbrain and pons act as pathways connecting various parts of the brain with each other. The medulla controls involuntary actions such as heartbeat, breathing, and blood pressure. The medulla also is involved in such actions as coughing, sneezing, swallowing, and vomiting.

122 ◆ D CHAPTER 5 Control and Coordination

Visual Learning

Figure 6 Have students describe how the brain is protected. Hair, skin, skull bones, membranes, and fluids protect the brain. L2

Differentiated Instruction

Visually Impaired and Learning Disabled Have students make a model of the brain from papier-mâché or craft foam. Have them paint each part a different color and label the areas of activity. These models can then be used by visually impaired and learning disabled students for study. L1 **Kinesthetic**

The Spinal Cord Your spinal cord, illustrated in **Figure 7,** is an extension of the brain stem. It is made up of bundles of neurons that carry impulses from all parts of the body to the brain and from the brain to all parts of your body. The adult spinal cord is about the width of an adult thumb and is about 43 cm long.

The Peripheral Nervous System

Your brain and spinal cord are connected to the rest of your body by the peripheral nervous system. The PNS is made up of 12 pairs of nerves from your brain called cranial nerves and 31 pairs from your spinal cord called spinal nerves. Spinal nerves are made up of bundles of sensory and motor neurons bound together by connective tissue. For this reason, a single spinal nerve can have impulses going to and from the brain at the same time. Some nerves contain only sensory neurons, and some contain only motor neurons, but most nerves contain both types of neurons.

Somatic and Autonomic Systems The peripheral nervous system has two major divisions. The somatic system controls voluntary actions. It is made up of the cranial and spinal nerves that go from the central nervous system to your skeletal muscles. The autonomic system controls involuntary actions—those not under conscious control—such as your heart rate, breathing, digestion, and glandular functions. These two divisions, along with the central nervous system, make up your body's nervous system.

Science Online

Topic: Nervous System
Visit bookd.msscience.com for Web links to information about the nervous system.

Activity In your Science Journal, make a brochure outlining recent medical advances.

Figure 7 A column of vertebrae, or bones, protects the spinal cord. The spinal cord is made up of bundles of neurons that carry impulses to and from all parts of the body, similar to a telephone cable.

IDENTIFYING Misconceptions

Alcohol Is a Depressant Alcohol is often perceived as a stimulant because it initially makes a person feel more energetic. However, alcohol actually slows down the actions of the central nervous system.

Make a Model
Protecting Vertebrae Have students make a model of the vertebral column and spinal cord by stringing 33 thread spools on a thin rope. Use circular pieces of foam rubber for the disks between the vertebrae. Have students note how the cord (rope) is protected. *The spools (vertebrae) protect the rope (spinal cord); vertebrae are cushioned by the foam rubber.* L2

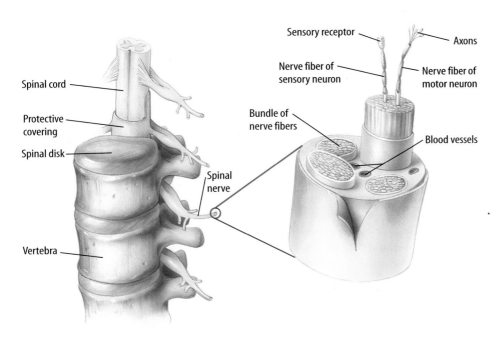

SECTION 1 The Nervous System **D** ◆ **123**

Differentiated Instruction

Challenge Have an interested student interview a pediatrician to find out which motor reflexes a child is born with. *A partial list includes gag reflex, blink reflex, pain avoidance reflex, shivering in response to cold, sucking reflex, and swallowing reflex.* L3

Curriculum Connection

History In the latter part of the eighteenth century, scientists investigated animals that were able to produce an electric shock such as the electric eel. These investigations led to research on the effects of electricity on nerves and the muscular contractions that could be produced. Have students research the results of such investigations and share their findings. L3

Discussion

Preventing Injury Have students discuss other types of reflex responses to stimuli that prevent injury to the body. Examples include holding hands over the ear when there are loud noises and rapid upward foot movement when stepping on a sharp object. L2

Discussion

Head Injuries What kinds of accidents at home might cause head injuries? Possible answers: slipping in the bathtub or falling off a ladder

Use Science Words

Word Origin When the brain is damaged, paralysis can result. Quadriplegics are individuals whose arms and legs are paralyzed. The word *quadriplegic* has its roots in the Latin word *quadra*, meaning "four," and the Greek word *plege*, meaning "stroke." How is this combination of words appropriate for its definition? A stroke can cause paralysis of all four limbs. Have students research the word origin of hemiplegia. Hemiplegia is total or partial paralysis of one side of the body (hemi = half). L2

Caption Answer

Figure 8 to prevent serious injuries and loss of life

Safety and the Nervous System

Every mental process and physical action of the body is associated with the structures of the central and peripheral nervous systems. Therefore, any injury to the brain or the spinal cord can be serious. A severe blow to the head can bruise the brain and cause temporary or permanent loss of mental and physical abilities. For example, the back of the brain controls vision. An injury in this region could result in the loss of vision.

Although the spinal cord is surrounded by the vertebrae of your spine, spinal cord injuries do occur. They can be just as dangerous as a brain injury. Injury to the spine can bring about damage to nerve pathways and result in paralysis (puh RA luh suhs), which is the loss of muscle movement. As shown in **Figure 8,** a neck injury that damages certain nerves could prevent a person from breathing. Major causes of head and spinal injuries include automobile, motorcycle, and bicycle accidents, as well as sports injuries. Just like wearing safety belts in automobiles, it is important to wear the appropriate safety gear while playing sports and riding on bicycles and skateboards.

Figure 8 Head and spinal cord damage can result in paralysis, depending on where the injury occurs.
Explain why it is important to wear safety equipment and safety belts.

Brain

Spinal cord

Key
- Site of damage
- Body area affected

Damage to one side of the brain can result in the paralysis of the opposite side of the body.

Damage to the middle or lower spinal cord can result in the legs and possibly part of the torso being paralyzed.

Damage to the spinal cord in the lower neck area can cause the body to be paralyzed from the neck down.

124 ◆ **D CHAPTER 5** Control and Coordination

Science Journal

Recovering from Injury Christopher Reeve, the actor who portrayed Superman in the movies, suffered severe injuries while horseback riding. Ask students to describe in their Science Journals his progress in adapting to and dealing with his paralysis. L2 IS **Linguistic**

Teacher FYI

Head Injuries A closed head injury does not involve any breaks in the skull. Loss of consciousness and diminished brain function may result. In an open head injury, the skull bones are penetrated. There is then the added risk of infection. Immediate surgery is necessary to clean and repair the wound.

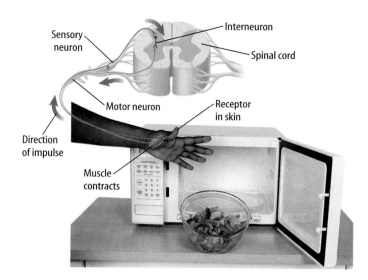

Sensory
neuron

Interneuron

Spinal cord

Motor neuron

Receptor
in skin

Direction
of impulse

Muscle
contracts

Figure 9 Your response in a
reflex is controlled in your spinal
cord, not your brain.

Teacher FYI

Dying Brain Alzheimer's disease is
the result of brain neurons slowly
dying. This results in less production of the chemical needed for
neurons to communicate with
each other.

Reading Check

Answer They allow quick reactions to
dangerous situations without having to
think about what to do.

Text Question Answer

If your breathing and heart rate hadn't
calmed down, you might have lost consciousness; your body systems would not
have been able to keep up with your high
rate of respiration and heartbeat.

Reflexes You experience a reflex if you accidentally touch
something sharp, something extremely hot or cold, or when you
cough or vomit. A **reflex** is an involuntary, automatic response
to a stimulus. You can't control reflexes because they occur
before you know what has happened. A reflex involves a simple
nerve pathway called a reflex arc, as illustrated in **Figure 9.**

Imagine that while walking on a sandy beach, a pain suddenly
shoots through your foot as you step on the sharp edge of a broken shell. Sensory receptors in your foot respond to this sharp
object, and an impulse is sent to the spinal cord. As you just
learned, the impulse passes to an interneuron in the spinal cord
that immediately relays the impulse to motor neurons. Motor neurons transmit the impulse to muscles in your leg. Instantly, without thinking, you lift up your leg in response to the sharp-edged
shell. This is a withdrawal reflex.

A reflex allows the body to respond without having to think
about what action to take. Reflex responses are controlled in your
spinal cord, not in your brain. Your brain acts after the reflex to
help you figure out what to do to make the pain stop.

Reading Check *Why are reflexes important?*

Do you remember reading at the beginning of this chapter
about being frightened after a lamp was broken? What would have
happened if your breathing and heart rate didn't calm down
within a few minutes? Your body systems can't be kept in a state of
continual excitement. The organs of your nervous system control
and coordinate body responses. This helps maintain homeostasis
within your body.

Science Online

**Topic: Reflexes and
Paralysis**

Visit bookd.msscience.com for Web
links to information about reflexes
and paralysis.

Activity Make a small poster
that illustrates what you learn.

Drugs and the Nervous System

Many drugs, such as alcohol and caffeine, directly affect your nervous system. When swallowed, alcohol passes directly through the walls of the stomach and small intestine into the circulatory system. After it is inside the circulatory system, it can travel throughout your body. Upon reaching neurons, alcohol moves through their cell membranes and disrupts their normal cell functions. As a result, this drug slows the activities of the central nervous system and is classified as a depressant. Muscle control, judgment, reasoning, memory, and concentration also are impaired. Heavy alcohol use destroys brain and liver cells.

A stimulant is a drug that speeds up the activity of the central nervous system. Caffeine is a stimulant found in coffee, tea, cocoa, and many soft drinks, as shown in **Figure 10.** Too much caffeine can increase heart rate and aggravates restlessness, tremors, and insomnia in some people. It also can stimulate the kidneys to produce more urine.

Think again about a scare from a loud noise. The organs of your nervous system control and coordinate responses to maintain homeostasis within your body. This task might be more difficult when your body must cope with the effects of drugs.

Figure 10 Caffeine, a substance found in colas, coffee, chocolate, and some teas, can cause excitability and sleeplessness.

section 1 review

Summary

How the Nervous System Works
- The nervous system responds to stimuli to maintain homeostasis.
- To move from one neuron to another, an impulse crosses a synapse.

The Central Nervous System
- The brain controls all body activities.
- Spinal neurons carry impulses from all parts of the body to the brain.

The Peripheral Nervous System
- The somatic system controls voluntary actions and the autonomic system controls involuntary actions.

Safety and the Nervous System
- The spinal cord controls reflex responses.

Drugs and the Nervous System
- Many drugs affect your nervous system.

Self Check

1. **Draw and label** the parts of a neuron.
2. **Compare and contrast** the central and peripheral nervous systems.
3. **Explain** why you have trouble falling asleep after drinking several cups of hot cocoa.
4. **Explain** the advantage of having reflexes controlled by the spinal cord.
5. **Think Critically** Explain why many medications caution the consumer not to operate heavy machinery.

Applying Skills

6. **Concept Map** Prepare an events-chain concept map of the different kinds of neurons that pass an impulse from a stimulus to a response.
7. **Use a Word Processor** Create a flowchart showing the reflex pathway of a nerve impulse when you step on a sharp object. Label the body parts involved in each step.

 Science Online booked.msscience.com/self_check_quiz

section 1 review

1. Drawings should resemble **Figure 2.**
2. The central nervous system is made up of the brain and spinal cord. The peripheral nervous system is made up of cranial and spinal nerves.
3. Cocoa contains caffeine, which is a stimulant that can cause sleeplessness.
4. Response time to stimuli is less.
5. Many drugs can slow your central nervous system and affect muscle control, judgment, reasoning, memory, and concentration.
6. The concept map should contain the following: stimulus—sensory neurons—interneurons—motor neurons—response.
7. Flowcharts should show an impulse moving from receptor to sensory neuron to interneuron in the spinal cord to motor neuron to muscles in the foot.

◉ Test Your Hypothesis

Make a Plan

1. As a group, agree upon and write the hypothesis statement.

2. As a group, list the steps you need to test your hypothesis. Describe exactly what you will do at each step. Consider the following as you list the steps. How will you know that sight is not a factor? How will you use the card shown on the right to determine sensitivity to touch? How will you determine that one or both points are sensed?

3. **Design** a data table in your Science Journal to record your observations.

4. Reread your entire experiment to make sure that all steps are in the correct order.

5. **Identify** constants, variables, and controls of the experiment.

Follow Your Plan

1. Make sure your teacher approves your plan before you start.

2. Carry out the experiment as planned.

3. While the experiment is going on, write down any observations that you make and complete the data table in your Science Journal.

◉ Analyze Your Data

1. **Identify** which part of the body is least sensitive and which part is most sensitive.

2. **Identify** which part of the body tested can distinguish between the closest stimuli.

3. **Compare** your results with those of other groups.

4. Rank body parts tested from most to least sensitive. Did your results from this investigation support your hypothesis? Explain.

◉ Conclude and Apply

1. Based on the results of your investigation, what can you infer about the distribution of touch receptors on the skin?

2. What other parts of your body would you predict to be less sensitive? Explain your predictions.

Communicating Your Data

Write a report to share with your class about body parts of animals that are sensitive to touch. **For more help, refer to the** Science Skill Handbook.

LAB **D** ◆ **137**

• With partner's eyes closed, carefully touch the skin with the pair 1 mm apart. If partner feels two points, record a plus (+). If partner feels one point, record a minus (−). Repeat using the other pairs.

Teaching Strategy Have students vary the order of toothpick pairs they use.

Expected Outcome The more sensitive areas are the fingertips, palms, and cheeks. Less sensitive are the backs of the hands, forearms, and back of the neck.

◉ Analyze Your Data

Answers to Questions

1. least: backs of the hands, forearms, back of neck; most: fingertips, palms, cheeks

2. fingertips and usually the palms

3. Results should be consistent.

4. Answers will vary.

Error Analysis Have students compare their results and their hypotheses and explain any differences that occurred.

◉ Conclude and Apply

1. Fingertip touch receptors are closer together than those of the backs of the hands and forearms. Receptors in the palms and back of the neck vary.

2. Answers may include the back and the legs because they rarely are used to sense an object.

✔ Assessment

Performance To further assess students' understanding of skin sensitivity, have them repeat this lab on the lower part of the leg and on the foot. Use **PASC**, p. 97. L2

Student Data Table

Felt two points (mm)					
Body Part Tested	**Predictions**	**1**	**3**	**5**	**10**
Fingertip	5	−	+	+	+
Palm	4	−	−	+	+
Back of hand	3	−	−	−	+
Forearm	1	−	−	−	−
Back of neck	2	−	−	−	−

Communicating Your Data

Students can use the Internet or texts from the school library to gather data on animals with special sense organs on their legs, ears, noses, and mouth parts.

Sula

by Toni Morrison

Understanding Literature

Diction and Tone Other examples of diction conveying a pleasant tone in the passage are *excitement of newly installed light, bright with iced drinks, easy sun-washed days* and *purple dusks.*

Respond to the Reading

1. Nel seems happy about the return of Sula.

2. The phrases that describe Nel doing "a little dance" and being "moved to smile" help the reader understand Nel's feelings.

3. **Linking Science and Writing** Students should convey their character's dislike through the description of his or her nervous system's response to stimuli from the January environment.

 Neurological Process Nel's dance is a complex neurological process. However, it is a response to other sensory systems that are also neurological processes, such as the process of seeing. The eye's retina contains receptors that respond to light. The retina is the back part of the eye that contains cells called photoreceptors. Photoreceptors respond to light by generating electrical impulses that travel out of the eye through the optic nerve. Nel is able to see the sheen and glimmer of May because of this neurological process.

In the following passage from Sula, *a novel by Toni Morrison, the author describes Nel's response to the arrival of her old friend Sula.*

Nel alone noticed the peculiar quality of the May that followed the leaving of the birds. It had a sheen, a glimmering as of green, rain-soaked Saturday nights (lit by the excitement of newly installed street lights); of lemon-yellow afternoons bright with iced drinks and splashes of daffodils. It showed in the damp faces of her children and the river-smoothness of their voices. Even her own body was not immune to the magic. She would sit on the floor to sew as she had done as a girl, fold her legs up under her or do a little dance that fitted some tune in her head. There were easy sun-washed days and purple dusks . . . .

Although it was she alone who saw this magic, she did not wonder at it. She knew it was all due to Sula's return to the Bottom.

Understanding Literature

Diction and Tone An author's choice of words, or diction, can help convey a certain tone in the writing. In the passage, Toni Morrison's word choices help the reader understand that the character Nel is enjoying the month of May. Find two more examples in which diction conveys a pleasant tone.

Respond to the Reading

1. Describe, in your own words, how Nel feels about the return of her friend Sula.

2. What parts of the passage help you determine Nel's feelings?

3. **Linking Science and Writing** Write a paragraph describing the month of January that clearly shows a person's dislike for the month.

 In the passage, Nel has a physical reaction to her environment. She is moved to "do a little dance" in response to the sights and sounds of May. This action is an example of a voluntary response to stimuli from outside the body. Movement of the body is a coordinated effort of the skeletal, muscular, and nervous system. Nel can dance because motor neurons conduct impulses from the brain to her muscles.

138 ◆ D CHAPTER 5 Control and Coordination

Resources for Teachers and Students

"A Symphony in the Brain: The Evolution of the New Brain Wave Biofeedback", by Jim Robbins, *Atlantic Monthly Press*, May 2000

The Bluest Eye, Penguin USA, 2000

"Beloved", *Plume*, reprint edition, September 1998

The Man Who Mistook His Wife for a Hat, by Oliver Sacks, Touchstone Books, April 1998

Reviewing Main Ideas

Section 1 The Nervous System

1. Your body constantly is receiving a variety of stimuli from inside and outside the body. The nervous system responds to these stimuli to maintain homeostasis.

2. A neuron is the basic unit of structure and function of the nervous system.

3. A stimulus is detected by sensory neurons. Electrical impulses are carried to the interneurons and transmitted to the motor neurons. The result is the movement of a body part.

4. A response that is made automatically is a reflex.

5. The central nervous system contains the brain and spinal cord. The peripheral nervous system is made up of cranial and spinal nerves.

6. Many drugs, such as alcohol and caffeine, have a direct effect on your nervous system.

Section 2 The Senses

1. Your senses respond to stimuli. The eyes respond to light energy, and the ears respond to sound waves.

2. Olfactory cells of the nose and taste buds of the tongue are stimulated by chemicals.

3. Sensory receptors in your internal organs and skin respond to touch, pressure, pain, and temperature.

4. Your senses enable you to enjoy or avoid things around you. You are able to react to the changing conditions of your environment.

Visualizing Main Ideas

Copy and complete the following concept map about the nervous system.

bookd.msscience.com/interactive_tutor

Reviewing Main Ideas

Summary statements can be used by students to review the major concepts of the chapter.

Visualizing Main Ideas

See student page.

Science Online

Visit bookd.msscience.com
/self_check_quiz
/interactive_tutor
/vocabulary_puzzlemaker
/chapter_review
/standardized_test

Assessment Transparency

For additional assessment questions, use the *Assessment Transparency* located in the transparency book.

Assessment

Assessment Transparency   **Control and Coordination**

Directions: *Carefully review the table and answer the following questions.*

Reaction Experiment Results

Students	Distance of catch (cm)	Reaction time (s)
Dorothea	5	0.10
Billy	10	0.13
Hans	15	0.16
Sandra	20	?
Martha	25	0.22
Leo	30	0.25

1. According to the information in the table, the student with the lowest reaction time is ___.
   A Leo   C Hans
   B Billy   D Dorothea

2. Based on the relationship between catch distance and reaction time, which is most likely Sandra's reaction time?
   F 0.10 s   H 0.19 s
   G 0.18 s   J 0.21 s

3. Eleanor, another student, is asked to participate in the experiment. Her reaction time was determined to be 0.23 seconds. Based on the information in the table, Eleanor's catch distance would be ___.
   A 31.15 cm   C 24.25 cm
   B 26.67 cm   D 21.67 cm

Control and Coordination

Identifying Misconceptions

Assess

Use this assessment as follow-up to the F page at the beginning of this chapter.

Procedure Draw on the board the correct model of how light reflects off an object and toward the eye to cause vision. Draw several other models, such as the misconception that light comes from the eye to cause vision. Have students individually assess the models and decide what is correct and incorrect about each diagram. Ask students to identify which diagram is most correct.

Expected Outcome After completing the Sight Box activity, students should be able to recognize a model which shows light from a light source reflecting off of an object and toward the eye as the most correct model.

Using Vocabulary

1. Axons carry messages away from the cell body. Dendrites receive and carry messages to the cell body.

2. central nervous system—brain and spinal cord; peripheral nervous system—all the nerves outside the central nervous system

3. The cerebellum coordinates voluntary muscle movement. The cerebrum is where impulses are interpreted, memory is stored, and movements are controlled.

4. A reflex is an involuntary, automatic response to a stimulus. A synapse is the small space between an axon and a dendrite.

5. The brain stem is part of the brain. A neuron is a nerve cell.

6. An olfactory cell detects odors; a taste bud detects tastes.

7. A dendrite is part of a neuron. A synapse is the small space between an axon and a dendrite.

8. The cerebrum is a part of the brain. The central nervous system consists of the brain and the spinal cord.

9. The retina is a tissue of the eye. The cochlea is a structure in the inner ear.

10. A synapse is a small space between an axon and a dendrite. A neuron is a nerve cell.

Checking Concepts

11. D	16. C
12. B	17. A
13. C	18. B
14. D	19. C
15. A	20. C

Thinking Critically

21. Possible responses: so messages do not get mixed; so that responses can be coordinated

Using Vocabulary

axon p.119	neuron p.119
brain stem p.122	olfactory cell p.133
central nervous system	peripheral nervous system
p.121	p.121
cerebellum p.122	reflex p.125
cerebrum p.122	retina p.129
cochlea p.132	synapse p.121
dendrite p.119	taste bud p.134
homeostasis p.119	

Explain the difference between the vocabulary words in each of the following sets.

1. axon—dendrite
2. central nervous system—peripheral nervous system
3. cerebellum—cerebrum
4. reflex—synapse
5. brain stem—neuron
6. olfactory cell—taste bud
7. dendrite—synapse
8. cerebrum—central nervous system
9. retina—cochlea
10. synapse—neuron

Checking Concepts

Choose the word or phrase that best answers the question.

11. How do impulses cross synapses between neurons?
   A) by osmosis
   B) through interneurons
   C) through a cell body
   D) by a chemical

12. Which of the following is in the inner ear?
   A) anvil   C) eardrum
   B) hammer   D) cochlea

13. What are neurons called that detect stimuli in the skin and eyes?
   A) interneurons   C) motor neurons
   B) synapses   D) sensory neurons

14. Which of the following does the skin not sense?
   A) pain   C) temperature
   B) pressure   D) taste

15. What part of the brain controls voluntary muscles?
   A) cerebellum   C) cerebrum
   B) brain stem   D) pons

16. What part of the brain has an outer layer called the cortex?
   A) pons   C) cerebrum
   B) brain stem   D) spinal cord

17. What does the somatic system of the PNS control?
   A) skeletal muscles C) glands
   B) heart   D) salivary glands

18. What part of the eye is light finally focused on?
   A) lens   C) pupil
   B) retina   D) cornea

19. What is the largest part of the brain?
   A) cerebellum   C) cerebrum
   B) brain stem   D) pons

Use the illustration below to answer question 20.

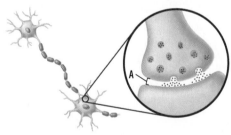

20. What is the name given to A?
   A) axon   C) synapse
   B) dendrite   D) nucleus

Thinking Critically

21. **Describe** why it is helpful to have impulses move only in one direction in a neuron.

22. **Describe** how smell and taste are related.

23. **Form a Hypothesis** If a fly were to land on your face and another one on your back, which might you feel first? How could you test your choice?

24. **Concept Map** Copy and complete this events-chain concept map to show the correct sequence of the structures through which light passes in the eye.

Cornea

Iris

Lens

Retina

Optic nerve

25. **Classify** Group the types of neurons as to their location and direction of impulse.

26. **Compare and contrast** the structures and functions of the cerebrum, cerebellum, and brain stem. Include in your discussion the following functions: balance, involuntary muscle movements, muscle tone, memory, voluntary muscles, thinking, and senses.

27. **Draw Conclusions** If an impulse traveled down one neuron but failed to move on to the next neuron, what might you conclude about the first neuron?

 Science Online bookd.msscience.com/chapter_review

Performance Activities

28. **Illustrate** In an emergency room, the doctor notices that a patient has uncoordinated body movements and has difficulty maintaining his balance. Draw and label the part of the brain that may have been injured.

Applying Math

29. **Sound Waves** How deep is a cave if you shout into the cave and it takes 1.5 seconds to hear your echo? Remember that the speed of sound is 340 m/s.

Use the paragraph and table below to answer question 30.

A police officer brought the following table into a school to educate students about the dangers of drinking and driving.

Approximate Blood Alcohol Percentage for Men

Drinks	Body Weight in Kilograms							
	45.4	54.4	63.5	72.6	81.6	90.7	99.8	108.9
1	0.04	0.03	0.03	0.02	0.02	0.02	0.02	0.02
2	0.08	0.06	0.05	0.05	0.04	0.04	0.03	0.03
3	0.11	0.09	0.08	0.07	0.06	0.06	0.05	0.05
4	0.15	0.12	0.11	0.09	0.08	0.08	0.07	0.06
5	0.19	0.16	0.13	0.12	0.11	0.09	0.09	0.08

Subtract 0.01% for each 40 minutes of drinking. One drink is 40 mL of 80-proof liquor, 355 mL of beer, or 148 mL of table wine.

30. **Blood Alcohol** A 72-kg man has been tested for blood alcohol content. His blood alcohol percentage is 0.07. Based upon the information in the table above, about how much has he had to drink?

A) 628 mL of 80-proof liquor

B) 1,064 mL of beer

C) 295 mL of table wine

D) four drinks

CHAPTER REVIEW D ◆ **141**

Thinking Critically

22. When food is put into the mouth and made moist, both the taste buds and olfactory cells are stimulated, and the food item is sensed by both.

23. The sense of touch is more pronounced on the face than on the back. One could check this by using something lightweight, such as a feather or small paintbrush, to test the sensitivity of the face and back.

24. See student page.

25. Sensory neurons are located in the sense organs and spinal cord; they carry impulses to the brain. Interneurons are located in the central nervous system; they carry impulses from the central nervous system to motor neurons. Motor neurons are in muscles and glands; they carry impulses from the brain to muscles and glands.

26. cerebrum—voluntary muscles, memory, senses, thinking; cerebellum—balance, muscle tone; brain stem—coordinates involuntary muscle movements, controls heartbeat, breathing, and blood pressure

27. It may be lacking the nerve-transmitting chemical released by axons.

Performance Activities

28. Drawings should indicate that the cerebellum is injured. Use **PASC**, p. 127.

Applying Math

National Math Standards

1, 5, 9

29. 510 m

30. B

✔ Assessment Resources

🗁 Reproducible Masters

Chapter *Fast File* Resources
  Chapter Review, pp. 35–36
  Chapter Tests, pp. 37–40
  Assessment Transparency Activity, p. 47

Glencoe Science Web site
  Chapter Review Test
  Standardized Test Practice

Glencoe Technology

  🔦 Assessment Transparency
  ⊕ Exam*View*® Pro Testmaker
  📼 MindJogger Videoquiz
  ⊕ Interactive Chalkboard

SAMPLE

Part 1 | Multiple Choice

1. B
2. B
3. B
4. C
5. C
6. D
7. A
8. D
9. B

Part 1 | Multiple Choice

Record your answers on the answer sheet provided by your teacher or on a sheet of paper.

1. An internal or external change that brings about a response is called a
   A. reflex.   C. receptor.
   B. stimulus.   D. heartbeat.

Use the illustration below to answer questions 2–4.

Cerebrum

Brain stem   Cerebellum

2. Which part of the brain helps in maintaining balance?
   A. cerebrum   C. brain stem
   B. cerebellum   D. no brain region

3. Which part of the brain controls involuntary actions?
   A. cerebrum   C. brain stem
   B. cerebellum   D. no brain region

4. In which part of the brain is memory stored?
   A. cerebrum   C. brain stem
   B. cerebellum   D. no brain region

5. Which of the following structures helps control the body's balance?
   A. retina   C. cochlea
   B. eardrum   D. cristae ampullaris

Test-Taking Tip

Focus On Your Test During the test, keep your eyes on your own paper. If you need to rest them, close them or look up at the ceiling.

Use the table below to answer questions 6 and 7.

Approximate Blood Alcohol Percentage for Men								
	Body Weight in Kilograms							
Drinks	45.4	54.4	63.5	72.6	81.6	90.7	99.8	108.9
1	0.04	0.03	0.03	0.02	0.02	0.02	0.02	0.02
2	0.08	0.06	0.05	0.05	0.04	0.04	0.03	0.03
3	0.11	0.09	0.08	0.07	0.06	0.06	0.05	0.05
4	0.15	0.12	0.11	0.09	0.08	0.08	0.07	0.06
5	0.19	0.16	0.13	0.12	0.11	0.09	0.09	0.08

Subtract 0.01% for each 40 minutes of drinking. One drink is 40 mL of 80-proof liquor, 355 mL of beer, or 148 mL of table wine.

6. In Michigan, it is illegal for drivers under 21 years of age to drink alcohol. Underage drivers can be arrested for drinking and driving if their blood alcohol percentage is more than 0.02 percent. According to this information, how many drinks would it take a 72-kg man to exceed this limit?
   A. three   C. one
   B. two   D. zero

7. In some states, the legal blood alcohol percentage limit for driving while under the influence of alcohol is 0.08 percent. According to this information, how many drinks would a 54-kg man have to consume to exceed this limit?
   A. four   C. two
   B. three   D. one

8. What neurons conduct impulses from the brain to glands?
   A. dendrites   C. sensory neurons
   B. interneurons   D. motor neurons

9. What carries impulses from the eye to the vision area of the brain?
   A. visual cortex   C. sensory neurons
   B. optic nerve   D. dendrites

Part 2 | Short Response/Grid In

10. Because the brain and spinal cord are surrounded by bone, the space where the fluid is cannot expand. If the amount of fluid increases, the pressure that the fluid exerts will be increased because there is nowhere for the fluid to go. Thus, more pressure will be put on the brain.

11. 658 + 99 = 757; 757 10% = 75.7. Approximately 76 people.

12. 605 + 76 = 681 deaths; 76/681 = .11 = 11%

13. 1997

14. Jeremy used a convex lens. Convex lenses can be used to magnify objects. A convex lens is thicker in the middle.

15. Alcohol is classified as a depressant because it slows the activities of the central nervous system.

Part 2 | Short Response/Grid In

Record your answers on the answer sheet provided by your teacher or on a sheet of paper.

10. Meningitis is an infection of the fluid that surrounds the spinal cord and the brain. Meningitis can be caused by bacteria or viruses. In bacterial meningitis, the amount of fluid in the brain and spinal cord may increase. What do you think might happen if the amount of fluid increases?

Use the table below to answer questions 11–13.

Number of Bicycle Deaths per Year		
Year	Male	Female
1996	654	107
1997	712	99
1998	658	99
1999	656	94
2000	605	76

Data from Insurance Institute for Highway Safety

11. Head injuries are the most serious injuries that are found in people who died in bicycle accidents. Ninety percent of the deaths were in people who were not wearing bicycle helmets. Using the data in the table, approximately how many of the people (male and female) who died in bicycle accidents in 1998 were wearing bicycle helmets?

12. In 2000, what percentage of the people who died were women?

13. Which of the years from 1996 to 2000 had the greatest total number of bicycle deaths?

14. Jeremy used a magnifying lens to study an earthworm. What kind of lens did he use? What part of this type of lens is the thickest?

15. Explain why alcohol is classified as a depressant.

Part 3 | Open Ended

Record your answers on a sheet of paper.

16. Compare and contrast the somatic and autonomic systems.

Use the illustration below to answer question 17.

17. Identify the structure in the illustration. Explain what might happen if chemical was not released here.

18. Inez and Maria went to the ice cream parlor. They both ordered strawberry sundaes. Marie thought that the sundae was made with fresh strawberries, because it tasted so great. Inez thought that her sundae did not have much flavor. What could be the reason that Inez's sundae was tasteless? Explain why.

Use the illustration below to answer question 19.

19. The person with this foot sore has diabetes. People with diabetes often lose sensation in their feet. Explain why a sore like the one in the photograph might develop if skin sensory receptors were not working properly.

nose prevents the food molecules from reaching the olfactory cells in the nasal passages and the strawberry sundae seems tasteless.

19. In a person without diabetes, the skin normally has pain receptors. Pain receptors would warn the person that there is an infection. Because the skin receptors for pain are not working, the person with diabetes will not feel the pain that would tell the person that there is an infection.

Rubrics

For more help evaluating open-ended assessment questions, see the rubric on p. 10T.

Part 3 | Open Ended

16. The somatic system controls voluntary actions. It is made up of the cranial and spinal nerves that go from the central nervous system to the skeletal muscles. The autonomic nervous system controls involuntary actions such as heart rate, breathing, digestion, and glandular functions.

17. The structure is a synapse. Neurons do not touch each other. Impulses travel from one axon to the next because of an impulse-transmitting chemical at the synapse. If the axon did not release the chemical, then the impulse will not be transmitted to the next axon. The impulse will stop there.

18. Inez may have a stuffy nose. Smell and taste are related. The sense of smell is needed to identify some foods. When saliva mixes in the mouth, the odors travel up the nasal passage in the back of the throat. The olfactory cells are stimulated, and the taste and smell of the strawberries is sensed. A stuffy

Section/Objectives	Standards		Labs/Features
	National	**State/Local**	
Chapter Opener	See p. 16–17T for a Key to Standards.		**Launch Lab:** Model a Chemical Message, p. 145 **Foldables,** p. 145
Section 1 The Endocrine System ⏱ 2 sessions ▤ 1 block 1. **Define** how hormones function. 2. **Identify** different endocrine glands and the effects of the hormones they produce. 3. **Describe** how a feedback system works in your body.	National Content Standards: UCP.1–UCP.3, UCP.5, A.1, A.2, C.1–C.3		**Applying Math:** Glucose Levels, p. 147 **Visualizing the Endocrine System,** p. 148
Section 2 The Reproductive System ⏱ 2 sessions ▤ 1 block 4. **Identify** the function of the reproductive system. 5. **Compare and contrast** the major structures of the male and female reproductive systems. 6. **Sequence** the stages of the menstrual cycle.	National Content Standards: UCP.1–UCP.3, UCP.5, A.1, A.2, C.1–C.3		**Science Online,** p. 153 **MiniLAB:** Graphing Hormone Levels, p. 154 **Lab:** Interpreting Diagrams, p. 156
Section 3 Human Life Stages ⏱ 3 sessions ▤ 1.5 blocks 7. **Describe** the fertilization of a human egg. 8. **List** the major events in the development of an embryo and fetus. 9. **Describe** the developmental stages of infancy, childhood, adolescence, and adulthood.	National Content Standards: UCP.1–UCP.3, UCP.5, A.1, A.2, B.2, C.1, C.3, C5		**Integrate Career,** p. 158 **MiniLAB:** Interpreting Fetal Development, p. 160 **Science Online,** p. 161 **Integrate Physics,** p. 164 **Lab:** Changing Body Proportions, p. 166 **Science Stats:** Facts About Infants, p. 168

Lab Materials	Reproducible Resources	Section Assessment	Technology
Launch Lab: filter paper; metric ruler; plastic, ceramic, or glass plate; baking soda; salt; dropper; vinegar	**Chapter *FAST FILE* Resources** Foldables Worksheet, p. 15 Directed Reading Overview, p. 17 Note-taking Worksheets, pp. 31–33	*GLENCOE'S* **ASSESSMENT** *ADVANTAGE*	TeacherWorks includes: • Interactive Teacher Edition • Lesson Planner with calendar • Access to all program blacklines • Correlations to standards • Web links 📼 Video Lab
Need materials? Contact Science Kit at 1-800-828-7777 or www.sciencekit.com on the Internet.	**Chapter *FAST FILE* Resources** Transparency Activity, p. 42 Enrichment, p. 28 Reinforcement, p. 25 Directed Reading, p. 18 Lab Activity, pp. 9–11 Transparency Activity, pp. 45–46	**Portfolio** Visual Learning, p. 149 **Performance** Applying Math, p. 147 Applying Skills, p. 150 **Content** Section Review, p. 150	🔦 Section Focus Transparency 🔦 Teaching Transparency 💿 Virtual Labs CD-ROM 🎧 Guided Reading Audio Program 💿 Interactive Chalkboard CD-ROM
MiniLAB: graph paper **Lab:** paper, pencil	**Chapter *FAST FILE* Resources** Transparency Activity, p. 43 MiniLAB, p. 3 Enrichment, p. 29 Reinforcement, p. 26 Directed Reading, p. 18 Lab Worksheet, pp. 5–6	**Portfolio** Science Journal, p. 153 **Performance** MiniLAB, p. 154 Applying Math, p. 155 **Content** Section Review, p. 155	🔦 Section Focus Transparency 💿 Virtual Labs CD-ROM 🎧 Guided Reading Audio Program 💿 Interactive Chalkboard CD-ROM
MiniLAB: graph paper **Lab:** tape measure, erasable pencil, graph paper	**Chapter *FAST FILE* Resources** Transparency Activity, p. 44 MiniLAB, p. 4 Enrichment, p. 30 Reinforcement, p. 27 Directed Reading, pp. 19, 20 Lab Worksheet, pp. 7–8 Lab Activity, pp. 13–14 **Lab Management and Safety,** p. 70	**Portfolio** Make a Model, p. 158 **Performance** MiniLAB, p. 160 Applying Skills, p. 165 **Content** Section Review, p. 165	🔦 Section Focus Transparency 💿 Virtual Labs CD-ROM 🎧 Guided Reading Audio Program 💿 Interactive Chalkboard CD-ROM

GLENCOE'S **ASSESSMENT** *ADVANTAGE* **End of Chapter Assessment**		
Blackline Masters	**Technology**	**Professional Series**
Chapter *FAST FILE* Resources Chapter Review, pp. 35–36 Chapter Tests, pp. 37–40 **Standardized Test Practice,** pp. 27–30	📼 MindJogger Videoquiz 💿 Virtual Labs CD-ROM 💿 Exam*View*® Pro Testmaker 💿 TeacherWorks CD-ROM 💿 Interactive Chalkboard CD-ROM	**Performance Assessment in the Science Classroom (PASC)**

Transparencies

Section Focus

Section 1 — Section Focus Transparency — Living with Diabetes

Diabetes is a disease that occurs when the body does not produce insulin in proper amounts. An insulin pump, like the one shown below, helps control insulin levels for a person with diabetes. It is worn all the time, but can be easily removed when participating in sports.

1. Why would a person with diabetes need to take insulin?
2. Why is maintaining a healthful diet important to a person with diabetes?

L2

Section 2 — Section Focus Transparency — Sprint to Home

Adult sea turtles lay about one hundred eggs in a nest on land, then promptly return to the water. After the eggs hatch, the young sea turtles race toward the sea in a struggle for survival on their own. In contrast, other species produce fewer eggs but give more care and protection to the young once they are born.

1. Compared to sea turtles, how many offspring do people have?
2. How does the amount of care young sea turtles receive differ from that of humans?

L2

Section 3 — Section Focus Transparency — Keep on Running

Growing older does not mean an end to fitness and competition. The National Senior Games will attract over 10,000 athletes, aged 50 and older. For young and old alike, exercise is essential for good health.

1. How can exercise help offset some of the effects of aging?
2. Other than exercise, what choices can people make that might affect the aging process?

L2

This is a representation of key blackline masters available in the Teacher Classroom Resources. See Resource Manager boxes within the chapter for additional information.

Assessment

Assessment Transparency — Regulation and Reproduction

Directions: *Carefully review the table and answer the following questions.*

Population by Country (in millions)				
Country	1970	1980	1990	2000
Japan	104	117	124	127
USA	205	223	250	281
India	555	690	851	1,014
Pakistan	66	85	114	142
Indonesia	94	155	189	225
Russia	130	148	148	146

1. According to this information, which country had the greatest increase in population between the years 1970 and 2000?
   A Russia   C India
   B United States   D Japan
2. Between the years 1990 and 2000, which country had a negative rate of population growth?
   F Japan   H Indonesia
   G Russia   J India
3. According to the table, the country that had a total population greater than Pakistan in 1970 but less than Pakistan in the year 2000 is ___.
   A India   C United States
   B Japan   D Russia

L2

Teaching

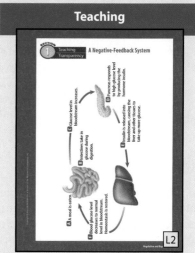

Section 1 — Teaching Transparency — A Negative-Feedback System

L2

Key to Teaching Strategies

The following designations will help you decide which activities are appropriate for your students.

L1 Level 1 activities should be appropriate for students with learning difficulties.

L2 Level 2 activities should be within the ability range of all students.

L3 Level 3 activities are designed for above-average students.

ELL ELL activities should be within the ability range of English-Language Learners.

COOP LEARN Cooperative Learning activities are designed for small group work.

LS Multiple Learning Styles logos, as described on page 12T, are used throughout to indicate strategies that address different learning styles.

P These strategies represent student products that can be placed into a best-work portfolio.

PBL Problem-Based Learning activities apply real-world situations to learning.

Hands-on Activities

Student Text Lab Worksheet

Activity — Interpreting Diagrams

Lab Preview
Directions: *Answer these questions before you begin the Activity.*
1. What does the diagram below show?
2. Where do eggs develop in a female?

Starting in adolescence, hormones cause the development of eggs in a female's ovaries and changes in the uterus. These changes prepare the uterus to accept a fertilized egg that can attach itself in the wall of the uterus. What happens to an unfertilized egg?

What You'll Investigate
What changes occur to the uterus during a female's monthly menstrual cycle?

Materials
paper and pencil

Goals
• Observe the stages in the diagram of the menstrual cycle.
• Relate the process of ovulation to the cycle.

Procedure
1. The diagrams below show what is explained in this chapter on the menstrual cycle.
2. Use the information in this chapter and the diagrams below to complete the table in the Data and Observations section.
3. On approximately what day in a 28-day cycle is the egg released from the ovary?

L2

Laboratory Activities

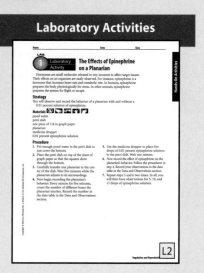

Laboratory Activity 1 — The Effects of Epinephrine on a Planarian

Hormones are small molecules released in tiny amounts to affect target tissues. Their effects on an organism are easily observed. For instance, epinephrine is a hormone that increases heart rate and metabolic rate. In humans, epinephrine prepares the body physiologically for stress. In other animals, epinephrine prepares the system for flight or escape.

Strategy
You will observe and record the behavior of a planarian with and without a 0.01 percent solution of epinephrine.

Materials
pond water
petri dish
one piece of 1/4 in. graph paper
planarian
medicine dropper
0.01 percent epinephrine solution

Procedure
1. Put enough pond water in the petri dish to just cover the bottom.
2. Place the petri dish on top of the sheet of graph paper so that the squares show through the bottom.
3. Carefully transfer your planarian to the center of the dish. Wait five minutes while the planarian adjusts to its surroundings.
4. Now begin recording the planarian's behavior. Every minute for five minutes, count the number of different boxes the planarian touches. Record the number in the data table in the Data and Observations section.
5. Use the medicine dropper to place five drops of 0.01 percent epinephrine solution to the petri dish. Wait one minute.
6. Now record the effect of epinephrine on the planarian's behavior. Follow the procedures in step 4. Record your observations in the data table in the Data and Observations section.
7. Repeat steps 5 and 6 two times. In all, you will then have observations for 5, 10, and 15 drops of epinephrine solution.

L2

Meeting Different Ability Levels

Content Outline

Note-taking Worksheet — Regulation and Reproduction

Section 1 The Endocrine System

A. _____ of the endocrine system—help regulate and coordinate body systems
   1. _____—chemical messengers manufactured in glands throughout the body
   2. Endocrine glands release hormones directly into the blood because they are _____.

B. Negative-feedback system—endocrine system gives _____ messages to control the production and release of hormones.

Section 2 The Reproductive System

A. Endocrine system hormones are key factors in the _____ of human reproduction systems.

B. Male reproductive system—has both internal and external organs
   1. _____—organs that produce male hormone testosterone and reproductive cells called sperm
   2. Internal organs combine sperm with a fluid energy source producing _____.

C. Female reproductive system—internal organs called _____ produce egg cells.
   1. Once a month the _____ process releases an egg.
   2. A hollow, pear-shaped, muscular organ in which fertilized egg develop is called the _____.
   3. The _____, or birth canal, is a muscular tube that opens to the outside of the body.

D. Menstrual cycle—monthly cycle of _____ in the female reproductive system
   1. Endocrine _____ including estrogen and progesterone control the menstrual cycle.
   2. _____, which is the release of blood and uterine lining tissue, occurs in phases.
      a. Phase 1 begins when _____ starts and usually lasts about 4 to 6 days.
      b. Phase 2 involves thickening of the uterus lining and _____, or egg release.
      c. Phase 3 continues with uterine preparation and ends with _____ hormone levels and uterine lining breakdown if no fertilized egg arrives.
   3. _____—the gradual shutdown of the ovaries which ends ovulation and menstrual periods

L2

Reinforcement

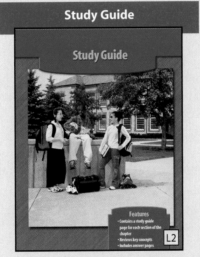

Reinforcement — The Endocrine System

Directions: Listed below are some of the endocrine glands. Describe the function of each gland and label the figure below.

1. pituitary gland

2. thyroid gland

3. parathyroid glands

4. adrenal glands

Directions: Answer the following question on the lines provided.
9. How does the endocrine system control its output of a hormone?

L2

Enrichment

Enrichment — Transplantation

Each year, millions of Americans develop Type 1 or insulin-dependent diabetes mellitus. People with Type 1 diabetes don't produce enough insulin because the disease destroys the cells in the pancreas that make insulin. Although diabetes is often managed with insulin injections, it is a serious—sometimes deadly—disease. It can cause heart disease, high blood pressure, blindness, and more. In fact, diabetes is the leading cause of kidney failure, effecting almost 30 percent of people with Type 1 diabetes.

A New Kidney
That's why diabetic patients with kidney failure often undergo surgery to get a new kidney. This surgery, called kidney transplantation, has a better success rate than another kind of treatment called dialysis. Dialysis acts as an artificial kidney that removes a patient's blood, purifies it, and returns it to the bloodstream. Unfortunately, Type 1 diabetic patients treated with dialysis for a long time are more likely to die at a young age.
Doctors trying to save lives have, in a single operation, transplanted both kidneys and pancreases into diabetic patients. The simultaneous transplantation of a pancreas and kidney, called SPK transplantation. With SPK transplantation, patients can live longer, healthier lives.

Ten years after SPK transplantation, between 70 and 80 percent of patients are still alive. With ten years on dialysis, less than 20 percent of patients survive. But SPK transplantation isn't perfect. There are risks involved, such as infection and organ rejection. Plus, patients must stay in the hospital for several days after surgery and recover at home for another four to six weeks.

Another Type of Transplant
Diabetes can also consider islet cell transplantation. With this procedure, islets or nests of hormone-producing cells are freed from nearby pancreatic tissue. The tissue is processed to purify the cells, then injected into a vein that leads directly to the liver. If the operation is successful, the islet cells survive and produce insulin.
Islet cell transplantation has none of the side effects of SPK transplantation. Even though it's been around as long as SPK transplantation, islet cell transplantation is still considered experimental. That's because its success rate is much lower than SPK transplantation. Only five to ten percent of islet cell transplantation patients are able to go off insulin after one year, compared with more than 80 percent of pancreatic transplant patients. But both methods provide hope to diabetic patients.

1. Explain the difference between SPK transplantation and islet cell transplantation.

2. What are the biggest advantages of either kind of transplantation surgery?

3. Do you think it's accurate to call SPK transplantation a "life-saving operation"? Why or why not?

4. Besides having a lower success rate than SPK transplantation, why else might islet cell transplantation be considered experimental?

L3

Directed Reading (English/Spanish)

Directed Reading for Content Mastery — Overview Regulation and Reproduction

Directions: Complete the sentences using the terms listed below.

hormones   endocrine   umbilical cord
adulthood   childhood   negative feedback

1. _____ secreted by glands in the _____ system are necessary for sexual development.
2. The endocrine system controls the level of hormones in the body by a _____ system.
3. At birth the baby is still attached to the _____.
4. The stages of life are infancy, _____, adolescence, and _____.

Directions: Use the following terms to complete the concept map below.

egg   oviduct   sperm
semen   fertilized egg   urethra

An ovary produces a(n) __5__ that travels through the __7__ and is penetrated by the male's sperm to become a(n) __9__

Testes produce __6__ that combine with semen and travel through the __8__ to penetrate the female's egg to create a(n) __9__

L1

Study Guide

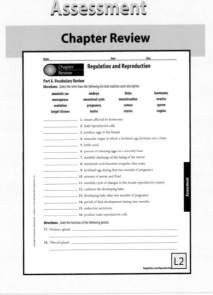

Study Guide

Features
- Contains a study guide page for each section of the chapter
- Reviews key concepts
- Includes answer pages

L2

Reading Essentials

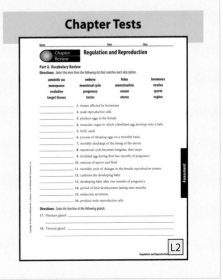

Reading Essentials for Glencoe Science
An Interactive Student Workbook

Features
- Condensed core content
- Actively involves students in reading
- Reinforces key vocabulary

L1

Assessment

Test Practice Workbook

Chapter 22 Regulation and Reproduction — Standardized Test Practice

DIRECTIONS
Read each question. Then, on your answer sheet, mark the answer choice that you think is best.

1. During the first two months of pregnancy, the developing child is called an embryo. After this period, it is called a
   A zygote
   B neo-embryo
   C fetus
   D baby

2. A similarity between the endocrine system and the nervous system is that they are both control systems. One difference is that the endocrine system
   F doesn't react as quickly as the nervous system
   G is made up of more neurons
   H reacts more quickly than the nervous system
   J does not release hormones into the blood

3. If the blood contains too little or too much glucose, the endocrine system will respond by increasing or decreasing the glucose level. The endocrine system is a type of
   A positive feedback system
   B equilibrium feedback system
   C negative feedback system
   D neutral feedback system

4. Sperm and testosterone are produced in the
   F urethra
   G prostate gland
   H penis
   J testes

5. In which of the following does fertilization of an egg usually take place?
   A ovary
   B oviduct
   C placenta
   D cilia

GO ON   L2

Glencoe Life Science

Chapter Review

Chapter Review — Regulation and Reproduction

Part A. Vocabulary Review
Directions: Select the term from the following list that matches each description.

amniotic sac   embryo   fetus   hormones
menopause   menstrual cycle   menstruation   ovaries
ovulation   pregnancy   semen   sperm
target tissues   testes   uterus   vagina

___ 1. tissues affected by hormones
___ 2. male reproductive cells
___ 3. produce eggs in the female
___ 4. muscular organ in which a fertilized egg develops into a baby
___ 5. birth canal
___ 6. process of releasing eggs on a monthly basis
___ 7. monthly discharge of the lining of the uterus
___ 8. menstrual cycle becomes irregular, then stops
___ 9. fertilized egg during first two months of pregnancy
___ 10. mixture of sperm and fluid
___ 11. monthly cycle of changes in the female reproductive system
___ 12. cushions the developing baby
___ 13. developing baby after two months of pregnancy
___ 14. period of fetal development lasting nine months
___ 15. endocrine secretions
___ 16. produce male reproductive cells

Directions: State the function of the following glands.

17. Pituitary gland:

18. Thyroid gland:

L2

Chapter Tests

Chapter Review — Regulation and Reproduction

Part A. Vocabulary Review
Directions: Select the term from the following list that matches each description.

amniotic sac   embryo   fetus   hormones
menopause   menstrual cycle   menstruation   ovaries
ovulation   pregnancy   semen   sperm
target tissues   testes   uterus   vagina

___ 1. tissues affected by hormones
___ 2. male reproductive cells
___ 3. produce eggs in the female
___ 4. muscular organ in which a fertilized egg develops into a baby
___ 5. birth canal
___ 6. process of releasing eggs on a monthly basis
___ 7. monthly discharge of the lining of the uterus
___ 8. menstrual cycle becomes irregular, then stops
___ 9. fertilized egg during first two months of pregnancy
___ 10. mixture of sperm and fluid
___ 11. monthly cycle of changes in the female reproductive system
___ 12. cushions the developing baby
___ 13. developing baby after two months of pregnancy
___ 14. period of fetal development lasting nine months
___ 15. endocrine secretions
___ 16. produce male reproductive cells

Directions: State the function of the following glands.

17. Pituitary gland:

18. Thyroid gland:

L2

Science Content Background

section 1 **The Endocrine System**
Regulation

The endocrine system uses hormones to control body functions such as defense, hunger, growth and reproduction. All organs of the endocrine system are glands that produce and empty hormones into the circulatory system.

The anterior lobe of the pituitary gland produces hormones that cause the stimulation of growth, the production of milk, the regulation of thyroid gland secretions, the regulation of adrenal cortex secretions, the stimulation of egg and sperm production, and egg release.

The posterior lobe of the pituitary gland aids in the regulation of water secretion by the kidneys, muscle contractions during labor, and the contraction of milk-producing glands.

The pituitary's intermediate lobe controls melanin production, which determines skin color.

section 2 **The Reproductive System**
Hormones

Hormones produced by the endocrine system control sexual development, maturation, and functioning of the reproductive system. Hormones stimulate the production and release of sperm and semen in the male reproductive system. In the female reproductive system, hormones stimulate the production and release of ova, or eggs. Hormones also play a role during labor and birth. In later years, menopause is brought on when the body stops producing certain hormones.

section 3 **Human Life Stages**
Embryonic Development

Fertilization is the union of a sperm cell from a male with an egg from a female. Fertilization results in two events: (1) fusion of the sperm and egg cells, including fusion of the two nuclei, to form a cell called a zygote, and (2) activation of the new cell to begin division and growth.

Once a sperm fertilizes an egg, the egg produces an outer protective layer. Next, the zygote divides into thousands of smaller cells that cling together like a ball of soap bubbles. After several days and until about two weeks later, the ball of cells begins to differentiate into three parts: an outer layer of cells that attaches to the uterus of the mother, an inner mass of cells that develops into the embryo, and a fluid-filled sac that surrounds the embryo.

The next phase, which occurs between two and eight weeks after fertilization, involves specialization of cells into primary organ systems. This set of events marks the end of the embryo stage and the beginning of the fetal stage.

chapter content resources

Internet Resources

For additional content background, visit
bookd.msscience.com to:

- access your book online
- find references to related articles in popular science magazines
- access Web links with related content background
- access current events with science journal topics

Print Resources

How the Endocrine System Works, by J. Matthew Neal, Blackwell Publishers, 2001

Endocrine and Reproductive Systems, by Susan Dudley Gold and Melissa Kim, Enslow Publishers, Inc., 2003

IDENTIFYING Misconceptions

Find Out What Students Think

Students may think that . . .

Fertilization and embryonic development are mysterious processes that are not understandable.

Many students may find the concepts of fertilization and embryonic development very abstract. Using concrete demonstrations and activities will help these students understand the processes and sequences of events that occur.

Demonstration

- Using two different colors of clay, form a large ball from one color, representing an egg cell, and many smaller balls from the second color, representing sperm cells. Fertilization can be modeled by molding the "egg" and "sperm" into one ball. Explain that this fertilized cell is called a zygote. No other sperm cells can fuse with the egg cell at this point because the zygote produces a protective barrier blocking other sperm cells. Emphasize that the molding together of the sperm and egg cells is a simulation of the combining of genetic material from both.

- Next, model the phase of rapid cell division by dividing the ball into many smaller, connected balls. Explain that these cells cling together like a ball of soap bubbles. Continue by drawing the "soap bubble" stage on the board and labeling it as time from fertilization to a few days.

- Next, draw the three-part stage and the specialization. Label these drawings as "a few days to 2 weeks" and "2 weeks to 8 weeks," respectively.

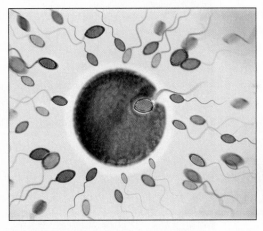

VCG/FPG International

Promote Understanding

Activity

After discussion, have students draw diagrams of the events that occur from fertilization through the stages of early development to the early fetal stage. Have students work in small groups to explain to one another their diagrams and the events that take place during each stage.

Assess

After completing the chapter, see *Identifying Misconceptions* in the Study Guide at the end of the chapter.

Chapter Vocabulary

Science Journal Student responses will vary, but may include dispatchers answering an incoming emergency call, dispatching emergency crews to the scene, and monitoring the situation to see if additional help is needed.

INTERACTIVE CHALKBOARD
with Image Bank

PowerPoint® Presentations

This CD-ROM is an editable Microsoft® PowerPoint® presentation that includes:

- a pre-made presentation for every chapter
- interactive graphics
- animations
- audio clips
- image bank
- all new section and chapter questions
- Standardized Test Practice
- transparencies
- pre-lab questions for all labs
- Foldables directions
- links to bookd.msscience.com

Regulation and Reproduction

chapter preview

sections

1 The Endocrine System

2 The Reproductive System
Lab Interpreting Diagrams

3 Human Life Stages
Lab Changing Body Proportions

Virtual Lab What are the stages of development before birth?

Where's the emergency?

The fire station control room blinks with panels of buttons and monitors. Dispatchers can access and relay emergency information quickly using this complex monitoring system. In a similar way, your body's endocrine system monitors and controls the actions of many of your body's functions.

Science Journal Write a paragraph describing how an emergency call might be handled at a fire station.

Theme Connection

Stability, Change, and Energy The endocrine system maintains stable body functions and responds to changes. The unique functioning of the reproductive system is dependent on energy for cell division and differentiation of cells.

About the Photo

Fighting Fires Fire department dispatchers must maintain a vigilant watch over the communications equipment in the control room. Emergency calls are received and monitored and information is passed along to the personnel responding to the scene of an emergency. The dispatchers also may be in contact with other emergency companies in order to receive or provide additional help.

Start-Up Activities

Launch LAB

Model a Chemical Message

Your body has systems that work together to coordinate your body's activities. One of these systems sends chemical messages through your blood to certain tissues, which, in turn, respond. Do the lab below to see how a chemical signal can be sent.

1. Cut a 10-cm-tall *Y* shape from filter paper and place it on a plastic, ceramic, or glass plate.

2. Sprinkle baking soda on one arm of the *Y* and salt on the other arm.

3. Using a dropper, place five or six drops of vinegar halfway up the leg of the *Y*.

4. **Think Critically** Describe in your Science Journal how the chemical moves along the paper and the reaction(s) it causes.

Science Online Preview this chapter's content and activities at bookd.msscience.com

FOLDABLES Study Organizer

Stages of Life Make the following Foldable to help you predict the stages of life.

STEP 1 Fold a vertical sheet of paper in half from top to bottom. Then fold it in half again top to bottom two more times. Unfold all the folds.

STEP 2 Refold the paper into a fan, using the folds as a guide. Unfold all the folds again.

STEP 3 Label as shown.

Fertilization/Embryo

Death

Read and Write Before you read the chapter, list as many stages of life as you can on your Foldable. Add to your list as you read the chapter.

Purpose Use the Launch Lab to introduce students to the endocrine system. L2 IS **Visual-Spatial**

Preparation Cut Y-shaped pieces of filter paper before class.

Materials filter paper or coffee filters; baking soda; salt; vinegar; plastic, ceramic, or glass plate; dropper

Teaching Strategy Have students observe the bubbles that form when the vinegar and baking soda react.

Think Critically

Students should observe the vinegar moving along the leg of the Y and then into the arms of the Y. The vinegar reacts with the baking soda and bubbles are produced.

Assessment

Performance Have students repeat this lab using baking powder in place of baking soda and water instead of vinegar and observe the reaction. Use **Performance Assessment in the Science Classroom,** p. 97.

FOLDABLES Study Organizer **Dinah Zike Study Fold**

Student preparation materials for this Foldable are available in the **Chapter *FAST FILE* Resources.**

The Endocrine System

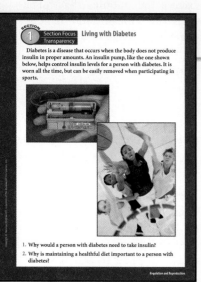

SECTION 1
Section Focus Transparency

Living with Diabetes

Diabetes is a disease that occurs when the body does not produce insulin in proper amounts. An insulin pump, like the one shown below, helps control insulin levels for a person with diabetes. It is worn all the time, but can be easily removed when participating in sports.

1. Why would a person with diabetes need to take insulin?
2. Why is maintaining a healthful diet important to a person with diabetes?

Regulation and Reproduction

Tie to Prior Knowledge

Stimuli Have students recall how their bodies react to stimuli such as the touching of a hot object or how they respond to a loud noise.

Reading Check

Answer to speed up and slow down certain cellular activities

as you read

What You'll Learn

- **Define** how hormones function.
- **Identify** different endocrine glands and the effects of the hormones they produce.
- **Describe** how a feedback system works in your body.

Why It's Important

The endocrine system uses chemicals to control many systems in your body.

Review Vocabulary

tissue: groups of cells that work together to perform a specific function

New Vocabulary

- hormone

Functions of the Endocrine System

You go through the dark hallways of a haunted house. You can't see a thing. Your heart is pounding. Suddenly, a monster steps out in front of you. You scream and jump backwards. Your body is prepared to defend itself or get away. Preparing the body for fight or flight in times of emergency, as shown in **Figure 1,** is one of the functions of the body's control systems.

Control Systems All of your body's systems work together, but the endocrine (EN duh krun) and the nervous systems are your body's control systems. The endocrine system sends chemical messages in your blood that affect specific tissues called target tissues. The nervous system sends rapid impulses to and from your brain, then throughout your body. Your body does not respond as quickly to chemical messages as it does to impulses.

Endocrine Glands

Tissues found throughout your body called endocrine glands produce the chemical messages called **hormones** (HOR mohnz). Hormones can speed up or slow down certain cellular processes.

Some glands in your body release their products through small tubes called ducts. Endocrine glands are ductless and each endocrine gland releases its hormone directly into the blood. Then, the blood transports the hormone to the target tissue. A target tissue usually is located in the body far from the location of the endocrine gland that produced the hormone to which it responds.

Reading Check
What is the function of hormones?

Figure 1 Your endocrine system enables many parts of your body to respond immediately in a fearful situation.

Gland Functions Endocrine glands have many functions in the body. The functions include the regulation of its internal environment, adaptation to stressful situations, promotion of growth and development, and the coordination of circulation, digestion, and the absorption of food. **Figure 2** on the next two pages shows some of the body's endocrine glands.

 Applying Math   **Use Percentages**

GLUCOSE LEVELS Calculate how much higher the blood sugar (glucose) level of a diabetic is before breakfast when compared to a nondiabetic before breakfast. Express this number as a percentage of the nondiabetic sugar level before breakfast.

Solution

1 *This is what you know:*
- nondiabetic blood sugar at 0 h = 0.85 g sugar/L blood
- diabetic blood sugar at 0 h = 1.8 g sugar/L blood

2 *This is what you need to find out:*
How much higher is the glucose level of a diabetic person than that of a nondiabetic person before breakfast?

3 *This is the procedure you need to use:*
- Find the difference in glucose levels:
  1.8 g/L − 0.85 g/L = 0.95 g/L
- Use this equation:
  $\dfrac{\text{difference between values}}{\text{nondiabetic value}} \times 100\% = \text{percent difference}$
- Substitute in the known values:
  $\dfrac{0.95}{0.85} \times 100\% = 112\%$
- Before breakfast, a diabetic's blood sugar is about 112 percent higher than that of a nondiabetic.

4 *Check your answer:*
Change 112% to a decimal then multiply it by 0.85. You should get 0.95.

Practice Problems

1. Express as a percentage how much higher the blood sugar value is for a diabetic person compared to a nondiabetic person 1 h after breakfast.

2. Express as a percentage how much higher the blood sugar value is for a diabetic person compared to a nondiabetic person 3 h and 6 h after breakfast.

 For more practice, visit bookd.msscience.com/ math_practice

Applying Math

National Math Standards
Correlation to Mathematics Objectives
1, 9

Answers to Practice Problems

1. Hour one = 130 / 110 × 100 = 118 %

2. Hour three = 95 / 85 × 100 = 111 %
   Hour six = 110 / 70 × 100 = 157%

Note: student answers may vary slightly due to the values read from the graph. Accept answers that are reasonably close.

Teacher FYI

Hormone Production In addition to hormones produced by endocrine glands, other organs also produce hormones. Endocrine cells in the stomach produce a hormone that regulates the release of its digestive enzymes. The kidneys release a hormone that controls the rate of production of red blood cells. The heart makes a hormone that regulates blood pressure and volume.

Differentiated Instruction

English-Language Learners Have students make flashcards with the name of a gland on one side and the hormone it produces on the other. Student pairs can quiz each other using the flashcards. L2

Visualizing the Endocrine System

Have students examine the pictures and read the captions. Then ask the following questions.

How do hormones from the thyroid gland and the parathyroid gland work together? Possible answers: Both glands release hormones that work together to regulate the levels of calcium in the blood.

What could be the result if a person's thymus gland was not functioning properly? Possible answer: The thymus gland produces hormones that stimulate the production of cells involved in immune reactions. Without these cells the body has difficulty fighting infection.

Activity

Negative Feedback Have students write and act out a skit that demonstrates the negative feedback cycle of hormone regulation. Students can break into groups of 6 or 7 and produce the skits. The instructor would need to provide a different sequence of events for each student group. Each student can play the role of the brain, a hormone or an endocrine gland, and one student can be the messenger between the body and the brain. L2

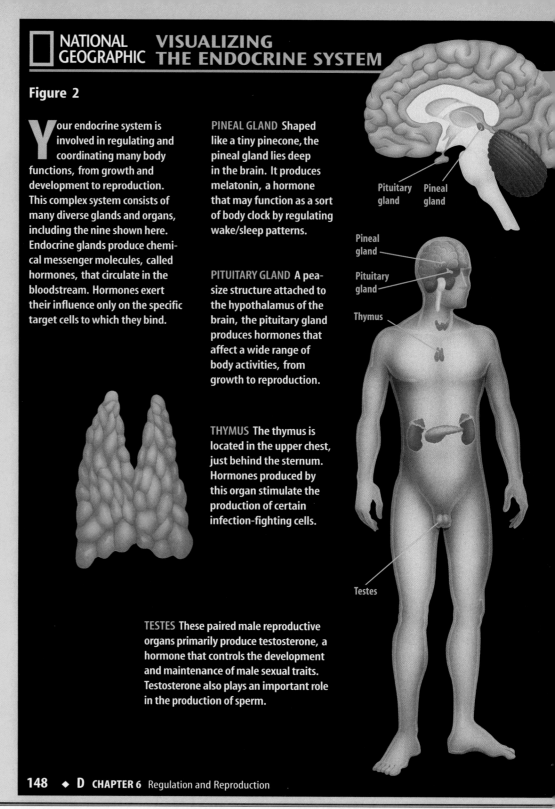

NATIONAL GEOGRAPHIC VISUALIZING THE ENDOCRINE SYSTEM

Figure 2

Your endocrine system is involved in regulating and coordinating many body functions, from growth and development to reproduction. This complex system consists of many diverse glands and organs, including the nine shown here. Endocrine glands produce chemical messenger molecules, called hormones, that circulate in the bloodstream. Hormones exert their influence only on the specific target cells to which they bind.

PINEAL GLAND Shaped like a tiny pinecone, the pineal gland lies deep in the brain. It produces melatonin, a hormone that may function as a sort of body clock by regulating wake/sleep patterns.

PITUITARY GLAND A pea-size structure attached to the hypothalamus of the brain, the pituitary gland produces hormones that affect a wide range of body activities, from growth to reproduction.

THYMUS The thymus is located in the upper chest, just behind the sternum. Hormones produced by this organ stimulate the production of certain infection-fighting cells.

TESTES These paired male reproductive organs primarily produce testosterone, a hormone that controls the development and maintenance of male sexual traits. Testosterone also plays an important role in the production of sperm.

Pituitary gland   Pineal gland

Pineal gland
Pituitary gland
Thymus
Testes

148 ◆ **D CHAPTER 6** Regulation and Reproduction

Differentiated Instruction

Challenge Have students research disorders of the endocrine system such as Graves' disease, Cushing's Syndrome, Addison's disease, diabetes, gigantism and acromegaly. Ask students to make a list of questions they would use to interview a person with one of these disorders. L3

Teacher FYI

SAD An overproduction of melatonin is hypothesized by scientists to be one cause of Seasonal Affective Disorder (SAD). SAD is a type of depression that some people suffer when there are fewer hours of daylight during winter months. The treatment of SAD includes exposing sufferers to artificial bright light for several hours at a time.

THYROID GLAND Located below the larynx, the bi-lobed thyroid gland is richly supplied with blood vessels. It produces hormones that regulate metabolic rate, control the uptake of calcium by bones, and promote normal nervous system development.

Thyroid (front)

PARATHYROID GLANDS Attached to the back surface of the thyroid are tiny parathyroids, which help regulate calcium levels in the body. Calcium is important for bone growth and maintenance, as well as for muscle contraction and nerve impulse transmission.

Parathyroid (back)

Thyroid and Parathyroid

Adrenal gland

Kidney

Pancreas

Ovaries

ADRENAL GLANDS On top of each of your kidneys is an adrenal gland. This complex endocrine gland produces a variety of hormones. Some play a critical role in helping your body adapt to physical and emotional stress. Others help stabilize blood sugar levels.

PANCREAS Scattered throughout the pancreas are millions of tiny clusters of endocrine tissue called the islets of Langerhans. Cells that make up the islets produce hormones that help control sugar levels in the bloodstream.

OVARIES Found deep in the pelvic cavity, ovaries produce female sex hormones known as estrogen and progesterone. These hormones regulate the female reproductive cycle and are responsible for producing and maintaining female sex characteristics.

SECTION 1 The Endocrine System **D** ◆ **149**

Visual Learning

Figure 2 Have students make a network tree concept map depicting the major endocrine glands in the human body and the function of each. L2 LS **Visual-Spatial** P

Quick Demo

Flight or Fight Hormone

Materials watch with second hand, loud bell

Estimated Time 10 minutes

Procedure Have one student count the number of pulse beats in one minute of another student volunteer. Then, have a third student not in view ring a loud bell. Have the first student immediately count the number of pulse beats in one minute of the other student. Ask students to describe what happened to the student's heart rate. The student's heart rate increased. When a person is startled, the hormone adrenaline is released into the bloodstream. It speeds up the heart to transport more oxygen to the muscles. L2

Curriculum Connection

Language Arts The word *adrenal* is derived from two Latin words: *ad-* meaning "to," and *renalis*, meaning "kidneys." How is this word related to the location of the adrenal glands? The adrenal glands are located on top of the kidneys.

Fun Fact

The pituitary gland produces TSH, a hormone that promotes the production of thyroxin by the thyroid gland. Thyroxin helps regulate growth and development in immature animals. It also speeds up metabolism in all animals.

Excessive Growth Hormones Infer the probable results of too much growth hormone in the blood of a young person. The person would grow at an accelerated rate and become abnormally tall. What if there were too little of the hormone produced? Shortness might result.

3 Assess

DAILY INTERVENTION

Check for Understanding

Visual-Spatial On simple diagrams of the human body, have students draw and label the glands of the endocrine system. L2

Reteach

Hormone Pathways Using a chart of the circulatory system, have students trace the pathway of a hormone to its target tissue. L2
LS **Kinesthetic**

Assessment

Content Make a table describing the characteristics and components of the endocrine system. Use **Performance Assessment in the Science Classroom,** p. 109.

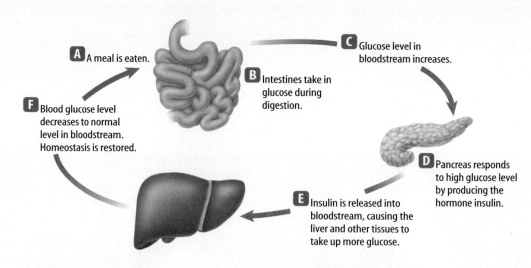

Figure 3 Many internal body conditions, such as hormone level, blood sugar level, and body temperature, are controlled by negative-feedback systems.

A A meal is eaten.

B Intestines take in glucose during digestion.

C Glucose level in bloodstream increases.

D Pancreas responds to high glucose level by producing the hormone insulin.

E Insulin is released into bloodstream, causing the liver and other tissues to take up more glucose.

F Blood glucose level decreases to normal level in bloodstream. Homeostasis is restored.

A Negative-Feedback System

To control the amount of hormones that are in your body, the endocrine system sends chemical messages back and forth within itself. This is called a negative-feedback system. It works much the way a thermostat works. When the temperature in a room drops below a set level, the thermostat signals the furnace to turn on. Once the furnace has raised the temperature in the room to the set level, the thermostat signals the furnace to shut off. It will continue to stay off until the thermostat signals that the temperature has dropped again. **Figure 3** shows how a negative-feedback system controls the level of glucose in your bloodstream.

section 1 review

Summary

Functions of the Endocrine System

- The nervous system and the endocrine system are the control systems of your body.
- The endocrine system uses hormones to deliver messages to the body.

Endocrine Glands

- Endocrine glands release hormones directly into the bloodstream.

A Negative-Feedback System

- The endocrine system uses a negative-feedback system to control the amount of hormones in your body.

Self Check

1. **Explain** the function of hormones.
2. **Choose** one endocrine gland. How does it work?
3. **Describe** a negative-feedback system.
4. **Think Critically** Glucose is required for cellular respiration, the process that releases energy within cells. How would a lack of insulin affect this process?

Applying Skills

5. **Predict** why the circulatory system is a good mechanism for delivering hormones throughout the body.
6. **Research** recent treatments for growth disorders involving the pituitary gland. Write a brief paragraph of your results in your Science Journal.

Science Online bookd.msscience.com/self_check_quiz

section 1 review

1. Hormones regulate certain cellular activities.
2. Pancreas—secretes insulin to regulate glucose levels; refer to **Figure 2** for other possible answers.
3. a system that uses blood hormone levels to signal when a gland should and should not secrete the hormone
4. Insulin causes tissues to take up more glucose, without which cells can't carry on respiration.
5. The circulatory system reaches every cell of the body.
6. Answers will vary. Possible topic: the use of hormone therapy to stimulate growth in young children.

The Reproductive System

Reproduction and the Endocrine System

Reproduction is the process that continues life on Earth. Most human body systems, such as the digestive system and the nervous system, are the same in males and females, but this is not true for the reproductive system. Males and females each have structures specialized for their roles in reproduction. Although structurally different, both the male and female reproductive systems are adapted to allow for a series of events that can lead to the birth of a baby.

Hormones are the key to how the human reproductive system functions, as shown in **Figure 4.** Sex hormones are necessary for the development of sexual characteristics, such as breast development in females and facial hair growth in males. Hormones from the pituitary gland also begin the production of eggs in females and sperm in males. Eggs and sperm transfer hereditary information from one generation to the next.

as you read

What You'll Learn
- **Identify** the function of the reproductive system.
- **Compare and contrast** the major structures of the male and female reproductive systems.
- **Sequence** the stages of the menstrual cycle.

Why It's Important

Human reproductive systems help ensure that human life continues on Earth.

Review Vocabulary
cilia: short, hairlike structures that extend from a cell

New Vocabulary
- testes
- sperm
- semen
- ovary
- ovulation
- uterus
- vagina
- menstrual cycle
- menstruation

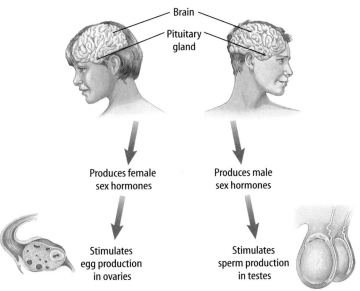

Brain
Pituitary gland

Produces female sex hormones
Produces male sex hormones

Stimulates egg production in ovaries
Stimulates sperm production in testes

Figure 4 The pituitary gland produces hormones that control the male and female reproductive systems.

Section 2 Resource Manager

Chapter FAST FILE Resources
- Transparency Activity, p. 43
- Directed Reading for Content Mastery, p. 18
- Enrichment, p. 29
- Reinforcement, p. 26
- MiniLAB, p. 3

Lab Worksheet, pp. 5–6

Activity

Sperm Shapes Have students draw a diagram of a sperm, like the one in **Figure 5**. Then ask them to draw a sperm with a very large, round head and a curly tail. Ask students to compare the two sperm and determine which one would be more likely to fertilize an egg. The sperm, like the one in **Figure 5,** would be more likely to fertilize an egg. The streamlined head reduces friction as it moves through liquids. The straight tail propels the sperm in a direction that can be against gravity. L2

Use an Analogy

Flagellate Protozoans The movement of sperm is not unlike the movement of flagellate protozoans. Wavelike movements of the tail propel the organism forward. ⬛ **Visual-Spatial**

Discussion

Functions of Semen What other functions does semen have in addition to carrying the sperm? Chemical substances in semen provide energy for sperm movement. Explain that because semen is slightly alkaline, it protects sperm from acidic conditions, such as those found in the female reproductive system.

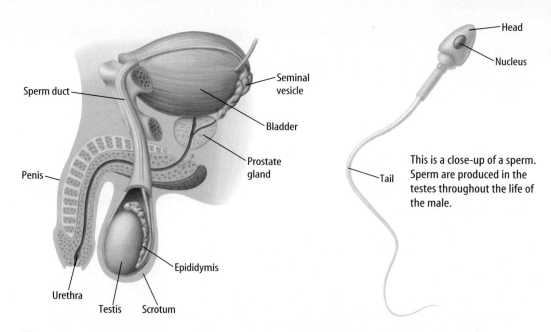

Figure 5 The structures of the male reproductive system are shown from the side of the body.

This is a close-up of a sperm. Sperm are produced in the testes throughout the life of the male.

The Male Reproductive System

The male reproductive system is made up of external and internal organs. The external organs of the male reproductive system are the penis and scrotum, shown in **Figure 5.** The scrotum contains two organs called testes (TES teez). As males mature sexually, the **testes** begin to produce testosterone, the male hormone, and **sperm,** which are male reproductive cells.

Sperm Each sperm cell has a head and tail. The head contains hereditary information, and the tail moves the sperm. Because the scrotum is located outside the body cavity, the testes, where sperm are produced, are kept at a lower temperature than the rest of the body. Sperm are produced in greater numbers at lower temperatures.

Many organs help in the production, transportation, and storage of sperm. After sperm are produced, they travel from the testes through sperm ducts that circle the bladder. Behind the bladder, a gland called the seminal vesicle provides sperm with a fluid. This fluid supplies the sperm with an energy source and helps them move. This mixture of sperm and fluid is called **semen** (SEE mun). Semen leaves the body through the urethra, which is the same tube that carries urine from the body. However, semen and urine never mix. A muscle at the back of the bladder contracts to prevent urine from entering the urethra as sperm leave the body.

152 ◆ **D CHAPTER 6** Regulation and Reproduction

Curriculum Connection

Language Arts Have students look up the words *sperm* and *ovary* and find out why the Latin roots are appropriate to their meanings. The Late Latin term *sperma* means seed; the Latin term *ovum* means egg. L1 ⬛ **Linguistic**

Differentiated Instruction

Learning Disabled Have students use tracing paper to trace the structures of the male and female reproductive systems shown in **Figures 5** and **6.** Ask them to label each structure and include the diagrams in their journals to use as study tools. L1

The Female Reproductive System

Unlike male reproductive organs, most of the reproductive organs of the female are inside the body. The **ovaries**—the female sex organs—are located in the lower part of the body cavity. Each of the two ovaries is about the size and shape of an almond. **Figure 6** shows the different organs of the female reproductive system.

The Egg When a female is born, she already has all of the cells in her ovaries that eventually will develop into eggs—the female reproductive cells. At puberty, eggs start to develop in her ovaries because of specific sex hormones.

About once a month, an egg is released from an ovary in a hormone-controlled process called **ovulation** (ahv yuh LAY shun). The two ovaries release eggs on alternating months. One month, an egg is released from an ovary. The next month, the other ovary releases an egg, and so on. After the egg is released, it enters the oviduct. If a sperm fertilizes the egg, it usually happens in an oviduct. Short, hairlike structures called cilia help sweep the egg through the oviduct toward the uterus (YEW tuh rus).

☑ Reading Check *When are eggs released by the ovaries?*

The **uterus** is a hollow, pear-shaped, muscular organ with thick walls in which a fertilized egg develops. The lower end of the uterus, the cervix, narrows and is connected to the outside of the body by a muscular tube called the **vagina** (vuh JI nuh). The vagina also is called the birth canal because during birth, a baby travels through this tube from the uterus to the outside of the mother's body.

Science Online

Topic: Ovarian Cysts
Visit bookd.msscience.com for Web links to information about ovarian cysts.

Activity Make a small pamphlet explaining what cysts are and how they can be treated.

Figure 6 The structures of the female reproductive system are internal.
Name *where eggs develop in the female reproductive system.*

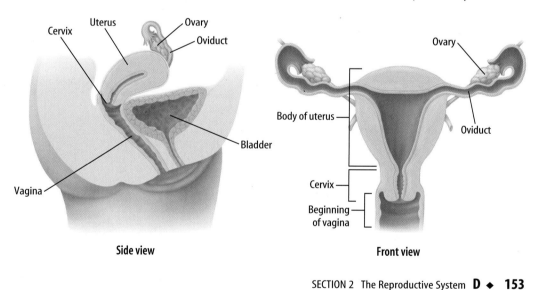

Side view

Front view

IDENTIFYING Misconceptions

Estrogen Ovaries produce the hormone estrogen, which controls the development of female secondary sex characteristics. Many people think males do not produce this hormone. However, small amounts of estrogen are produced by adrenal and certain testicular cells in males.

☑ Reading Check

Answer once a month

Visual Learning

Figure 6 Have students trace the movement of an egg after ovulation.

Caption Answer
Figure 6 in the ovaries

Teacher FYI

Abdominal Pregnancies Rarely, an egg from the ovary does not enter the opening of the oviduct but enters the abdominal cavity and becomes fertilized. Abdominal pregnancies rarely are carried to term. If so, the baby is delivered by a C-section. Usually, the fetus does not survive and must be surgically removed.

Science Journal

Conception Have students investigate and write a short paragraph about the chances of conception. Fertilization can occur only during a two- to three-day time period, when the cervical mucus forms small channels that allow sperm to enter the uterus. Once in the mucus, the sperm can live up to 48 hours. A sexually-active 30-year-old female has a 20% chance each month of conceiving. L2

LS Logical-Mathematical P

Use Science Words

Word Origin The Greek word for egg is *oion*. It is the root for many words related to eggs or the shape of an egg. Have students look up words with this root and explain their meanings. Possible answers: oocyte—an egg before maturation, oology—the study of bird eggs, oogenesis—the formation and maturation of an egg L2 [IS] **Linguistic**

Answer the monthly cycle of changes in the female reproductive system

Purpose Students observe and interpret data illustrating changes in hormone levels during the menstrual cycle. L2
[IS] **Logical-Mathematical**
Materials graph paper
Teaching Strategy Have students note the range of the data figures before constructing their graphs.
Analysis
1. day 13
2. ovulation

Assessment

Process Have students correlate the data in the MiniLAB chart with the events shown in **Figure 7.** Use **Performance Assessment in the Science Classroom,** p. 99.

Caption Answer

Figure 7 to support and nourish the developing embryo

Graphing Hormone Levels

Procedure
Make a line graph of this table.

Hormone Changes	
Day	**Level of Hormone**
1	12
5	14
9	15
13	70
17	13
21	12
25	8

Analysis
1. On what day is the highest level of hormone present?
2. What event takes place around the time of the highest hormone level?

The Menstrual Cycle

How is the female body prepared for having a baby? The **menstrual cycle** is the monthly cycle of changes in the female reproductive system. Before and after an egg is released from an ovary, the uterus undergoes changes. The menstrual cycle of a human female averages 28 days. However, the cycle can vary in some individuals from 20 to 40 days. Changes include the maturing of an egg, the production of female sex hormones, the preparation of the uterus to receive a fertilized egg, and menstrual flow.

Reading Check *What is the menstrual cycle?*

Endocrine Control Hormones control the entire menstrual cycle. The pituitary gland responds to chemical messages from the hypothalamus by releasing several hormones. These hormones start the development of eggs in the ovary. They also start the production of other hormones in the ovary, including estrogen (ES truh jun) and progesterone (proh JES tuh rohn). The interaction of all these hormones results in the physical processes of the menstrual cycle.

Phase One As shown in **Figure 7,** the first day of phase 1 starts when menstrual flow begins. Menstrual flow consists of blood and tissue cells released from the thickened lining of the uterus. This flow usually continues for four to six days and is called **menstruation** (men STRAY shun).

Figure 7 The three phases of the menstrual cycle make up the monthly changes in the female reproductive system.
Explain *why the uterine lining thickens.*

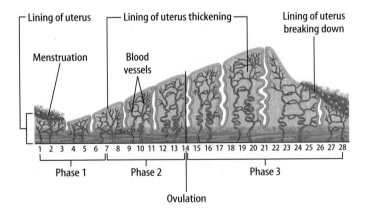

Differentiated Instruction

Challenge Some women going through menopause experience some of the same symptoms as women beginning their menstrual cycles. Have students research to find out why this happens. Both are experiencing changing levels of hormones. L3

Teacher FYI

Premenstrual Syndrome During the week before menstruation, a woman may experience premenstrual syndrome (PMS). Symptoms include depression, fatigue, headache, irritability, nervousness, and lack of concentration. Diet, exercise, and aspirin or other medicines are used to lessen the discomfort.

Phase Two Hormones cause the lining of the uterus to thicken in phase 2. Hormones also control the development of an egg in the ovary. Ovulation occurs about 14 days before menstruation begins. Once the egg is released, it must be fertilized within 24 h or it usually begins to break down. Because sperm can survive in a female's body for up to three days, fertilization can occur soon after ovulation.

Phase Three Hormones produced by the ovaries continue to cause an increase in the thickness of the uterine lining during phase 3. If a fertilized egg does arrive, the uterus is ready to support and nourish the developing embryo. If the egg is not fertilized, the lining of the uterus breaks down as the hormone levels decrease. Menstruation begins and the cycle repeats itself.

Menopause For most females, the first menstrual period happens between ages nine years and 13 years and continues until 45 years of age to 60 years of age. Then, a gradual reduction of menstruation takes place as hormone production by the ovaries begins to shut down. Menopause occurs when both ovulation and menstrual periods end. It can take several years for the completion of menopause. As **Figure 8** indicates, menopause does not inhibit a woman's ability to enjoy an active life.

Figure 8 This older woman enjoys exercising with her grand-daughter.

section 2 review

Summary

Reproduction and the Endocrine System
- Reproduction is the process that continues life.
- The human reproductive system needs hormones to function.

The Male Reproductive System
- Sperm are produced in the testes and leave the male through the penis.

The Female Reproductive System
- Eggs are produced in the ovaries and, if fertilized, can develop in the uterus.

The Menstrual Cycle
- A female's menstrual cycle occurs approximately every 28 days.
- If an egg is not fertilized, the lining of the uterus breaks down and is shed in a process called menstruation.

Self Check

1. **Identify** the major function of male and female reproductive systems in humans.
2. **Explain** the movement of sperm through the male reproductive system.
3. **Compare and contrast** the major organs and structures of the male and female reproductive systems.
4. **Sequence** the stages of the menstrual cycle in a human female using diagrams and captions.
5. **Think Critically** Adolescent females often require additional amounts of iron in their diet. Explain.

Applying Math

6. **Order of Operations** Usually, one egg is released each month during a female's reproductive years. If menstruation begins at 12 years of age and ends at 50 years of age, calculate the number of eggs her body can release during her reproductive years.

Quick Demo
Human Eggs
Materials paper, sharp-tipped pencil
Estimated Time 5 minutes
Procedure With the pencil, make a tiny dot on the paper. This dot is about 0.5 mm in diameter. The human egg is about 5 times smaller in size. After demonstrating this, have students do it so they can get an idea of the size of a human egg. [L1]

3 Assess

DAILY INTERVENTION

Check for Understanding
Visual-Spatial Have students write brief summaries of the three phases of the menstrual cycle. [L2]

Reteach
Egg Pathway Have students diagram the pathway an egg follows as it moves from the ovary to the uterus. [L1] [LS] **Visual-Spatial**

✔ Assessment

Performance Further assess students' abilities by having them sequence the thickness of the uterus during the menstrual cycle using **Figure 7**. Use **Performance Assessment in the Science Classroom,** p. 163.

section 2 review

1. to allow for a series of events that can lead to the birth of a baby
2. testes→tubes that encircle the bladder→seminal vesical→urethra
3. Sex cell production: female— ovaries within the body; male— testes in scrotum outside of body; movement of sex cells: female—

eggs released from ovary and swept into oviduct and uterus; male— sperm swim from testes through sperm duct and into the urethra.
4. Phase one: menstrual flow begins; phase two: wall of uterus thickens, ovulation occurs; phase three: wall of uterus continues to thicken; if a

fertilized egg arrives, it implants into the wall; if a fertilized egg does not arrive, the lining deteriorates.
5. The body may have a temporary iron deficiency resulting from loss of blood during menstruation.
6. 50 years — 12 years = 38 years; 38 years × 1 egg/month × 12 month/year = 456 eggs

Interpreting Diagrams

Starting in adolescence, hormones cause the development of eggs in the ovary and changes in the uterus. These changes prepare the uterus to accept a fertilized egg that can attach itself in the wall of the uterus. What happens to an unfertilized egg?

▶ Real-World Question

What changes occur to the uterus during a female's monthly menstrual cycle?

Goals
- **Observe** the stages of the menstrual cycle in the diagram.
- **Relate** the process of ovulation to the cycle.

Materials

paper   pencil

▶ Procedure

1. The diagrams below illustrate the menstrual cycle.
2. Copy and complete the data table using information in this chapter and diagrams below.
3. On approximately what day in a 28-day cycle is the egg released from the ovary?

Menstruation Cycle		
Days	**Condition of Uterus**	**What Happens**
1–6	breakdown of lining	menstruation
7–12	lining begins to thicken	egg matures in ovary
13–14	lining is thicker	ovulation
15–18	lining thickens	egg moves to uterus

▶ Conclude and Apply

1. **Infer** how many days the average menstrual cycle lasts.
2. **State** on what days the lining of the uterus builds up.
3. **Infer** why this process is called a cycle.
4. **Calculate** how many days before menstruation ovulation usually occurs.

Communicating Your Data

Compare your data table with those of other students in your class. **For more help, refer to the** Science Skill Handbook.

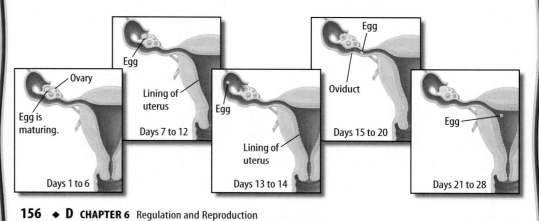

Days 1 to 6 — Ovary — Egg is maturing.
Days 7 to 12 — Egg — Lining of uterus
Days 13 to 14 — Egg — Lining of uterus
Days 15 to 20 — Egg — Oviduct
Days 21 to 28 — Egg

156 ◆ **D CHAPTER 6** Regulation and Reproduction

✓ Assessment

Communicating Your Data

Human Life Stages

The Function of the Reproductive System

Before the invention of powerful microscopes, some people imagined an egg or a sperm to be a tiny person that grew inside a female. In the latter part of the 1700s, experiments using amphibians showed that contact between an egg and sperm is necessary for the development of life. With the development of the cell theory in the 1800s, scientists recognized that a human develops from an egg that has been fertilized by a sperm. The uniting of a sperm and an egg is known as fertilization. Fertilization, as shown in **Figure 9,** usually takes place in the oviduct.

Fertilization

INTEGRATE Chemistry

Although 200 million to 300 million sperm can be deposited in the vagina, only several thousand reach an egg in the oviduct. As they enter the female, the sperm come into contact with chemical secretions in the vagina. It appears that this contact causes a change in the membrane of the sperm. The sperm then become capable of fertilizing the egg. The one sperm that makes successful contact with the egg releases an enzyme from the saclike structure on its head. Enzymes help speed up chemical reactions that have a direct effect on the protective membranes on the egg's surface. The structure of the egg's membrane is disrupted, and the sperm head can enter the egg.

Zygote Formation Once a sperm has entered the egg, changes in the electric charge of the egg's membrane prevent other sperm from entering the egg. At this point, the nucleus of the successful sperm joins with the nucleus of the egg. This joining of nuclei creates a fertilized cell called the zygote. It begins to undergo many cell divisions.

as you read

What **You'll Learn**

- **Describe** the fertilization of a human egg.
- **List** the major events in the development of an embryo and fetus.
- **Describe** the developmental stages of infancy, childhood, adolescence, and adulthood.

Why **It's Important**

Fertilization begins the entire process of human growth and development.

Review Vocabulary
nutrient: substance in food that provides energy and materials for cell development, growth, and repair

New Vocabulary
- pregnancy
- embryo
- amniotic sac
- fetus
- fetal stress

Figure 9 After the sperm releases enzymes that disrupt the egg's membrane, it penetrates the egg.

Color-enhanced SEM Magnification: 340×

Bellringer

Section Focus Transparencies also are available on the Interactive Chalkboard CD-ROM.
[L2] [ELL]

Section Focus Transparency — Keep on Running

Growing older does not mean an end to fitness and competition. The National Senior Games will attract over 10,000 athletes, aged 50 and older. For young and old alike, exercise is essential for good health.

1. How can exercise help offset some of the effects of aging?
2. Other than exercise, what choices can people make that might affect the aging process?

Tie to Prior Knowledge

Life Stages Display photographs of people in different life stages, e.g., an infant, a small child, an adolescent, a young adult, and an older adult. Explain that these represent life stages and ask how many students can identify. Ask what stage they are in.

Section 3 Resource Manager

Chapter *FAST FILE* Resources
Transparency Activity, p. 44
Directed Reading for Content Mastery, pp. 19, 20
MiniLAB, p. 4
Enrichment, p. 30
Reinforcement, p. 27

Lab Activity, pp. 13–14
Lab Worksheet, pp. 7–8
Home and Community Involvement, p. 43
Life Science Critical Thinking/Problem Solving, p. 19
Reading and Writing Skill Activities, p. 39
Lab Management and Safety, p. 70

Use Science Words

Word Usage Have students compare the biological use of the word *fertilization* to the agronomic use of the word. Biologists use fertilization to refer to the process by which two sex cells join to produce offspring. Agronomists use fertilization to refer to the application of manure or chemicals to make soil more fertile. L2 **IS** **Linguistic**

Visual Learning

Figure 10 What are the differences between the development of fraternal and identical twins? Fraternal twins develop from two separate eggs that have been fertilized by two different sperm. Identical twins result when one egg is fertilized by one sperm and the resulting zygote splits.

Make a Model

Zygote Growth Have students use polystyrene foam balls to construct four- and eight-cell models to illustrate the earliest stages of zygote growth. L2 **IS** **Kinesthetic** P

Midwives education: nursing degree or a science or health background; skills: monitor the baby and mother during pregnancy and labor, guide the birthing process, examine and care for newborns, maintain health records and write reports

Research the requirements needed to become a midwife in your state.

Figure 10 The development of fraternal and identical twins is different.

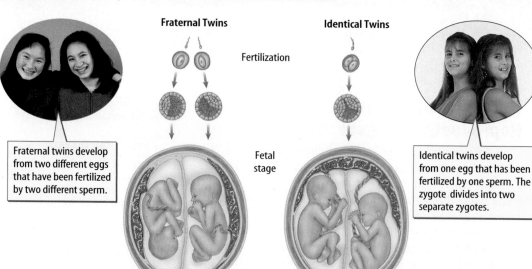

Fraternal Twins　　　**Identical Twins**

Fertilization

Fetal stage

Fraternal twins develop from two different eggs that have been fertilized by two different sperm.

Identical twins develop from one egg that has been fertilized by one sperm. The zygote divides into two separate zygotes.

Midwives Some women choose to deliver their babies at home rather than at a hospital. An at-home birth can be attended by a certified nurse-midwife. Research to find the educational and skill requirements of a nurse-midwife.

Multiple Births

Sometimes two eggs leave the ovary at the same time. If both eggs are fertilized and both develop, fraternal twins are born. Fraternal twins, as shown in **Figure 10,** can be two girls, two boys, or a boy and a girl. Because fraternal twins come from two eggs, they only resemble each other.

Because identical twin zygotes develop from the same egg and sperm, as explained in **Figure 10,** they have the same hereditary information. These identical zygotes develop into identical twins, which are either two girls or two boys. Multiple births also can occur when three or more eggs are produced at one time or when the zygote separates into three or more parts.

Development Before Birth

After fertilization, the zygote moves along the oviduct to the uterus. During this time, the zygote is dividing and forming into a ball of cells. After about seven days, the zygote attaches to the wall of the uterus, which has been thickening in preparation to receive a zygote, as shown in **Figure 11.** If attached to the wall of the uterus, the zygote will develop into a baby in about nine months. This period of development from fertilized egg to birth is known as **pregnancy.**

Curriculum Connection

Health Have students research ectopic pregnancies. How frequently do they occur? 1 in every 250–300 pregnancies How does the female know there is a problem? She experiences pain and bleeding. What is the treatment? Ectopic pregnancies often end in a miscarriage; if not miscarried, surgical removal of the fetus is sometimes necessary; abdominal pregnancies can be carried to term and the baby delivered by C-section. L2

Active Reading

Speculation About Effects/Prediction Journal This strategy allows students to examine events and speculate about their possible long-term effects. Have students divide their papers in half. On the left side record "What happened." On the right side, write "What might/should happen as a result of this." Have students use this strategy to write about an aspect of human life stages.

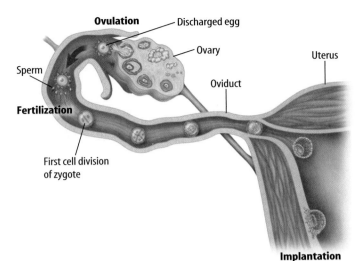

Ovulation · Discharged egg

Sperm

Ovary

Fertilization

Oviduct

Uterus

First cell division of zygote

Implantation

Figure 11 After a few days of rapid cell division, the zygote, now a ball of cells, reaches the lining of the uterus, where it attaches itself to the lining for development.

Understanding Fertilization Students may think that fertilization and embryonic development are mysterious processes that are not understandable. Refer to page F at the beginning of this chapter for teaching strategies that address this misconception.

The Embryo After the zygote attaches to the wall of the uterus, it is known as an **embryo,** illustrated in **Figure 12.** It receives nutrients from fluids in the uterus until the placenta (plu SEN tuh) develops from tissues of the uterus and the embryo. An umbilical cord develops that connects the embryo to the placenta. In the placenta, materials diffuse between the mother's blood and the embryo's blood, but their bloods do not mix. Blood vessels in the umbilical cord carry nutrients and oxygen from the mother's blood through the placenta to the embryo. Other substances in the mother's blood can move into the embryo, including drugs, toxins, and disease organisms. Wastes from the embryo are carried in other blood vessels in the umbilical cord through the placenta to the mother's blood.

✓ **Reading Check** *Why must a pregnant woman avoid alcohol, tobacco, and harmful drugs?*

Pregnancy in humans lasts about 38 to 39 weeks. During the third week, a thin membrane called the **amniotic** (am nee AH tihk) **sac** begins to form around the embryo. The amniotic sac is filled with a clear liquid called amniotic fluid, which acts as a cushion for the embryo and stores nutrients and wastes.

During the first two months of development, the embryo's major organs form and the heart structure begins to beat. At five weeks, the embryo has a head with eyes, nose, and mouth features. During the sixth and seventh weeks, fingers and toes develop.

✓ **Reading Check**

Answer Any substances taken in by the mother and carried in her blood can pass to the embryo through the umbilical cord and cause the embryo damage.

Figure 12 By two months, the developing embryo is about 2.5 cm long and is beginning to develop recognizable features.

SECTION 3 Human Life Stages **D ◆ 159**

Inquiry Lab

Fetal Development

Purpose to familiarize students with the stages of development during pregnancy

Possible Materials library or Internet sources

Estimated Time 50 minutes

Teaching Strategies

• Divide students into three groups and have each group study a trimester of pregnancy.

• Students can describe body features and organs that have formed, length and weight of the baby, and which senses have developed.

• Students could also describe developmental milestones reached during the trimester. L2 PBL

• Students could also research the effects of alcohol, drugs, and smoking on the fetus. Have them make posters to share with the health class about these dangers.

For additional inquiry activities, see *Science Inquiry Labs.*

Differentiated Instruction

Challenge Have students research the unusual breeding processes of such animals as the sea horse and midwife toad. In both, the fertilized eggs are carried by the male until the young are ready to be born. L3

Mini LAB

Purpose Students observe data on the growth rate of a fetus.

L2 **IS** **Logical-Mathematical**

Materials graph paper

Teaching Strategy Have students note the range of the data before constructing their graphs.

Analysis

1. during the ninth month
2. about 5.7 cm per month

Assessment

Performance To further assess students' understanding of fetus size, have them find and measure common household items that correspond to the various fetus sizes. Set up a display of these items. Use **Performance Assessment in the Science Classroom**, p. 97.

Activity

Fetal Cutouts Have students prepare a series of actual-size cutouts of the fetus from three months to birth to have a visual demonstration of its size while developing.

L2 **ELL** **IS** **Visual-Spatial**

Caption Answer

Figure 13 fetus is 30 cm to 38 cm in length and looks less wrinkled because fatty tissue has built up under the skin

Figure 13 A fetus at about 16 weeks is approximately 15 cm long and weighs 140 g. **Describe** *the changes that take place in a fetus by the end of the seventh month.*

Mini LAB

Interpreting Fetal Development

Procedure
Make a bar graph of the following data.

Fetal Development	
End of Month	Length (cm)
3	8
4	15
5	25
6	30
7	35
8	40
9	51

Analysis

1. During which month does the greatest increase in length occur?
2. On average, how many centimeters does the baby grow per month?

The Fetus After the first two months of pregnancy, the developing embryo is called a **fetus,** shown in **Figure 13.** At this time, body organs are present. Around the third month, the fetus is 8 cm to 9 cm long. The mother may feel the fetus move. The fetus can even suck its thumb. By the fourth month, an ultrasound test can determine the sex of the fetus. The fetus is 30 cm to 38 cm in length by the end of the seventh month of pregnancy. Fatty tissue builds up under the skin, and the fetus looks less wrinkled. By the ninth month, the fetus usually has shifted to a head-down position within the uterus, a position beneficial for delivery. The head usually is in contact with the opening of the uterus to the vagina. The fetus is about 50 cm in length and weighs from 2.5 kg to 3.5 kg.

The Birthing Process

The process of childbirth, as shown in **Figure 14,** begins with labor, the muscular contractions of the uterus. As the contractions increase in strength and number, the amniotic sac usually breaks and releases its fluid. Over a period of hours, the contractions cause the opening of the uterus to widen. More powerful and more frequent contractions push the baby out through the vagina into its new environment.

Delivery Often a mother is given assistance by a doctor during the delivery of the baby. As the baby emerges from the birth canal, a check is made to determine if the umbilical cord is wrapped around the baby's neck or any body part. When the head is free, any fluid in the baby's nose and mouth is removed by suction. After the head and shoulders appear, contractions force the baby out completely. Up to an hour after delivery, contractions occur that push the placenta out of the mother's body.

LAB DEMONSTRATION

Purpose to observe the proportions of girls and boys born in the population

Materials pennies

Preparation Collect small foam trays to deaden the sound and catch the tossed pennies.

Procedure Have students toss a penny one hundred times and record the order and number of times it lands on heads or tails.

Expected Outcome About a 50:50 ratio; there may be sequences of one side landing faceup repeatedly. Relate this to families of several boys or several girls.

Assessment

Infer the chances of a family with five girls or a family with five boys having a girl if there were a sixth child born. The chance of a girl being born into either family as the next child is 50:50.

Cesarean Section Sometimes a baby must be delivered before labor begins or before it is completed. At other times, a baby cannot be delivered through the birth canal because the mother's pelvis might be too small or the baby might be in the wrong birthing position. In cases like these, surgery called a cesarean (suh SEER ee uhn) section is performed. An incision is made through the mother's abdominal wall, then through the wall of the uterus. The baby is delivered through this opening.

✓ **Reading Check** *What is a cesarean section?*

After Birth When the baby is born, it is attached to the umbilical cord. The person assisting with the birth clamps the cord in two places and cuts it between the clamps. The baby does not feel any pain from this procedure. The baby might cry, which is the result of air being forced into its lungs. The scar that forms where the cord was attached is called the navel.

Science Online

Topic: Cesarean Sections
Visit bookd.msscience.com for Web links to information about cesarean section delivery.

Activity Make a chart listing the advantages and disadvantages of a cesarean section delivery.

Figure 14 Childbirth begins with labor. The opening to the uterus widens, and the baby passes through.

The fetus moves into the opening of the birth canal, and the uterus begins to widen.

The base of the uterus is completely dilated.

The fetus is pushed out through the birth canal.

✓ **Reading Check**

Answer a surgical procedure in which an incision in the mother's abdomen and uterus is made and the baby removed

Use Science Words

Word Meaning Have students find out why the surgical removal of a baby from the mother is called a "cesarean section." It was named after Julius Caesar, who was supposedly delivered in this manner. L2 **LS**
Linguistic

Visual Learning

Figure 14 Have students list the stages involved in childbirth. Fetus moves to opening of birth canal, base of uterus dilates, muscle contractions push fetus through the birth canal. L2 **LS** **Visual-Spatial**

Virtual Labs

Stages of Development
What are the stages of development before birth?

Curriculum Connection

Health Arrange a visit to an X-ray lab to view X rays of bones of infants or young children and compare them with X rays of adults to show the differences in cartilage and bone. If a visit is impractical, arrange to view X-ray photos in class. L2 **LS** **Visual-Spatial**

Stages After Birth

Defined stages of development occur after birth, based on the major developments that take place during those specific years. Infancy lasts from birth to around 18 months of age. Childhood extends from the end of infancy to sexual maturity, or puberty. The years of adolescence vary, but they usually are considered to be the teen years. Adulthood covers the years of age from the early 20s until life ends, with older adulthood considered to be over 60. The age spans of these different stages are not set, and scientists differ in their opinions regarding them.

Infancy What type of environment must the infant adjust to after birth? The experiences the fetus goes through during birth cause **fetal stress.** The fetus has emerged from an environment that was dark, watery, a constant temperature, and nearly soundless. In addition, the fetus might have been forced through the constricted birth canal. However, in a short period of time, the infant's body becomes adapted to its new world.

The first four weeks after birth are known as the neonatal (nee oh NAY tul) period. The term *neonatal* means "newborn." During this time, the baby's body begins to function normally. Unlike the newborn of some other animals, human babies, such as the one shown in **Figure 15,** depend on other humans for their survival. In contrast, many other animals, such as the young horse also shown in **Figure 15,** begin walking a few hours after they are born.

Figure 15 Human babies are more dependent upon their caregivers than many other mammals are.

Infants and toddlers are completely dependent upon caregivers for all their needs.

Other young mammals are more self-sufficient. This colt is able to stand within an hour after birth.

Differentiated Instruction

Behaviorally Disordered Have students bring photos of themselves at various stages and describe favorite activities they remember from these stages. L1

Science Journal

Immunizations Babies and young children need certain vaccines to prevent disease. Have students find out what vaccinations are recommended between birth and age 6. Between birth and 6 yrs. old, the following vaccines are recommended: Polio; Hepatitis B; Diphtheria, Tetanus, Pertussis; Varicella or Chicken Pox; Haemophilus Influenza B; Measles, Mumps, Rubella; Pneumococcal. L2

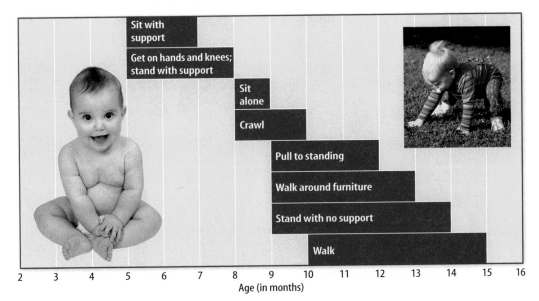

Sit with support

Get on hands and knees; stand with support

Sit alone

Crawl

Pull to standing

Walk around furniture

Stand with no support

Walk

Age (in months)
2 3 4 5 6 7 8 9 10 11 12 13 14 15 16

During these first 18 months, infants show increased physical coordination, mental development, and rapid growth. Many infants will triple their weight in the first year. **Figure 16** shows the extremely rapid development of the nervous and muscular systems during this stage, which enables infants to start interacting with the world around them.

Figure 16 Infants show rapid development in their nervous and muscular systems through 18 months of age.

Childhood After infancy is childhood, which lasts until about puberty, or sexual maturity. Sexual maturity occurs around 12 years of age. Overall, growth during early childhood is rather rapid, although the physical growth rate for height and weight is not as rapid as it is in infancy. Between two and three years of age, the child learns to control his or her bladder and bowels. At age two to three, most children can speak in simple sentences. Around age four, the child is able to get dressed and undressed with some help. By age five, many children can read a limited number of words. By age six, children usually have lost their chubby baby appearance, as seen in **Figure 17.** However, muscular coordination and mental abilities continue to develop. Throughout this stage, children develop their abilities to speak, read, write, and reason. These ages of development are only guidelines because each child develops at a different rate.

Figure 17 Children, like these kindergartners, grow and develop at different rates.

SECTION 3 Human Life Stages **D** ◆ **163**

Figure 18 The proportions of body parts change over time as the body develops.
Describe how the head changes proportion.

Adolescent Growth During adolescence, body parts do not all grow at the same rate. Legs grow longer before the upper body lengthens. This changes the body's center of gravity, the point at which the body maintains its balance. This is one cause of teenager clumsiness. In your Science Journal, write a paragraph about how this might affect playing sports.

Adolescence

Adolescence Adolescence usually begins around age 12 or 13. A part of adolescence is puberty—the time of development when a person becomes physically able to reproduce. For girls, puberty occurs between ages nine and 13. For boys, puberty occurs between ages 13 and 16. During puberty, hormones produced by the pituitary gland cause changes in the body. These hormones produce reproductive cells and sex hormones. Secondary sex characteristics also develop. In females, the breasts develop, pubic and underarm hair appears, and fatty tissue is added to the buttocks and thighs. In males, the hormones cause a deepened voice, an increase in muscle size, and the growth of facial, pubic, and underarm hair.

Adolescence usually is when the final growth spurt occurs. Because the time when hormones begin working varies among individuals and between males and females, growth rates differ. Girls often begin their final growth phase at about age 11 and end around age 16. Boys usually start their growth spurt at age 13 and end around 18 years of age.

Adulthood The final stage of development, adulthood, begins with the end of adolescence and continues through old age. This is when the growth of the muscular and skeletal system stops. **Figure 18** shows how body proportions change as you age.

People from age 45 to age 60 are sometimes considered middle-aged adults. During these years, physical strength begins to decline. Blood circulation and respiration become less efficient. Bones become more brittle, and the skin becomes wrinkled.

Cultural Diversity

Rites of Passage Have students research and write a report on ceremonies in other societies, past or present, that mark the transition of young people to adults. These ceremonies are often referred to as "rites of passage." L3 IS **Linguistic**

Older Adulthood People over the age of 60 may experience an overall decline in their physical body systems. The cells that make up these systems no longer function as well as they did at a younger age. Connective tissues lose their elasticity, causing muscles and joints to be less flexible. Bones become thinner and more brittle. Hearing and vision are less sensitive. The lungs and heart work less efficiently. However, exercise and eating well over a lifetime can help extend the health of one's body systems. Many healthy older adults enjoy full lives and embrace challenges, as shown in **Figure 19.**

Figure 19 Astronaut and Senator John Glenn traveled into space twice. In 1962, at age 40, he was the first U.S. citizen to orbit Earth. He was part of the space shuttle crew in 1998 at age 77. Senator Glenn has helped change people's views of what many older adults are capable of doing.

 What physical changes occur during late adulthood?

Human Life Spans Seventy-seven years is the average life span—from birth to death—of humans in the United States, although an increasing number of people live much longer. However, body systems break down with age, resulting in eventual death. Death can occur earlier than old age for many reasons, including diseases, accidents, and bad health choices.

section 3 review

Summary

Fertilization
- Fertilization is the uniting of a sperm and an egg.

Development Before Birth
- Pregnancy begins when an egg is fertilized and lasts until birth.

The Birthing Process
- Birth begins with labor. Contractions force the baby out of the mother's body.

Stages After Birth
- Infancy (birth to 18 months) and childhood (until age 12) are periods of physical and mental growth.
- A person becomes physically able to reproduce during adolescence. Adulthood is the final stage of development.

Self Check

1. **Describe** what happens when an egg is fertilized in a female.
2. **Explain** what happens to an embryo during the first two months of pregnancy.
3. **Describe** the major events that occur during childbirth.
4. **Name** the stage of development that you are in. What physical changes have occurred or will occur during this stage of human development?
5. **Think Critically** Why is it hard to compare the growth and development of different adolescents?

Applying Skills

6. **Use a Spreadsheet** Using your text and other resources, make a spreadsheet for the stages of human development from a zygote to a fetus. Title one column *Zygote,* another *Embryo,* and a third *Fetus.* Complete the spreadsheet.

Reading Check

Answer Connective tissue loses elasticity, bones become brittle, hearing and vision are less sensitive, and the lungs and heart work less efficiently.

3 Assess

DAILY INTERVENTION

Check for Understanding
Logical-Mathematical Have students graph the length of time a developing human is termed a *zygote,* an *embryo,* and a *fetus.*

Reteach
Life Stages Divide the class into groups and have each group write descriptions of a particular life stage—one per index card. Mix up the cards, divide the class into teams, and read the descriptions. Students take turns stating the life stage. The team with the greatest number of correct answers wins. L2 ELL
Visual-Spatial

Assessment

Performance To further assess students' understanding of neonatal development, have them construct a time line to correspond with the stages of neonatal development. Use **Performance Assessment in the Science Classroom,** p. 163.

section 3 review

1. sperm and egg nuclei combine, producing a zygote; egg membrane changes; cell division begins
2. Amniotic sac and placenta develop, major organs form, and the heart structure begins to beat.
3. Events include contraction, rupture of the amniotic sac, and widening

of the uterus's opening to allow the baby to pass through the cervix and the birth canal.
4. Adolescence; sex hormones are produced, secondary sex characteristics develop, last growth spurt occurs.
5. Each person has his or her own rate of development.

6. Zygote undergoes cell divisions, forms a ball of cells, and attaches to the uterine wall; see information in "Development Before Birth".

● Real-World Question

Purpose Students measure the body proportions of adolescents and infer how body proportions differ between males and females.

[L2] [IS] **Logical-Mathematical**

Process Skills calculate, compare, graph, infer

Time Required 40 minutes

● Procedure

Alternate Materials Students may use metersticks instead of a tape measure. Masking tape can be used to mark heights on the wall instead of pencil marks.

Teaching Strategy Encourage students to measure each dimension twice to improve accuracy.

Goals
- **Measure** specific body proportions of adolescents.
- **Infer** how body proportions differ between adolescent males and females.

Materials
tape measure
erasable pencil
graph paper

Changing Body Proportions

● Real-World Question

The ancient Greeks believed that the perfect body was completely balanced. Arms and legs should not be too long or short. A person's head should not be too large or small. The extra-large muscles of a body builder would have been ugly to the Greeks. How do you think they viewed the bodies of infants and children? Infants and young children have much different body proportions than adults, and teenagers often go through growth spurts that quickly change their body proportions. How do the body proportions differ between adolescent males and females?

● Procedure

1. Copy the data table in your Science Journal and record the gender of each person that you measure.

2. Measure each person's head circumference by starting in the middle of the forehead and wrapping the tape measure once around the head. Record these measurements.

Alternative Inquiry Lab

Measuring Body Changes Students can observe many people of different ages to decide which body parts they will choose to measure. Encourage them to observe a broad age range of people from infants to the elderly. From their observations, students can design an experiment to test how different body proportions change over the life spans of humans.

Students can create a data table for their measurements, graphing their data using line graphs or bar graphs. Encourage students to generate charts and graphs electronically. Encourage students to explore and test other body changes such as weight.

3. Measure each person's arm length from the top of the shoulder to the tip of the middle finger while the arm is held straight out to the side of the body. Record these measurements.

4. Ask each person to remove his or her shoes and stand next to a wall. Mark their height with an erasable pencil and measure their height from the floor to the mark. Record these measurements in the data table.

5. **Combine** your data with that of your classmates. Find the averages of head circumference, arm length, and height. Then, find these averages for males and females.

6. Make a bar graph of your calculations in step 5. Plot the measurements on the *y*-axis and plot all of the averages along the *x*-axis.

7. **Calculate** the proportion of average head circumference to average height for everyone in your class by dividing the average head circumference by the average height. Repeat this calculation for males and females.

8. **Calculate** the proportion of average arm length to average height for everyone in your class by dividing the average arm length by the average height. Repeat this calculation for males and females.

Age and Body Measurements

Gender of Person	Head Circumference (cm)	Arm Length (cm)	Height (cm)
		Answers will vary.	

Analyze Your Data

Analyze whether adolescent males or females have larger head circumferences or longer arms. Which group has the larger proportion of head circumference or arm length to height?

Conclude and Apply

Explain if this lab supports the information in this chapter about the differences between growth rates of adolescent males and females.

Communicating
Your Data

Construct data tables on poster board showing your results and those of your classmates. Discuss with your classmates why these results might be different.

Analyze Your Data

Expected Outcome Because adolescent girls generally undergo growth sooner than adolescent males, their body parts will be in different proportions than those of adolescent males.

Answers to Questions Answers will vary depending on students' measurements.

Error Analysis Form students into groups of four or five and have each student compare his or her data with that of other group members. If data disagree, have each group list reasons for discrepancies.

Conclude and Apply

Answers will vary but data should support chapter information about differences in growth rates between adolescent males and females.

✔ Assessment

Portfolio Ask students to draw what they envision as the Greek ideal of a perfectly proportioned body.

Communicating
Your Data

Encourage students to use a spreadsheet program to construct their data tables.

Content Background

Mammals can be divided into three groups based on their development. Humans are placentals: a mammal whose young develop in the female parent's uterus. The offspring of placental mammals are usually comparatively well developed. Marsupials, like the kangaroo shown in this feature, give birth to less-developed young, which usually develop in a pouch, or attached to the mother's body. Monotremes are mammals that lay eggs.

Discussion

Kangaroo Babies Why might a baby kangaroo need to spend such a long period of time in its mother's pouch after it is born? Possible answer: Kangaroo babies are not developed enough to survive outside of the pouch when they are born, they need a period of protected growth and development.

Activity

Animal Independence Assign small groups of students an animal to research. Have the students find the age at which the young become independent from their parents. Have the students compare their findings on a bar graph.

Applying Math

elephant, about 5%

Find Out About It

Students can use reference material to explore the life spans of different animals. Explain that the life span of humans varies greatly between countries, so the statistic that different students use for this number may vary.

SCIENCE Stats

Facts About Infants

Did you know...

...Humans and chimpanzees share about 99 percent of their genes. Although humans look different than chimps, reproduction is similar and gestation is the same—about nine months. Youngsters of both species lose their baby teeth at about six years of age.

Mammal Facts

Mammal	Average Gestation	Average Birth Weight	Average Adult Weight	Average Life Span (years)
African elephant	22 months	136 kg	4,989.5 kg	35
Blue whale	12 months	1,800 kg	135,000 kg	60
Human	9 months	3.3 kg	59–76 kg	77*
Brown bear	7 months	0.23–0.5 kg	350 kg	22.5
Cat	2 months	99 g	2.7–7 kg	13.5
Kangaroo	1 month	0.75–1.0 g	45 kg	5
Golden hamster	2.5 weeks	0.3 g	112 g	2

*In the United States

Applying Math Assume that a female of each mammal listed in the table above is pregnant once during her life. Which mammal is pregnant for the greatest proportion of her life?

...Of about 4,000 species of mammals, only three lay eggs: the platypus, the short-beaked echidna (ih KIHD nuh), and the long-beaked echidna.

Echidna

Find Out About It

Visit bookd.msscience.com/science_stats to research which species of vertebrate animals has the longest life span and which has the shortest. Present your findings in a table that also shows the life span of humans.

Visual Learning

Mammal Facts Ask students to compare the birth weights of humans and whales as a percent of adult weight. They will find that whales are born at about 1.5% of the weight they will be as adults, while humans are born at 4.5% to 5.5% of their adult weight. Proportionately, newborn humans are larger than newborn whales. Have students determine which animals listed in the chart are born at the smallest (brown bear) and the largest (human) proportion of their adult weight.

Reviewing Main Ideas

Section 1 — The Endocrine System

1. Endocrine glands secrete hormones directly into the bloodstream. They affect specific tissues in the body.

2. A change in the body causes an endocrine gland to function. Hormone production slows or stops when homeostasis is reached.

Section 2 — The Reproductive System

1. Reproductive systems allow new organisms to be formed.

2. The testes produce sperm, which leave the male body through the penis.

3. The female ovaries produce eggs. If fertilized, an egg develops into a fetus within the uterus.

4. An unfertilized egg and the built-up lining of the uterus are shed in menstruation.

Section 3 — Human Life Stages

1. After fertilization, the zygote becomes an embryo, then a fetus. Twins occur when two eggs are fertilized or when a zygote divides after fertilization.

2. Birth begins with labor. The amniotic sac breaks. Then, usually after several hours, contractions force the baby out of the mother's body.

3. Infancy, from birth to 18 months of age, is a period of rapid growth of mental and physical skills. Childhood lasts until age 12 and involves further physical and mental development.

4. Adolescence is when a person becomes physically able to reproduce. In adulthood, physical development is complete and body systems become less efficient. Death occurs at the end of life.

Visualizing Main Ideas

Copy and complete the following table on life stages.

Human Development		
Stages of Life	Age Range	Physical Development
Infant	birth–18 months	sits, stands, words spoken
Childhood	18 months–12 years	walks, speaks, writes, reads
Adolescent	12–18 years	physically able to reproduce, sexual characteristics develop, final growth spurt
Adulthood	18 years–death	end of muscular and skeletal growth

Reviewing Main Ideas

Summary statements can be used by students to review the major concepts of the chapter.

Visualizing Main Ideas

See student page.

Science Online

Visit bookd.msscience.com
/self_check_quiz
/interactive_tutor
/vocabulary_puzzlemaker
/chapter_review
/standardized_test

Assessment Transparency

For additional assessment questions, use the *Assessment Transparency* located in the transparency book.

Assessment

Assessment Transparency — Regulation and Reproduction

Directions: Carefully review the table and answer the following questions.

Population by Country (in millions)				
Country	1970	1980	1990	2000
Japan	104	117	124	127
USA	205	223	250	281
India	555	690	851	1,014
Pakistan	66	85	114	142
Indonesia	94	155	189	225
Russia	130	148	148	146

1. According to this information, which country had the greatest increase in population between the years 1970 and 2000?
   A Russia
   B United States
   C India
   D Japan

2. Between the years 1990 and 2000, which country had a negative rate of population growth?
   F Japan
   G Russia
   H Indonesia
   J India

3. According to the table, the country that had a total population greater than Pakistan in 1970 but less than Pakistan in the year 2000 is ___.
   A India
   B Japan
   C United States
   D Russia

Regulation and Reproduction

Identifying Misconceptions

Assess

Use this assessment as follow-up to page F at the beginning of this chapter.

Activity Ask students to describe the events that take place during fertilization and what the new cell is called. Give students a handout or write on the board the stages of development (0 to a few days, a few days to 2 weeks, and 2 weeks to 8 weeks). Have students fill in the stages with diagrams and/or verbal descriptions.

Expected Outcome Students should know that during fertilization sperm and egg cells fuse, their nuclei fuse, and the new cell is called a zygote. Only one sperm can fuse with an egg cell. They should draw or describe the "soap bubble" stage, the three-part state, and the differentiation stage.

Using Vocabulary

1. Semen
2. pregnancy
3. an embryo
4. uterus
5. amniotic sac
6. ovary

Checking Concepts

7. A	12. B
8. C	13. A
9. D	14. B
10. C	15. C
11. A	16. B

Using Vocabulary

amniotic sac p.159	ovulation p.153
embryo p.159	pregnancy p.158
fetal stress p.162	semen p.152
fetus p.160	sperm p.152
hormone p.146	testes p.152
menstrual cycle p.154	uterus p.153
menstruation p.154	vagina p.153
ovary p.153	

Fill in the blank with the correct vocabulary word or words.

1. _____ is a mixture of sperm and fluid.

2. The time of the development until the birth of a baby is known as _____.

3. During the first two months of pregnancy, the unborn child is known as a(n) _____.

4. The _____ is a hollow, pear-shaped muscular organ.

5. The _____ is the membrane that protects the unborn child.

6. The _____ is the organ that produces eggs.

Checking Concepts

Choose the word or phrase that best answers the question.

7. Where is the egg usually fertilized?
   A) oviduct   C) vagina
   B) uterus   D) ovary

8. What are the chemicals produced by the endocrine system?
   A) enzymes   C) hormones
   B) target tissues   D) saliva

9. Which gland produces melatonin?
   A) adrenal   C) pancreas
   B) thyroid   D) pineal

10. Where does the embryo develop?
    A) oviduct   C) uterus
    B) ovary   D) vagina

Use the figure below to answer question 11.

Prevalence of Diabetes per 100 Adults, United States, 2001

KEY: □ < 4%   □ 4–4.9%   ▨ 5–5.9%   ■ 6+%

11. Using the figure above, which state has the lowest incidence of diabetes?
    A) Wyoming   C) Michigan
    B) Florida   D) Washington

12. What is the monthly process that releases an egg called?
    A) fertilization   C) menstruation
    B) ovulation   D) puberty

13. What is the union of an egg and a sperm?
    A) fertilization   C) menstruation
    B) ovulation   D) puberty

14. During what stage of development does the amniotic sac form?
    A) zygote   C) fetus
    B) embryo   D) newborn

15. When does puberty occur?
    A) childhood   C) adolescence
    B) adulthood   D) infancy

16. During which period does growth stop?
    A) childhood   C) adolescence
    B) adulthood   D) infancy

 Science Online bookd.msscience.com/vocabulary_puzzlemaker

Use the Exam*View*® Pro Testmaker CD-ROM to:

• create multiple versions of tests
• create modified tests with one mouse click for inclusion students
• edit existing questions and add your own questions
• build tests aligned with state standards using built-in State Curriculum Tags
• change English tests to Spanish with one mouse click and vice versa

Thinking Critically

17. **List** the effects that adrenal gland hormones can have on your body as you prepare to run a race.

18. **Explain** the similar functions of the ovaries and testes.

Use the diagram below to answer question 19.

19. **Identify** the structure in the above diagram in which each process occurs: ovulation, fertilization, and implantation.

20. **Compare and contrast** your endocrine system with the thermostat in your home.

21. **Explain** if quadruplets—four babies born at one birth—are always identical or always fraternal, or if they can be either.

22. **Predict** During the ninth month of pregnancy, the fetus develops a white, greasy coating. Predict what the function of this coating might be.

23. **Form a hypothesis** about the effect of raising identical twins apart from each other.

24. **Classify** each of the following structures as female or male and internal or external: ovary, penis, scrotum, testes, uterus, and vagina.

 Science nline bookd.msscience.com/chapter_review

Performance Activities

25. **Letter** Find newspaper or magazine articles on the effects of smoking on the health of the developing embryo and newborn. Write a letter to the editor about why a mother's smoking is damaging to her unborn baby's health.

Applying Math

26. **Blood Sugar Levels** Carol is diabetic and has a fasting blood sugar level of 180 mg/dL. Luisa does not have diabetes and has a fasting blood sugar level of 90 mg/dL. Express as a percentage how much higher the fasting blood sugar level is for Carol as compared to that for Luisa.

Use the graph below to answer questions 27 and 28.

Sam's Growth Chart

27. **Early Childhood Growth** The graph above charts Sam's growth from birth to 18 years of age. According to the graph, how much taller was Sam at 12 years of age than he was at 3 years of age?

28. **Adolescent Growth** According to the graph, how much did Sam grow between 12 and 18 years of age?

CHAPTER REVIEW D ◆ 171

Thinking Critically

17. Adrenal hormones cause your heart to beat faster, increasing blood flow to major organs and giving a sense of increased strength.

18. Both are paired organs that produce sex cells.

19. ovulation—ovary; fertilization—oviduct; implantation—uterus

20. According to the level of hormone in the blood, the target tissue sends a chemical message back to the gland to stop or start hormone secretion. Likewise, the thermostat in a house signals the heating or air conditioning unit to start or stop according to the temperature in the house. Both are negative-feedback systems.

21. Either; zygote splits into four parts—identical quadruplets; four eggs fertilized by four different sperm—fraternal quadruplets.

22. This coating aids in the movement of the baby through the birth canal.

23. Students might hypothesize that they will be the same because of their genes or that the environment will have an effect, making them different.

24. female internal: ovary, uterus, vagina; male external: penis, scrotum, testes

Performance Activities

25. Information in the letter might include how smoking reduces the oxygen supply to the fetus, increases the heart rate and blood pressure, and interferes with body chemistry. Use **Performance Assessment in the Science Classroom,** p. 139.

Applying Math

National Math Standards

1, 5, 9

26. $\dfrac{180-90}{90} \times 100 = 100\%$

27. $145-90 = 55$ cm

28. $175-145 = 30$ cm

✓ Assessment Resources

Reproducible Masters
Chapter *Fast File* **Resources**
  Chapter Review, pp. 35–36
  Chapter Tests, pp. 37–40
  Assessment Transparency Activity, p. 47
Glencoe Science Web site
  Chapter Review Test
  Standardized Test Practice

Glencoe Technology
  Assessment Transparency
  Exam*View*® Pro Testmaker
  MindJogger Videoquiz
  Interactive Chalkboard

FAST FILE

Answer Sheet A practice answer sheet can be found at bookd.msscience.com/answer_sheet.

SAMPLE

Part 1 | Multiple Choice

1. B	4. C	7. A
2. A	5. A	8. B
3. D	6. C	

Part 1 | Multiple Choice

Record your answers on the answer sheet provided by your teacher or on a sheet of paper.

1. When do eggs start to develop in the ovaries?
   - **A.** before birth
   - **B.** at puberty
   - **C.** during childhood
   - **D.** during infancy

Use the graph below to answers questions 2 and 3.

United States Syphilis Rates (1970–1997)

Year

2. According to the information in the graph, in which year was the syphilis rate the lowest?
   - **A.** 1976
   - **B.** 1982
   - **C.** 1988
   - **D.** 1993

3. According to the information in the graph, during which years was there a decrease in the syphilis rate?
   - **A.** 1970–1972
   - **B.** 1976–1982
   - **C.** 1988–1990
   - **D.** 1990–1993

4. Which of the following glands is found in the neck?
   - **A.** pineal
   - **B.** adrenal
   - **C.** thyroid
   - **D.** pancreas

> **Test-Taking Tip**
>
> **Bar Graphs** On a bar graph, line up each bar with its corresponding value by laying your pencil between the two points.

5. What is the mixture of sperm and fluid called?
   - **A.** semen
   - **B.** testes
   - **C.** seminal vesicle
   - **D.** epididymis

Use the table below to answer questions 6–8.

Results of Folic Acid on Development of Neural Tube Defect		
Group	**Babies with Neural Tube Defect**	**Babies without Neural Tube Defect**
Group I—Folic Acid	6	497
Group II—No Folic Acid	21	581

(From CDC)

6. Researchers have found that the B-vitamin folic acid can prevent neural tube defects. In a study done in Europe in 1991, one group of pregnant women was given extra folic acid, and the other group did not receive extra folic acid. What percentage of babies were born with a neural tube defect in Group II?
   - **A.** 1.0%
   - **B.** 2.5%
   - **C.** 3.0%
   - **D.** 4.0%

7. What percentage of babies were born with a neural tube defect in Group I?
   - **A.** 1.0%
   - **B.** 2.5%
   - **C.** 3.0%
   - **D.** 4.0%

8. Which of the following statements is true regarding the data in this table?
   - **A.** Folic acid had no effect on the percentage of babies with a neural tube defect.
   - **B.** Extra folic acid decreased the percentage of babies with a neural tube defect.
   - **C.** Extra folic acid increased the percentage of babies with a neural tube defect.
   - **D.** Group I and Group II had the same percentage of babies born with a neural tube defect.

172 ◆ **D** STANDARDIZED TEST PRACTICE

Part 2 | Short Response/Grid In

9. Endocrine glands are ductless. Hormones from endocrine glands pour directly into the blood. Saliva from salivary glands goes through tubes called ducts.

10. Parathyroid hormone helps regulate calcium levels in the body.

11. The cilia help sweep the egg through the oviduct toward the uterus.

12. $14/28 = 1/2 = 50\%$

13. $7/28 = 1/4 = 25\%$

14. day 14

15. Amniotic fluid is made during the embryo stage. Amniotic fluid acts as a cushion for the embryo and stores nutrients and wastes.

16. during infancy

17. During the first two months of development, because this is when the embryo's major organs form.

Part 2 | Short Response/Grid In

*Record your answers on the answer sheet
provided by your teacher or on a sheet of paper.*

9. How are endocrine glands different from salivary glands?

10. What does parathyroid hormone do for the body?

11. What is the function of the cilia in the oviduct?

Use the illustration below to answer questions 12 and 13.

| 1 2 3 4 5 6 7 8 9 10 11 12 13 14 15 16 17 18 19 20 21 22 23 24 25 26 27 28 |
| Phase 1 — Phase 2 — Phase 3 |

12. According to the illustration, what percentage of the menstrual cycle is phase 3?

13. According to the illustration, what percentage of the menstrual cycle is phase 2?

14. According to the illustration, on which day does ovulation occur?

15. During which stage of development before birth does amniotic fluid develop? What is the purpose of amniotic fluid?

16. During which stage of development after birth is physical growth and development the most rapid?

17. Rubella, also know as German measles, is caused by a virus. If a pregnant woman is infected with rubella, the virus can affect the formation of major organs, such as the heart, in the fetus. During which stage of development before birth would a rubella infection be most dangerous?

Part 3 | Open Ended

Record your answers on a sheet of paper.

18. Predict how each of the following factors may affect sperm production: hot environment, illness with fever, testes located inside the body cavity, and injury to the testes. Explain your answer.

19. Sexually transmitted diseases can cause infection of the female reproductive organs, including the oviduct. Infection of the oviduct can result in scarring. What might happen to an egg that enters a scarred oviduct?

Use the table below to answer question 20.

Pre-eclampsia Risk in Pregnancy	
Risk Factors	**Risk Ratio**
First pregnancy	3:1
Over 40 years of age	3:1
Family history	5:1
Chronic hypertension	10:1
Chronic renal disease	20:1
Antiphospholipid syndrome	10:1
Diabetes mellitus	2:1
Twin birth	4:1
Angiotensinogen gene T235	
Homozygous	20:1
Heterozygous	4:1

20. Pre-eclampsia is a condition that can develop in a woman after 20 weeks of pregnancy. It involves the development of hypertension or high blood pressure, an abnormal amount of protein in urine, and swelling. Infer why a woman with chronic hypertension has a higher risk of developing pre-eclampsia than a woman without hypertension.

Part 3 | Open Ended

18. All these will result in a decrease in sperm production. Sperm are produced in greater numbers at lower temperatures.

19. Because of the scarring, the egg will not travel normally through the oviduct. It may become stuck in the oviduct.

20. A woman with chronic hypertension is ten times more likely to develop pre-eclampsia during pregnancy than a woman without hypertension. Pre-eclampsia could make her hypertension worse.

Rubrics

The following rubrics are sample scoring devices for short response and open-ended questions.

Short Response

Points	Description
2	The student demonstrates a thorough understanding of the science of the task. The response may contain minor flaws that do not detract from the demonstration of a thorough understanding.
1	The student has provided a response that is only partially correct.
0	The student has provided a completely incorrect solution or no response at all.

Open Ended

Points	Description
4	The student demonstrates a thorough understanding of the science of the task. The response may contain minor flaws that do not detract from the demonstration of a thorough understanding.
3	The student demonstrates an understanding of the science of the task. The response is essentially correct and demonstrates an essential but less than thorough understanding of the science.
2	The student demonstrates only a partial understanding of the science of the task. Although the student may have used the correct approach to a solution or may have provided a correct solution, the work lacks an essential understanding of the underlying science concepts.
1	The student demonstrates a very limited understanding of the science of the task. The response is incomplete and exhibits many flaws.
0	The student provides a completely incorrect solution or no response at all.

Section/Objectives	Standards		Labs/Features
	National	**State/Local**	
Chapter Opener	See pp.16T–17T for a Key to Standards.		**Launch Lab:** How do diseases spread?, p. 175 **Foldables,** p. 175
Section 1 The Immune System ⏱ 2 sessions 📦 1 block 1. **Describe** the natural defenses your body has against disease. 2. **Explain** the difference between an antigen and an antibody. 3. **Compare and contrast** active and passive immunity.	National Content Standards: UCP.2, UCP.5, A.1, A.2, C.1–C.3, C.5, F.1, G.2		**Science Online,** p. 178 **MiniLAB:** Determining Reproduction Rates, p. 179
Section 2 Infectious Diseases ⏱ 2 sessions 📦 1 block 4. **Describe** the work of Pasteur, Koch, and Lister in the discovery and prevention of disease. 5. **Identify** diseases caused by viruses and bacteria. 6. **List** sexually transmitted diseases, their causes, and treatments. 7. **Explain** how HIV affects the immune system.	National Content Standards: UCP.2, UCP.5, A.1, C.1–C.3, C.5, E.1, F.1, F.4, F.5		**Integrate Social Studies,** p. 182 **Visualizing Koch's Rules,** p. 183 **MiniLAB:** Observing Antiseptic Action, p. 184 **Applying Science:** Has the annual percentage of deaths from major diseases changed?, p. 185 **Science Online,** p. 187 **Lab:** Microorganisms and Disease, p. 189
Section 3 Noninfectious Diseases ⏱ 3 sessions 📦 1.5 blocks 8. **Define** noninfectious diseases and list causes of them. 9. **Describe** the basic characteristics of cancer. 10. **Explain** what happens during an allergic reaction.	National Content Standards: UCP.2, UCP.5, A.1, A.2, C.1–C.3, C.5, F.1, F.3–F.5, G.1, G.2		**Integrate Environment,** p. 193 **Lab:** Defensive Saliva, p. 196 **Science Stats:** Battling Bacteria, p. 198

Lab Materials	Reproducible Resources	Section Assessment	Technology
Launch Lab: cotton ball, peppermint food flavoring	**Chapter FAST FILE Resources** Foldables Worksheet, p. 15 Directed Reading Overview, p. 17 Note-taking Worksheets, pp. 31–33	GLENCOE'S ASSESSMENT ADVANTAGE	**TeacherWorks** includes: • Interactive Teacher Edition • Lesson Planner with calendar • Access to all program blacklines • Correlations to standards • Web links
MiniLAB: 31 pennies, calculator *Need materials?* Contact Science Kit at 1-800-828-7777 or www.sciencekit.com on the Internet.	**Chapter FAST FILE Resources** Transparency Activity, p. 42 MiniLAB, p. 3 Lab Activity, pp. 9–12 Enrichment, p. 28 Reinforcement, p. 25 Directed Reading, p. 18 Transparency Activity, pp. 45–46	**Portfolio** Differentiated Instruction, p. 177 **Performance** MiniLAB, p. 179 Applying Skills, p. 190 **Content** Section Review, p. 190	Section Focus Transparency Teaching Transparency Virtual Labs CD-ROM Guided Reading Audio Program Interactive Chalkboard CD-ROM
MiniLAB: glass plate, dried yeast, hydrogen peroxide, dropper **Lab:** 6 fresh apples, rotting apple, rubbing alcohol, 6 self-sealing plastic bags, labels, gloves, paper towels, sandpaper, cotton ball, soap and water, newspaper	**Chapter FAST FILE Resources** Transparency Activity, p. 43 MiniLAB, p. 4 Enrichment, p. 29 Reinforcement, p. 26 Directed Reading, p. 19 Lab Worksheet, pp. 5–6 **Cultural Diversity,** p. 17 **Mathematics Skill Activities,** p. 1 **Reading and Writing Skill Activities,** pp. 25, 31	**Portfolio** Science Journal, p. 184 **Performance** MiniLAB, p. 184 Applying Science, p. 185 Applying Skills, p. 188 **Content** Section Review, p. 188	Section Focus Transparency Virtual Labs CD-ROM Guided Reading Audio Program Interactive Chalkboard CD-ROM Video Lab
Lab: head of red cabbage, cooking pot, coffee filter, drinking glasses, clear ammonia, baking soda, water, spoon, white vinegar, lemon juice, orange juice	**Chapter FAST FILE Resources** Transparency Activity, p. 44 Lab Activity, pp. 13–14 Enrichment, p. 30 Reinforcement, p. 27 Directed Reading, pp. 19, 20 Lab Worksheet, pp. 7–8 **Lab Management and Safety,** p. 70	**Performance** Applying Skills, p. 195 **Content** Section Review, p. 195	Section Focus Transparency Virtual Labs CD-ROM Guided Reading Audio Program Interactive Chalkboard CD-ROM

End of Chapter Assessment

GLENCOE'S ASSESSMENT ADVANTAGE

Blackline Masters	Technology	Professional Series
Chapter FAST FILE Resources Chapter Review, pp. 35–36 Chapter Tests, pp. 37–40 **Standardized Test Practice,** pp. 31–34	MindJogger Videoquiz Virtual Labs CD-ROM ExamView® Pro Testmaker TeacherWorks CD-ROM Interactive Chalkboard CD-ROM	**Performance Assessment in the Science Classroom (PASC)**

Transparencies

Section Focus

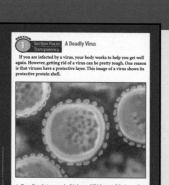

1 Section Focus Transparency **A Deadly Virus**

If you are infected by a virus, your body works to help you get well again. However, getting rid of a virus can be pretty tough. One reason is that viruses have a protective layer. This image of a virus shows its protective protein shell.

1. Describe what you see in this image. Which part of the image do you think shows the protective shell?
2. How might this protein shell protect a virus?
3. In general, what are some steps you can take to stay healthy?

L2

2 Section Focus Transparency **The Invisible World**

The first person to see many microorganisms, including bacteria, was Antonie van Leeuwenhoek (1632–1723). Leeuwenhoek wasn't a scientist by training, and he didn't invent the microscope. But he did learn to grind lenses very skillfully, and his small but powerful microscopes allowed him to see what no one else ever had.

1. What advantages do microscopes give researchers?
2. How would a more powerful microscope help Leeuwenhoek see what other people could not?
3. One of Leeuwenhoek's microscopes is shown on the right. Where do you think he placed the sample he wished to magnify?

L2

3 Section Focus Transparency **Ah-Chooo! (Gesundheit)**

Organisms are not the only things that can make you sick. Matter present in the environment, such as toxic chemicals, particles, and certain types of fibers, also can cause disease. The spiny spheres you see below are responsible for a certain type of allergic reaction that afflicts many people. Can you guess what they are?

1. How do allergies affect people?
2. What kind of help is there for allergy sufferers?
3. If people work around materials such as asbestos, burning tar, or smoke, what kinds of safety equipment should they use?

L2

This is a representation of key blackline masters available in the Teacher Classroom Resources. See Resource Manager boxes within the chapter for additional information.

Key to Teaching Strategies

The following designations will help you decide which activities are appropriate for your students.

L1 Level 1 activities should be appropriate for students with learning difficulties.

L2 Level 2 activities should be within the ability range of all students.

L3 Level 3 activities are designed for above-average students.

ELL ELL activities should be within the ability range of English-Language Learners.

COOP LEARN Cooperative Learning activities are designed for small group work.

LS Multiple Learning Styles logos, as described on page 12T, are used throughout to indicate strategies that address different learning styles.

P These strategies represent student products that can be placed into a best-work portfolio.

PBL Problem-Based Learning activities apply real-world situations to learning.

Assessment

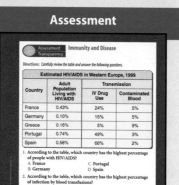

Assessment Transparency **Immunity and Disease**

Directions: Carefully review the table and answer the following questions.

Estimated HIV/AIDS in Western Europe, 1999

Country	Adult Population Living with HIV/AIDS	Transmission	
		IV Drug Use	Contaminated Blood
France	0.43%	24%	5%
Germany	0.10%	15%	5%
Greece	0.16%	5%	9%
Portugal	0.74%	49%	3%
Spain	0.58%	66%	2%

1. According to the table, which country has the highest percentage of people with HIV/AIDS?
   A France   C Portugal
   B Germany   D Spain
2. According to the table, which country has the highest percentage of infection by blood transfusions?
   F France
   G Germany
   H Greece
   J Portugal
3. According to the table, which country has the highest percentage of people infected by drug use?
   A France
   B Germany
   C Spain
   D Greece

L2

Teaching

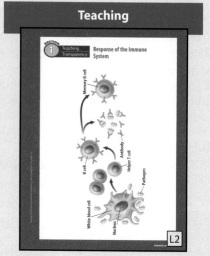

1 Teaching Transparency **Response of the Immune System**

L2

Hands-on Activities

Student Text Lab Worksheet

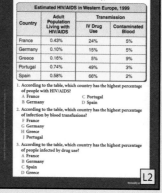

Activity **Microorganisms and Disease**

Lab Preview
Directions: Answer these questions before you begin the Activity.

1. Which safety symbols are associated with this activity?

2. What is the source of microorganisms in this activity?

Microorganisms are everywhere. Washing your hands and disinfecting items you use helps remove some of these organisms.

What You'll Investigate
How do microorganisms cause infection?

Materials
fresh apples (6)   self-sealing plastic bags (6)   soap and water
5 beakers, glass   labels and pencil   sandpaper   newspaper
rubbing alcohol (5 mL)   latex gloves   cotton ball

Goals
• **Observe** the transmission of microorganisms.
• **Relate** microorganisms to infections.

Safety Precautions
CAUTION: *Do not eat the apples.* Do not remove goggles until the activity and cleanup are completed. When you complete the experiment, give all bags to your teacher for disposal, then wash your hands.

Procedure
1. **Label** the plastic bags 1 through 6. Put on gloves. Place a fresh apple in bag 1.
2. Rub the rotting apple over the other five apples. This is your source of micro-organisms. CAUTION: *Don't touch your face.*
3. Put one apple in bag 2.
4. Hold one apple 1.5 m above the floor and drop it on a newspaper. Put it in bag 3.
5. Rub one apple with sandpaper. Place this apple in bag 4.
6. Wash one apple with soap and water. Dry it well. Put this apple in bag 5.
7. Use a cotton ball to spread alcohol over the last apple. Let it air dry. Place it in bag 6.
8. Seal all bags and put them in a dark place.
9. On day 3 and day 7, compare all of the apples without removing them from the bags. **Record** your observations in Table 1.

L2

Laboratory Activities

1 Laboratory Activity **Immunity Simulation**

To defend itself against disease, the human body is able to chemically "recognize" proteins and chemicals that are foreign to its system. Any protein or chemical that the body recognizes as not one of its own is called an antigen. When an antigen enters the body, a healthy immune system responds by producing a protein called an antibody. The antibody binds with the antigen, making the antigen useless. Large white blood cells then digest the antigen. In this way, the body develops an immunity to that antigen.

Strategy
You will simulate antigens in the blood.
You will simulate antibodies in the blood.
You will infer from the results of the simulation how antibody immunity works in the human body.

Materials
10 labels and pencils   5 stirring rods, glass   test-tube rack
5 beakers, glass   water   mortar and pestle
cylinder, graduated   lemon juice   antacid, tablets
milk   vinegar   antacid, liquid
food coloring, red   5 test tubes, glass
CAUTION: *Use care when handling sharp objects. Do not taste, eat, or drink any materials used in the lab.*

Figure 1

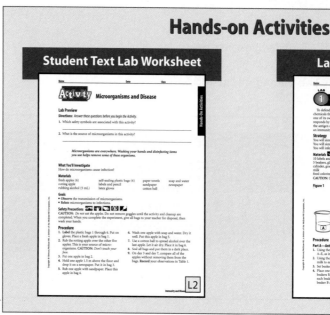

Procedure
Part A—Antibodies Attack Antigens
1. Using the labels, mark the glass beakers A–E, as in Figure 1.
2. Using the graduated cylinder, add 25 mL of milk to each of the glass beakers.
3. Set beaker A aside.
4. Place one drop of red food coloring into beakers B, C, D, and E. Stir the contents of each beaker with a glass stirring rod. Set beaker B aside.
5. Using the graduated cylinder, add 10 mL of tap water to beaker C. Stir the contents with a glass stirring rod and set beaker C aside.
6. Clean the graduated cylinder and add 10 mL of lemon juice to beaker D. Stir the contents with a glass stirring rod and set beaker D aside.
7. Clean the graduated cylinder and add 10 mL of vinegar to beaker E. Stir the contents with a glass stirring rod and set beaker E aside.
8. Wait 5 min. Then, observe each beaker and write your observations in Table 1.

L2

Meeting Different Ability Levels

Content Outline

L2

Reinforcement

L2

Enrichment

L3

Directed Reading (English/Spanish)

L1

Study Guide

Study Guide

Features
• Contains a study guide page for each section of the chapter
• Reviews key concepts
• Includes answer pages

L2

Reading Essentials

Reading Essentials for Glencoe Science
An Interactive Student Workbook

Features
• Condensed core content
• Actively involves students in reading
• Reinforces key vocabulary

L1

Assessment

Test Practice Workbook

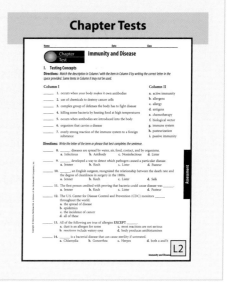

GO ON L2

Chapter Review

L2

Chapter Tests

L2

Science Content Background

The Immune System

Immunity

The lymphatic system produces various white blood cells, each of which fights a specific type of antigen. This type of defense is called specific immunity.

Active Immunity

Active immunity can be natural or induced. A natural active immunity develops after a person contracts and recovers from diseases such as measles or mumps. Defensive proteins, called antibodies, produced in the body counteract the invading microorganism's proteins called antigens. The interaction between antigens and antibodies stimulates the release of histamine and complement compounds.

Artificial active immunity is an induced immunity. A person is given an injection or an oral dose of a noninfectious disease antigen. The body forms antibodies against the antigen, providing immunity. The noninfectious antigens come from three sources:

1) microorganism secretions that have been detoxified,
2) dead microorganisms, and
3) living microorganisms.

Booster shots may be required to keep the artificial immunity active.

Passive Immunity

Passive immunity can be either natural or induced. Passive artificial immunity is acquired when antibodies produced in another animal are injected into the body. The serum containing the antibodies is often obtained from horses that were inoculated with disease antigens and then produced antibodies within their own body systems.

Passive natural immunity is that which an infant receives from its mother via the placenta. Because this protection only lasts for a few months, the child must be given inoculations to establish his or her own immunity to diseases.

Aaron Haupt/Photo Researchers, Inc.

chapter content resources

Internet Resources
For additional content background, visit
bookd.msscience.com to:
- access your book online
- find references to related articles in popular science magazines
- access Web links with related content background
- access current events with science journal topics

Print Resources
How the Immune System Works, by Lauren Sompayrac, Blackwell Publishers, 2002
Immune System, by Pam Walker and Elaine Wood, Gale Group, 2002
The Human Body for Every Kid, by Janice VanCleave, Wiley, John & Sons, Incorporated, 1995

section 2 | Infectious Diseases
Germ Theory

In early history, the causes of diseases were associated with the anger of the gods, sorcerers, evil vapors, or imbalances of body fluids. By the early and mid 1800s, researchers, such as French chemist Louis Pasteur, developed a germ theory that indicated microorganisms might be responsible for disease. It is now known that pathogenic organisms such as viruses, bacteria, yeasts, protozoans, flatworms, roundworms, and hookworms cause disease by secreting toxins, by destroying red blood cells, or by ingesting tissues. Infectious, or communicable diseases, can be transmitted from one organism to another by food, through the air, by insects, by parasites, or by sexual contact or exchange of body fluids. Bacteria and viruses cause sexually transmitted diseases.

Preventing Food Spoilage

Before the causes of diseases were discovered, various methods were used to prevent foods from spoiling. Foods were dried, smoked, pickled, or salted to prevent the growth of microorganisms. Establishment of the germ theory led to the use of chemicals and Pasteur's idea of the use of heat to destroy pathogens. Additional modern methods of safeguarding food include the use of extreme cold, steam, and radiation.

Germs in the Body

Some organisms are able to gain entrance to the body through the thin membranes of the eyes, nose, and mouth. Good hygiene habits such as washing with soap and water, remove many potentially troublesome organisms from the surface of the skin. After germs enter the body, some are unable to function because body temperature is either too warm or too cool, the pH of body fluids is unsuitable, or the available nutrients are inappropriate for their metabolism.

section 3 | Noninfectious Diseases
Causes and Cures

Some diseases and disorders are noninfectious. Although they are not contracted from other people or from objects, these conditions are usually unavoidable. Some noninfectious diseases are the result of poor nutrition. People who do not have access to a proper diet or people who do not choose a balanced diet are prone to such diseases. Other noninfectious diseases and disorders are the result of inheriting certain genes. Such genetic disorders include cystic fibrosis, hemophilia, Huntington's chorea, muscular dystrophy, sickle-cell anemia, and Tay-Sachs disease.

Toxins, or chemicals, introduced into the body through breathing, touching, drinking, or eating, can cause noninfectious diseases such as allergies, emphysema, and cancer. Prevention is the first line of defense for these diseases. Early detection of some diseases, such as cancer, paired with appropriate drug treatment and/or surgery, is a second line of defense.

Teacher to Teacher

Jeff Remington
Palmyra Middle School
Palmyra, Pennsylvania

"I obtain a non-toxic 100% synthetic organic colorant whose plastic particles are 5 microns and smaller (available at hospital supply stores in orange or blue) to simulate germs. Sprinkle a small amount of the powder on the hands of a few students and/or on classroom surfaces. After your students shake hands or touch the surfaces, use an ultra-violet lamp (black light) to demonstrate the transfer of 'germs' to one another."

Jeff Remington

Chapter Vocabulary

immune system, p. 176
antigen, p. 178
antibody, p. 178
active immunity, p. 179
passive immunity, p. 179
vaccination, p. 179
pasteurization, p. 182
virus, p. 182
infectious disease, p. 185
biological vector, p. 185
sexually transmitted disease
  (STD), p. 186
noninfectious diseases, p. 190
allergy, p. 190
allergen, p. 191
chemotherapy, p. 194

Science Journal Student responses should include a foreign substance invading the blood and being attacked by white blood cells.

INTERACTIVE CHALKBOARD
with Image Bank

PowerPoint® Presentations

This CD-ROM is an editable Microsoft® PowerPoint® presentation that includes:

- a pre-made presentation for every chapter
- interactive graphics
- animations
- audio clips
- image bank
- all new section and chapter questions
- Standardized Test Practice
- transparencies
- pre-lab questions for all labs
- Foldables directions
- links to bookd.msscience.com

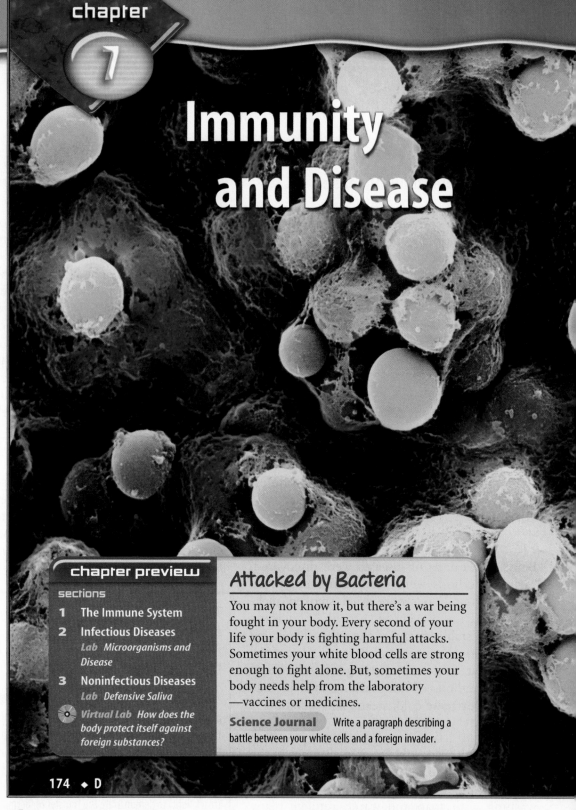

Immunity and Disease

chapter preview

sections

1 The Immune System

2 Infectious Diseases
   Lab Microorganisms and Disease

3 Noninfectious Diseases
   Lab Defensive Saliva

   Virtual Lab How does the body protect itself against foreign substances?

Attacked by Bacteria

You may not know it, but there's a war being fought in your body. Every second of your life your body is fighting harmful attacks. Sometimes your white blood cells are strong enough to fight alone. But, sometimes your body needs help from the laboratory —vaccines or medicines.

Science Journal Write a paragraph describing a battle between your white cells and a foreign invader.

174 ◆ D

Theme Connection

Systems and Interactions One major theme of science is interaction among systems. This chapter focuses on interactions within the body. Natural defenses in the body aid in preventing disease. Vaccines also provide active immunity to body systems.

About the Photo

Fighting Infection The yellow spheres in this scanning electron micrograph are *Streptococcus pyrogens* bacteria. These bacteria grow like a string of beads and are among the most common disease-causing bacteria in humans. *S. pyrogens* can cause a sore throat and is associated with strep throat and scarlet fever. The bacteria can spread from person to person when bacteria-containing droplets are coughed or exhaled into the air.

Start-Up Activities

How do diseases spread?

Knowing how diseases are spread will help you understand how your body fights disease. You can discover one way diseases are spread by doing the following lab.

1. Wash your hands before and after this lab. Don't touch your face until the lab is completed and your hands are washed.

2. Work with a partner. Place a drop of peppermint food flavoring on a cotton ball. Pretend that the flavoring is a mass of cold viruses.

3. Use the cotton ball to rub an X over the palm of your right hand. Let it dry.

4. Shake hands with your partner.

5. Have your partner shake hands with another student. Then each student should smell their hands.

6. **Think Critically** In your Science Journal, note how many persons your "virus" infected. Write a paragraph describing some ways the spread of diseases could be stopped.

FOLDABLES
Study Organizer

Classifying Diseases Make the following Foldable to classify human diseases as either infectious or noninfectious.

| **STEP 1** | Fold a sheet of paper in half lengthwise. |

| **STEP 2** | Fold paper down 2.5 cm from the top. (Hint: From the tip of your index finger to your middle knuckle is about 2.5 cm.) |

| **STEP 3** | Open and draw lines along the 2.5-cm fold. Label as shown. |

Read and Write As you read the chapter, classify human diseases as infectious or noninfectious by listing them on the proper fold.

 Preview this chapter's content and activities at bookd.msscience.com

Purpose Use this Launch Lab to introduce students to how disease can spread. L1 ELL

KS Kinesthetic

Preparation Before beginning this activity, obtain food flavoring and cotton balls.

Materials peppermint food flavoring, one cotton ball for each pair

Alternate Materials Other flavors, such as orange, almond, or banana, can be used.

Teaching Strategies
• Have students discuss how the mass of cold virus could have gotten on the hands in the first place.
• Have students infer whether the infection could be passed around on drinking glasses and handkerchiefs.

Safety Precautions Following the activity, have students wash their hands thoroughly.

Think Critically

Possible answer: Many diseases are spread through physical contact. The spread of some diseases can be stopped by carefully washing eating utensils and hands with warm water and soap.

Assessment

Oral Have students determine whether any flavoring remains on their hands after washing them. Discuss how washing hands affects the spread of disease. Use **Performance Assessment in the Science Classroom,** p. 89.

 Dinah Zike Study Fold

Student preparation materials for this Foldable are available in the **Chapter FAST FILE Resources.**

D ◆ 175

176 ◆ **D CHAPTER 7** Immunity and Disease

Bellringer

Section Focus Transparencies also are available on the Interactive Chalkboard CD-ROM.

L2 ELL

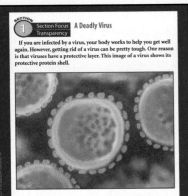

Section Focus Transparency — **A Deadly Virus**

If you are infected by a virus, your body works to help you get well again. However, getting rid of a virus can be pretty tough. One reason is that viruses have a protective layer. This image of a virus shows its protective protein shell.

1. Describe what you see in this image. Which part of the image do you think shows the protective shell?
2. How might this protein shell protect a virus?
3. In general, what are some steps you can take to stay healthy?

Tie to Prior Knowledge

Immunizations Ask students to recall the shots they received before entering school. Have them describe any immunizations they have been given in recent years.

Answer first-line (general) and second-line (specific) defenses

---

The Immune System

as you read

What You'll Learn

- **Describe** the natural defenses your body has against disease.
- **Explain** the difference between an antigen and an antibody.
- **Compare and contrast** active and passive immunity.

Why It's Important

Your body's defenses fight the pathogens that you are exposed to every day.

Review Vocabulary

enzyme: a type of protein that speeds up chemical reactions in the body

New Vocabulary

- immune system
- antigen
- antibody
- active immunity
- passive immunity
- vaccination

Lines of Defense

The Sun has just begun to peek over the horizon, casting an orange glow on the land. A skunk ambles down a dirt path. Behind the skunk, you and your dog come over a hill for your morning exercise. Suddenly, the skunk stops and raises its tail high in the air. Your dog creeps forward. "No!" you shout. The dog ignores your command. Without further warning, the skunk sprays your dog. Yelping pitifully and carrying an awful stench, your dog takes off. The skunk used its scent to protect itself. Its first-line defense was to warn your dog with its posture. Its second-line defense was its spray. Just as the skunk protects itself from predators, your body also protects itself from harm.

Your body has many ways to defend itself. Its first-line defenses work against harmful substances and all types of disease-causing organisms, called pathogens (PA thuh junz). Your second-line defenses are specific and work against specific pathogens. This complex group of defenses is called your **immune system.** Tonsils, shown in **Figure 1,** are one of the immune system organs that protect your body.

✓ Reading Check *What types of defenses does your body have?*

First-Line Defenses Your skin and respiratory, digestive, and circulatory systems are first-line defenses against pathogens. As shown in **Figure 2,** the skin is a barrier that prevents many pathogens from entering your body. Although most pathogens can't get through unbroken skin, they can get into your body easily through a cut or through your mouth and the membranes in your nose and eyes. The conditions on the skin can affect pathogens. Perspiration contains substances that can slow the growth of some pathogens. At times, secretions from the skin's oil glands and perspiration are acidic. Some pathogens cannot grow in this acidic environment.

Tonsils

Figure 1 Tonsils help prevent infection in your respiratory and digestive tract.

Section 1 Resource Manager

Chapter *FAST FILE* Resources

Transparency Activity, pp. 42, 45–46
Note-taking Worksheets, pp. 31–33
MiniLAB, p. 3
Lab Activity, pp. 9–12
Enrichment, p. 28

Reinforcement, p. 25
Directed Reading for Content Mastery, pp. 17, 18

Stained LM Magnification: 1000×

Internal First-Line Defenses Your respiratory system traps pathogens with hairlike structures, called cilia (SIH lee uh), and mucus. Mucus contains an enzyme that weakens the cell walls of some pathogens. When you cough or sneeze, you get rid of some of these trapped pathogens.

Your digestive system has several defenses against pathogens—saliva, enzymes, hydrochloric acid, and mucus. Saliva in your mouth contains substances that kill bacteria. Also, enzymes (EN zimez) in your stomach, pancreas, and liver help destroy pathogens. Hydrochloric acid in your stomach helps digest your food. It also kills some bacteria and stops the activity of some viruses that enter your body on the food that you eat. The mucus found on the walls of your digestive tract contains a chemical that coats bacteria and prevents them from binding to the inner lining of your digestive organs.

Your circulatory system contains white blood cells, like the one in **Figure 3,** that surround and digest foreign organisms and chemicals. These white blood cells constantly patrol your body, sweeping up and digesting bacteria that invade. They slip between cells of tiny blood vessels called capillaries. If the white blood cells cannot destroy the bacteria fast enough, you might develop a fever. Many pathogens are sensitive to temperature. A slight increase in body temperature slows their growth and activity but speeds up your body's defenses.

Inflammation When tissue is damaged by injury or infected by pathogens, it becomes inflamed. Signs of inflammation include redness, temperature increase, swelling, and pain. Chemical substances released by damaged cells cause capillary walls to expand, allowing more blood to flow into the area. Other chemicals released by damaged tissue attract certain white blood cells that surround and take in pathogenic bacteria. If pathogens get past these first-line defenses, your body uses another line of defense called specific immunity.

Figure 2 Most pathogens, like the staphylococci bacteria shown above, cannot pass through unbroken skin.
Infer *what happens if staphylococci bacteria enter your body through your skin.*

Figure 3 A white blood cell leaves a capillary. It will search out and destroy harmful microorganisms in your body tissues.

Color-enhanced SEM Magnification: 3450×

SECTION 1 The Immune System **D** ◆ **177**

SECTION 1 The Immune System **D** ◆ **177**

Differentiated Instruction

Challenge Have students research the discovery of chemicals that destroy or inhibit the functions of viruses. Have them write two or three paragraphs on what they find. L3 ELL IS **Linguistic** P

Visual Learning

Figure 2 Have students discuss how the surface of the skin may be broken. Possible answers: Falls and accidents may cause cuts, punctures, and scrapes of the skin that can allow the entrance of bacteria.

Caption Answer

Figure 2 The pathogen could infect the wound and could enter the bloodstream to infect the rest of the body.

Activity

Sweat Acidity Have students test the acidity of their sweat using pH indicator paper. Sweat may range from pH 3.0 to slightly alkaline. L2 IS **Kinesthetic**

Fun Fact

The saliva of cats and dogs contains various substances that can kill bacteria. The licking of wounds aids in the healing process.

Discussion

Fevers Why should a fever not be ignored? Fevers are an indication of infection, a sign that the body is fighting a pathogen. Temperatures over 104°F are potentially dangerous and medical help should be sought immediately.

IDENTIFYING Misconceptions

Fever Cures There is an old adage that "sweating out a fever" will rid the body of it. Extra blankets and keeping a room extra warm will only cause the patient's temperature to rise. Drinking lots of fluids and taking medicines recommended by a physician are better remedies.

Science Online

Topic: Disease Theory

Visit bookd.msscience.com for Web links to information about one of the historical theories of disease—the four body humors.

Activity Make a picture book describing the humoral theory of disease.

Figure 4 The response of your immune system to disease-causing organisms can be divided into four steps—recognition, mobilization, disposal, and immunity.
Explain the function of B cells.

Specific Immunity When your body fights disease, it is battling complex molecules that don't belong there. Molecules that are foreign to your body are called **antigens** (AN tih junz). Antigens can be separate molecules or they can be found on the surface of a pathogen. For example, the protein in the cell membrane of a bacterium can be an antigen. When your immune system recognizes molecules as being foreign to your body, as in **Figure 4,** special lymphocytes called T cells respond. Lymphocytes are a type of white blood cell. One type of T cells, called killer T cells, releases enzymes that help destroy invading foreign matter. Another type of T cells, called helper T cells, turns on the immune system. They stimulate other lymphocytes, known as B cells, to form antibodies.

An **antibody** is a protein made in response to a specific antigen. The antibody attaches to the antigen and makes it useless. This can happen in several ways. The pathogen might not be able to stay attached to a cell. It might be changed in such a way that a killer T cell can capture it more easily or the pathogen can be destroyed.

☑ Reading Check *What is an antibody?*

Another type of lymphocyte, called memory B cells, also has antibodies for the specific pathogen. Memory B cells remain in the blood ready to defend against an invasion by that same pathogen another time.

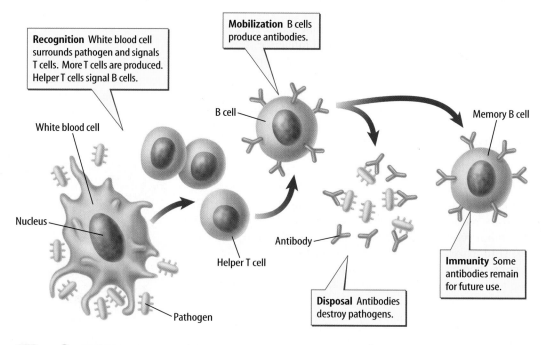

Recognition White blood cell surrounds pathogen and signals T cells. More T cells are produced. Helper T cells signal B cells.

Mobilization B cells produce antibodies.

White blood cell

B cell

Memory B cell

Nucleus

Helper T cell

Antibody

Disposal Antibodies destroy pathogens.

Immunity Some antibodies remain for future use.

Pathogen

Active Immunity Antibodies help your body build defenses in two ways—actively and passively. In **active immunity** your body makes its own antibodies in response to an antigen. **Passive immunity** results when antibodies that have been produced in another animal are introduced into your body.

When a pathogen invades your body and quickly multiplies, you get sick. Your body immediately starts to make antibodies to attack the pathogen. After enough antibodies form, you usually get better. Some antibodies stay on duty in your blood, and more are produced rapidly if the pathogen enters your body again. Because of this defense system you usually get certain diseases such as chicken pox only once. Why can you catch a cold over and over? There are many different cold viruses that give you similar symptoms. As you grow older and are exposed to many more types of pathogens, you will build immunity to each one.

Vaccination A vaccine is a form of an antigen that gives you immunity against a disease. A vaccine only can prevent a disease, not cure it. The process of giving a vaccine by injection or by mouth is called **vaccination.** If a specific vaccine is injected into your body, your body forms antibodies against that pathogen. If you later encounter the same pathogen, your bloodstream already has antibodies that are needed to fight and destroy it. Vaccines have helped reduce cases of childhood diseases, as shown in **Table 1.**

Mini LAB

Determining Reproduction Rates

Procedure

1. Place **one penny** on a table. Imagine that the penny is a bacterium that can divide every 10 min.
2. Place **two pennies** below the first penny to form a triangle. These represent the two new bacteria after the first bacterium divides.
3. Repeat three more divisions, placing two pennies under each penny as described above.
4. Calculate how many bacteria you would have after 5 h of reproduction. Graph your data.

Analysis

1. How many bacteria are present after 5 h?
2. Why is it important to take antibiotics promptly if you have an infection?

Try at Home

Mini LAB

Purpose to model bacterial reproduction

Materials pennies, paper, pencil, calculator

Teaching Strategies

• Make sure students understand that bacteria reproduce exponentially, allowing their populations to grow very quickly.
• Students should label the vertical axis of the graph *Bacteria* (thousands) and the horizontal axis *Time* (hours).

Analysis

1. At the five-hour point, there will be 1,073,741,824 bacteria.
2. Taking antibiotics promptly will inhibit the reproduction of bacteria. It is also important to take all of the antibiotic prescribed. Failing to do so will leave a few bacteria that can reinfect the body.

Assessment

Performance To further assess students' understanding of bacterial infections, have them research a variety of bacteria that cause common infections. Possible topics: staphylococci, streptococci, *Mycobacterium tuberculosis, Treponema pallidum* Use **Performance Assessment in the Science Classroom,** p. 97.

Try at Home

Table 1 Annual Cases of Disease Before and After Vaccine Availability in the U.S.		
Disease	**Before**	**After**
Measles	503,282	89
Diptheria	175,885	1
Tetanus	1,314	34
Mumps	152,209	606
Rubella	47,745	345
Pertussis (whooping cough)	147,271	6,279

Data from the National Immunization Program, CDC

Differentiated Instruction

Visually Impaired Photocopy and enlarge Figure 4. Use a felt-tip pen to outline the edges of the cells and the arrows in the illustration for use by visually impaired students. L2

Curriculum Connection

History In 1796, Edward Jenner pioneered the use of vaccines by inoculating a young boy with cowpox material to keep him from contracting the deadly disease smallpox. Editorial cartoons in the newspaper ridiculed the treatment and showed illustrations of people growing cow parts on their bodies as a result of being vaccinated. Have students find out more about Jenner's work. L2

DAILY INTERVENTION

Check for Understanding
Visual-Spatial Have students make a flowchart detailing the four steps of an immune system response. L2

Reteach
Body Defenses Use an anatomy chart or model to illustrate the various body systems involved in defense against microbes. L2 LS
Visual-Spatial

☑ Assessment

Portfolio To assess students' understanding of active and passive immunity, have them draw a concept map comparing and contrasting the two. Use **Performance Assessment in the Science Classroom,** p. 161.

Virtual Labs

Foreign Invaders *How does the body protect itself against foreign substances?*

Figure 5 The Td vaccine, which protects against tetanus and diphtheria, usually is injected into the arm.

Passive Immunity Passive immunity does not last as long as active immunity does. For example, you were born with all the antibodies that your mother had in her blood. However, these antibodies stayed with you for only a few months. Because newborn babies lose their passive immunity in a few months, they need to be vaccinated to develop their own immunity.

Tetanus Tetanus is a disease caused by a common soil bacterium. The bacterium produces a chemical that paralyzes muscles. Puncture wounds, deep cuts, and other wounds can be infected by this bacterium. Several times in early childhood you received active vaccines, as shown in **Figure 5,** that stimulated antibody production to tetanus toxin. You should continue to get vaccines or boosters every ten years to maintain protection. Booster shots for diphtheria, which is a dangerous infectious respiratory disease, are given in the same vaccine with tetanus.

section 1 review

Summary

Lines of Defense

- Your body's immune system protects you from harmful substances called pathogens.
- First-line defenses work against harmful substances and all types of pathogens.
- Second-line defenses work against specific pathogens.
- Antibodies help protect your body against specific foreign molecules called antigens.
- Your body gets antibodies through active immunity and passive immunity.
- Vaccines help you develop active immunity against a disease.
- You need to receive booster shots for some vaccines to maintain protection.

Self Check

1. **Describe** how harmful bacteria cause infections in your body.
2. **List** the natural defenses your body has against disease.
3. **Explain** how your immune system reacts when it detects an antigen.
4. **Compare and contrast** active and passive immunity.
5. **Think Critically** Several diseases have symptoms similar to those of measles. Why doesn't the measles vaccine protect you from all of these diseases?

Applying Skills

6. **Make Models** Create models of the different types of T cells, antigens, and B cells from clay, construction paper, or other art materials. Use them to explain how T cells function in the immune system.

180 ◆ D CHAPTER 7 Immunity and Disease

Science online bookd.msscience.com/self_check_quiz

section 1 review

1. Harmful bacteria enter your body and rapidly reproduce, causing you to get sick.
2. white blood cells, cilia, mucus, coughing, enzymes in the digestive system, hydrochloric acid solution, active immunity, sneezing, saliva, skin, perspiration, fever
3. The body starts to make antibodies against the antigen to destroy it. After the antigen is destroyed, some antibodies remain in the bloodstream to combat the return of the antigen.
4. Both confer immunity; active immunity—the body makes its own antibodies, long-term immunity; passive immunity—antibodies are introduced, short-term immunity.
5. Antibodies formed to fight a specific antigen will protect only against that antigen.
6. Models should show the role of T cells in the response of the immune system to antigens.

section 2

Infectious Diseases

Disease in History

For centuries, people have feared outbreaks of disease. The plague, smallpox, and influenza have killed millions of people worldwide. Today, the causes of these diseases are known, and treatments can prevent or cure them. But even today, there are diseases such as the Ebola virus in Africa that cannot be cured. Outbreaks of new diseases, such as severe acute respiratory syndrome (SARS), shown in **Table 2,** also occur.

Microorganisms With the invention of the microscope in the latter part of the seventeenth century, bacteria, yeast, and mold spores were seen for the first time. However, it took almost 200 years more to discover the relationship between some of them and disease. Scientists gradually learned that microorganisms were responsible for fermentation and decay. If decay-causing microorganisms could cause changes in other organisms, it was hypothesized that microorganisms could cause diseases and carry them from one person to another. Scientists did not make a connection between viruses and disease transmission until the late 1800s and early 1900s.

Table 2 Probable Cases of SARS (November 1, 2002 to July 7, 2003)		
Country	**Number of Cases**	**Number of Deaths**
Canada	251	38
China	7,756	730
Singapore	206	32
United States	73	0
Vietnam	63	5
Other countries	90	7

Data from the World Health Organization

as you read

What You'll Learn

- **Describe** the work of Pasteur, Koch, and Lister in the discovery and prevention of disease.
- **Identify** diseases caused by viruses and bacteria.
- **List** sexually transmitted diseases, their causes, and treatments.
- **Explain** how HIV affects the immune system.

Why It's Important

You can help prevent certain illnesses if you know what causes disease and how disease spreads.

Review Vocabulary

protist: a one- or many-celled organism that lives in moist or wet surroundings

New Vocabulary

- pasteurization
- virus
- infectious disease
- biological vector
- sexually transmitted disease (STD)

1 Motivate

Bellringer

Section Focus Transparencies also are available on the Interactive Chalkboard CD-ROM.
L2 ELL

Tie to Prior Knowledge

SARS Have students compare the student population figure of their school with the 812 people who died of SARS worldwide. This is a graphic way of illustrating the effect disease has on history.

SECTION 2 Infectious Diseases **D ◆ 181**

Section 2 Resource Manager	
Chapter _FAST FILE_ Resources	Lab Worksheet, pp. 5–6
Transparency Activity, p. 43	**Cultural Diversity,** p. 17
MiniLAB, p. 4	**Mathematics Skill Activities,** p. 1
Reinforcement, p. 26	**Reading and Writing Skill Activities,** pp. 25, 31
Enrichment, p. 29	
Directed Reading for Content Mastery, p. 19	

Quick Demo

Bacteria

Materials microscope, prepared microscope slides of various stained bacteria (different sizes and shapes)

Estimated Time 10 minutes

Procedure Using a microscope, show students prepared slides of various bacteria. Ask students to compare the sizes and shapes of the different bacteria.

Reading Check

Answer The virus invades the host cell and multiples within it; the host cell dies when the viruses break out of it.

INTEGRATE History

Jenner realized that dairy workers were resistant to catching smallpox if they had acquired cowpox, a similar, but milder disease. To test his theory, he infected a young boy with cowpox, then later with smallpox. The boy became ill, then made a full recovery.

Make a Model

Display Koch's Rules Have students prepare a display of Koch's rules. Use agar or gelatin petri dishes. Place several bright-colored cake decorations (nonpareils) on the surface of the medium. The color will diffuse onto the surface to give the appearance of bacterial colonies. L2 IS **Kinesthetic and Visual-Spatial**

INTEGRATE History

Disease Immunity Edward Jenner demonstrated that a vaccine could be produced to prevent smallpox. However, it wasn't until Louis Pasteur applied his germ theory to the process that the mechanism of vaccinations was understood. Pasteur demonstrated that germs cause diseases and that vaccines, which contained small amounts of disease organisms, could cause the body to build immunity to that disease without causing it. Research Jenner and write a summary in your Science Journal about his discovery of the smallpox vaccine.

Disease Organisms The French chemist Louis Pasteur learned that microorganisms cause disease in humans. Many scientists of his time did not believe that microorganisms could harm larger organisms, such as humans. However, Pasteur discovered that microorganisms could spoil wine and milk. He then realized that microorganisms could attack the human body in the same way. Pasteur invented **pasteurization** (pas chuh ruh ZAY shun), which is the process of heating a liquid to a specific temperature that kills most bacteria.

Today, it is known that many diseases are caused by bacteria, certain viruses, protists (PROH tihsts), or fungi. Bacteria cause tetanus, tuberculosis, strep throat, and bacterial pneumonia. Malaria and sleeping sickness are caused by protists. Fungi are the pathogens for athlete's foot and ringworm. Viruses are the cause of many common diseases—colds, influenza, AIDS, measles, mumps, smallpox, and SARS.

Many harmful bacteria that infect your body can reproduce rapidly. The conditions in your body, such as temperature and available nutrients, help the bacteria grow and multiply. Bacteria can slow down the normal growth and metabolic activities of body cells and tissues. Some bacteria even produce toxins that kill cells on contact.

A **virus** is a minute piece of genetic material surrounded by a protein coating that infects and multiplies in host cells. The host cells die when the viruses break out of them. These new viruses infect other cells, leading to the destruction of tissues or the interruption of vital body activities.

Reading Check *What is the relationship between a virus and a host cell?*

Pathogenic protists, such as the organisms that cause malaria, can destroy tissues and blood cells or interfere with normal body functions. In a similar manner, fungus infections can cause athlete's foot, nonhealing wounds, chronic lung disease, or inflammation of the membranes of the brain.

Koch's Rules Many diseases caused by pathogens can be treated with medicines. In many cases, these organisms need to be identified before specific treatment can begin. Today, a method developed in the nineteenth century still is used to identify organisms.

Pasteur may have shown that bacteria cause disease, but he didn't know how to tell which specific organism causes which disease. It was a young German doctor, Robert Koch, who first developed a way to isolate and grow one type of bacterium at a time, as shown in **Figure 6.**

LAB DEMONSTRATION

Purpose to observe microorganism growth

Materials sterile agar or gelatin plates, masking tape

Preparation Make or obtain prepared sterile agar petri plates. Have students wash their hands.

Procedure Have students lightly press their fingertips onto the surface of a sterile agar plate. Tape plates shut and place them in a dark place. Observe daily for several days. Do not open plates. Properly dispose of plates. Wash hands thoroughly.

Expected Outcome Small bacterial colonies and mold growth should be observed.

Assessment

Why was there microbial growth even after hands were washed? Not all microorganisms were washed off the hands; some may have been in the air. How could more microorganisms have been removed from the hands? by washing them with antiseptic

Figure 6

In the 1880s, German doctor Robert Koch developed a series of methods for identifying which organism was the cause of a particular disease. Koch's Rules are still in use today. Developed mainly for determining the cause of particular diseases in humans and other animals, these rules have been used for identifying diseases in plants as well.

A In every case of a particular disease, the organism thought to cause the disease—the pathogen—must be present.

Anthrax bacteria

B The suspected pathogen must be separated from all other organisms and grown on agar gel with no other organisms present.

C When inoculated with the suspected pathogen, a healthy host must come down with the original illness.

Anthrax bacteria

D Finally, when the suspected pathogen is removed from the host and grown on agar gel again, it must be compared with the original organism. Only when they match can that organism be identified as the pathogen that causes the disease.

SECTION 2 Infectious Diseases **D** ◆ **183**

Visualizing Koch's Rules

Have students examine the pictures and read the captions. Then ask the following questions.

Why does the suspected pathogen need to be grown on agar with no other organisms present? A suspected organism needs to be isolated (grown in a pure culture) to make sure that the suspected pathogen and only the suspected pathogen is inoculated into the healthy host. If not, there would be no way to know which organism caused the disease.

Why is it important to prove that a particular pathogen causes a particular disease? Possible answer: Knowing which pathogen causes a disease can help scientists develop treatments and preventative measures.

Activity

Skit Have students write and perform a skit demonstrating Koch's rules. Possible characters include Robert Koch, and a person or animal with a disease. Props: mouse, microscope, and petri dishes. L2 LS **Interpersonal**

Differentiated Instruction

English-Language Learners Have students prepare a chart of the contributions made by Pasteur, Koch, and Lister to the discovery and prevention of disease. Use the charts to check their understanding of these concepts. L2

Challenge Have students find out more about anthrax, a disease that Koch studied. Possible topics to investigate include which animals are affected, symptoms of the disease, how the disease is detected, and treatment. Have students make posters to explain what they learned. L3

Mini LAB

Purpose to observe the action of an antiseptic L2 IS **Kinesthetic**

Materials dried yeast, glass plate or saucer, dropper, 3% hydrogen peroxide solution

Teaching Strategy If time is short, do this MiniLAB as a demonstration. Then have students answer the questions on their own.

Analysis

1. The bubbling action moves dirt and other substances out of the wound.
2. The oxygen that is released destroys bacteria in the wound and cleanses the tissue.

Assessment

Process Have students observe the action of hydrogen peroxide on a piece of raw meat and relate this to its antiseptic action. Use **Performance Assessment in the Science Classroom,** p. 89.

✔ **Reading Check**

Possible answers use of antiseptics, filtering of air, sterilization techniques

Figure 7 Antiseptics and strictly followed rules of cleanliness have made surgical procedures safer than they once were.

Describe *the differences you see in the two operating scenes shown.*

Mini LAB

Observing Antiseptic Action

Procedure 🔊 ⚗️ 🧪 🥽

1. Place a few grains of **dried yeast** onto a **glass plate** or a saucer.
2. Add two drops of **hydrogen peroxide** to the yeast. Observe.
3. Clean up and wash hands before removing goggles.

Analysis

1. How does the action of hydrogen peroxide mechanically clean a wound?
2. Explain why hydrogen peroxide is classified as an antiseptic.

Keeping Clean Washing your hands before or after certain activities should be part of your daily routine. Restaurant employees are required to wash their hands immediately after using the rest room. Medical professionals wash their hands before examining each patient. However, hand washing was not always a routine, even for doctors. Into the late 1800s, doctors such as those in **Figure 7** regularly operated in their street clothes and with bare, unwashed hands. A bloody apron and well-used tools were considered signs of prestige for a surgeon. More patients died from the infections that they contracted during or after the surgery than from the surgery itself.

Joseph Lister, an English surgeon, recognized the relationship between the infection rate and cleanliness. Lister dramatically reduced the number of deaths among his patients by washing their skin and his hands with carbolic (kar BAH lihk) acid, which is a liquid that kills pathogens. Lister also used carbolic acid to clean his instruments and soak bandages, and he even sprayed the air with it. The odor was strong and it irritated the skin, but more and more people began to survive surgical procedures.

Modern Operating Procedures Today antiseptics and antiseptic soaps are used to kill pathogens on skin. Every person on the surgical team washes his or her hands thoroughly and wears sterile gloves and a covering gown. The patient's skin is cleaned around the area of the body to be operated on and then covered with sterile cloths. Tools that are used to operate on the patient and all operating room equipment also are sterilized. Even the air is filtered.

✔ **Reading Check** *What are three ways that pathogens are reduced in today's operating room?*

Visual Learning

Figure 7 Note the contrast in concern for cleanliness in these illustrations. Have students explain why cleanliness is especially important in the emergency room of a hospital. Because so many people are treated there, rules of cleanliness are strictly observed to prevent the spread of pathogens.

Science Journal

Joseph Lister Have students research Lister's use of a carbolic spray in the operating room to reduce infection. They should infer how this might affect the surgeon's work and write a brief report. L2 IS **Linguistic** P

How Diseases Are Spread

You walk into your kitchen before school. Your younger sister sits at the table eating a bowl of cereal. She has a fever, a runny nose, and a cough. She coughs loudly. "Hey, cover your mouth! I don't want to catch your cold," you tell her. A disease that is caused by a virus, bacterium, protist, or fungus and is spread from an infected organism or the environment to another organism is called an **infectious disease.** Infectious diseases are spread by direct contact with the infected organism, through water and air, on food, by contact with contaminated objects, and by disease-carrying organisms called **biological vectors.** Examples of vectors that have been sources of disease are rats, birds, cats, dogs, mosquitoes, fleas, and flies, as shown in **Figure 8.**

People also can be carriers of disease. When you have influenza and sneeze, you expel thousands of virus particles into the air. Colds and many other diseases are spread through contact. Each time you turn a doorknob, press the button on a water fountain, or use a telephone, your skin comes in contact with bacteria and viruses, which is why regular handwashing is recommended. The Centers for Disease Control and Prevention (CDC) in Atlanta, Georgia, monitors the spread of diseases throughout the United States. The CDC also tracks worldwide epidemics and watches for diseases brought into the United States.

Figure 8 When flies land on food, they can transport pathogens from one location to another.

SECTION 2 Infectious Diseases **D** ◆ **185**

Sexually Transmitted Diseases

Infectious diseases that are passed from person to person during sexual contact are called **sexually transmitted diseases (STDs)**. STDs are caused by bacteria or viruses.

Bacterial STDs Gonorrhea (gah nuh REE uh), chlamydia (kluh MIH dee uh), and syphilis (SIH fuh lus) are STDs caused by bacteria. The bacteria that cause gonorrhea and syphilis are shown in **Figure 9.** A person may have gonorrhea or chlamydia for some time before symptoms appear. When symptoms do appear, they can include painful urination, genital discharge, and genital sores. Antibiotics are used to treat these diseases. Some of the bacteria that cause gonorrhea may be resistant to the antibiotics usually used to treat the infection. However, the disease usually can be treated with other antibiotics. If they are untreated, gonorrhea and chlamydia can leave a person sterile because the reproductive organs can be damaged permanently.

Syphilis has three stages. In stage 1, a sore that lasts 10 to 14 days appears on the mouth or genitals. Stage 2 may involve a rash, fever, and swollen lymph glands. Within weeks to a year, these symptoms usually disappear. The person with syphilis often believes that the disease has gone away, but it hasn't. If he or she does not seek treatment, the disease advances to stage 3, when syphilis may infect the cardiovascular and nervous systems. In all stages, syphilis is treatable with antibiotics. However, the damage to body organs in stage 3 cannot be reversed and death can result.

Viral STDs Genital herpes, a lifelong viral disease, causes painful blisters on the sex organs. This type of herpes can be transmitted during sexual contact or from an infected mother to her child during birth. The herpes virus hides in the body for long periods of time and then reappears suddenly. Herpes has no cure, and no vaccine can prevent it. However, the symptoms of herpes can be treated with antiviral medicines.

Figure 9 Bacteria that cause gonorrhea and syphilis can be destroyed with antibiotics.
Explain why a person might not get treatment for a syphilis infection.

Gonorrhea bacteria

Color-enhanced TEM Magnification: 12000×

Syphilis bacteria

Color-enhanced SEM Magnification: 45000×

Curriculum Connection

Health The previous indiscriminate use of antibiotics in the treatment of STDs has resulted in the development of drug-resistant strains of bacteria. Modern methods of treatment use more potent forms of antibiotics and combinations of drugs. Ask students to write a paragraph about the problems that drug-resistant bacteria pose for individuals and society. L2 ELL IS **Linguistic**

HIV and Your Immune System

Human immunodeficiency virus (HIV) can exist in blood and body fluids. This virus can hide in body cells, sometimes for years. You can become infected with HIV by having sex with an HIV-infected person or by reusing an HIV-contaminated hypodermic needle for an injection. However, a freshly unwrapped sterile needle cannot transmit infection. The risk of getting HIV through blood transfusion is small because all donated blood is tested for the presence of HIV. A pregnant female with HIV can infect her child when the virus passes through the placenta. The child also may become infected from contacts with blood during the birth process or when nursing after birth.

Reading Check *What are ways that a person can become infected with HIV?*

HIV cannot multiply outside the body, and it does not survive long in the environment. The virus cannot be transmitted by touching an infected person, by handling objects used by the person unless they are contaminated with body fluids, or from contact with a toilet seat.

AIDS An HIV infection can lead to Acquired Immune Deficiency Syndrome (AIDS), which is a disease that attacks the body's immune system. HIV, as shown in **Figure 10,** is different from other viruses. It attacks the helper T cells in the immune system. The virus enters the T cell and multiplies. When the infected cell bursts open, it releases more HIV. These infect other T cells. Soon, so many T cells are destroyed that not enough B cells are stimulated to produce antibodies. The body no longer has an effective way to fight invading antigens. The immune system then is unable to fight HIV or any other pathogen. For this reason, when people with AIDS die it is from other diseases such as tuberculosis (too bur kyuh LOH sus), pneumonia, or cancer.

From 1981 to 2001, more than 816,000 cases of AIDS were documented in the United States. At this time the disease has no known cure. However, several medications help treat AIDS in some patients. One group of medicines interferes with the way that the virus multiplies in the host cell and is effective if it is used in the early stages of the disease. Another group of medicines that is being tested blocks the entrance of HIV into the host cell. These medicines prevent the pathogen from binding to the cell's surface.

Figure 10 A person can be infected with HIV and not show any symptoms of the infection for several years.
Infer *why this characteristic makes the spread of AIDS more likely.*

Color-enhanced TEM Magnification: 40000×

187

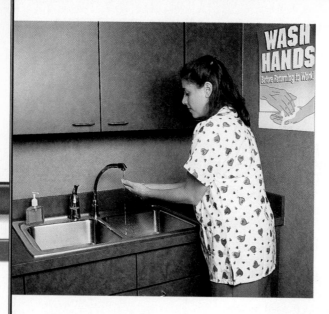

Figure 11 Proper hand washing includes using warm water and soap. The soapy lather must be rubbed over the hands, wrists, fingers, and thumbs for 15–20 s. Thoroughly rinse and dry with a clean towel.

Fighting Disease

Washing a small wound with soap and water is the first step in preventing an infection. Cleaning the wound with an antiseptic and covering it with a bandage are other steps. Is it necessary to wash your body to help prevent diseases? Yes! In addition to reducing body odor, washing your body removes and destroys some surface microorganisms. In medical facilities, hand washing, shown in **Figure 11,** is important to reduce the spread of pathogens. It is also important for everyone to wash his or her hands to reduce the spread of disease.

In your mouth, microorganisms are responsible for mouth odor and tooth decay. Using dental floss and routine tooth brushing keep these organisms under control.

Exercise and good nutrition help the circulatory and respiratory systems work more effectively. Good health habits, including getting enough rest and eating well-balanced meals, can make you less susceptible to the actions of disease organisms such as those that cause colds and flu. Keeping up with recommended immunizations and having annual health checkups also can help you stay healthy.

section 2 review

Summary

Disease in History
- Pasteur, Koch, and Lister played key roles in disease discovery and prevention.

How Diseases Are Spread
- Diseases are spread by air, water, food, animals, and through contact with pathogens.

Sexually Transmitted Diseases
- STDs, such as gonorrhea and herpes, are caused by either bacteria or viruses.

HIV and Your Immune System
- HIV can lead to AIDS, a disease of the immune system.

Fighting Disease
- Cleanliness, exercise, and good health habits can help prevent disease.

Self Check

1. **Explain** how the discoveries of Pasteur, Koch, and Lister help in the battle against the spread of disease.
2. **Identify** three infectious diseases caused by a virus and three caused by a bacterium.
3. **Define** sexually transmitted diseases. How are they contracted and treated?
4. **Describe** the way HIV affects the immune system and how it is different from other viruses.
5. **Think Critically** In what ways does Koch's procedure demonstrate the use of scientific methods?

Applying Skills

6. **Recognize Cause and Effect** How is poor cleanliness related to the spread of disease? Write your answer in your Science Journal.

 Science Online bookd.msscience.com/self_check_quiz

section 2 review

1. Pasteur: discovered bacteria could cause disease; Koch: developed methods to isolate bacteria; Lister: related infection to lack of cleanliness.
2. Possible answer: virus—colds, AIDS, measles; bacterium—tetanus, strep throat, tuberculosis
3. contracted through sexual activity with an infected person; bacterial STDs are treated with antibiotics; symptoms of viral STDs often can be alleviated with antiviral medicines
4. HIV destroys T cells so not enough B cells are stimulated to produce antibodies. Unlike other viruses, HIV attacks the helper T cells.
5. Possible answer: Koch used strict isolation techniques and retested suspected pathogens.
6. Poor cleanliness can allow disease organisms on the body to be transmitted to other people through physical contact or contact with a common object.

MICROORGANISMS AND DISEASE

Microorganisms are everywhere. Washing your hands and disinfecting items you use helps remove some of these organisms.

Real-World Question

How do microorganisms cause infection?

Goals

- **Observe** the transmission of microorganisms.
- **Relate** microorganisms to infections.

Materials

fresh apples (6)	paper towels
rotting apple	sandpaper
rubbing alcohol (5 mL)	cotton ball
self-sealing plastic bags (6)	soap and water
labels and pencil	newspaper
gloves	

Safety Precautions

WARNING: *Do not eat the apples.* When you complete the experiment, give all bags to your teacher for disposal.

Procedure

1. **Label** the plastic bags *1* through *6*. Put on gloves. Place a fresh apple in bag *1*.
2. Rub the rotting apple over the other five apples. This is your source of microorganisms. **WARNING:** *Do not touch your face.*
3. Put one apple in bag *2*.
4. Hold one apple 1.5 m above a newspaper on the floor and drop it. Put it in bag *3*.
5. Rub one apple with sandpaper. Place this apple in bag *4*.

6. Wash one apple with soap and water. Dry well and put it in bag *5*.
7. Use a cotton ball to spread alcohol over the last apple. Let it air dry. Place it in bag *6*.
8. Seal all bags and put them in a dark place.
9. Copy the data table below. On days 3 and 7, compare all apples without removing them from the bags. **Record** your observations.

Apple Observations

Condition	Day 3	Day 7
1. Fresh	no change	no change
2. Untreated	no change	some decay
3. Dropped	brown spots	some decay
4. Rubbed with sandpaper	some brown at soft areas	decay at soft areas
5. Washed with soap and water	no change	little or no change
6. Covered with alcohol	no change	no change

Conclude and Apply

1. **Infer** how this experiment relates to infections on your skin.
2. **Explain** why it is important to clean a wound.

Communicating Your Data

Prepare a poster illustrating the advantages of washing hands to avoid the spread of disease. Get permission to put the poster near a school rest room.

LAB D ◆ 189

Communicating Your Data

Students may want to include other good health habits that will help them fight disease. Posters dealing with good nutrition might be posted near the school cafeteria.

Real-World Question

Purpose to predict and explain how microbes spread [L2] [IS] **Visual-Spatial**

Process Skills observe and infer, predict, interpret data, compare and contrast, recognize cause and effect, separate and control variables

Time Required 30 minutes for initial setup; 15 minutes of observation time on days 3 and 7

Procedure

Safety Precautions Have students wash their hands after handling microorganisms. Provide for safe disposal of the rotting apples.

Teaching Strategy Point out that bruises may be caused by bacteria.

Conclude and Apply

1. Pathogens can cause infections by entering damaged or cut surfaces on an organism's skin.
2. Cleaning a wound removes pathogens and prevents infection.

☑ Assessment

Performance To further assess students' understanding of microorganisms and disease, repeat the activity using 3% hydrogen peroxide to clean an infected apple. Determine whether it stops bacterial growth. Use **Performance Assessment in the Science Classroom**, p. 97.

1 Motivate

Bellringer

INTERACTIVE CHALKBOARD
PowerPoint® Presentations

Section Focus Transparencies
also are available on the
Interactive Chalkboard CD-ROM.

L2 ELL

SECTION 3 Section Focus Transparency Ah-Chooo! (Gesundheit)

Organisms are not the only things that can make you sick. Matter present in the environment, such as toxic chemicals, particles, and certain types of fibers, also can cause disease. The spiny spheres you see below are responsible for a certain type of allergic reaction that afflicts many people. Can you guess what they are?

1. How do allergies affect people?
2. What kind of help is there for allergy sufferers?
3. If people work around materials such as asbestos, burning tar, or smoke, what kinds of safety equipment should they use?

Immunity and Disease

Tie to Prior Knowledge

Can't Catch It Have students recall that some diseases are not "catching." This means they are not transmitted by pathogens. Have students list as many of these diseases as they can. Possible answers: cancer, heart disease, leukemia, diabetes

---

as you read

What **You'll Learn**

- **Define** noninfectious diseases and list causes of them.
- **Describe** the basic characteristics of cancer.
- **Explain** what happens during an allergic reaction.
- **Explain** how chemicals in the environment can be harmful to humans.

Why **It's Important**

Knowing the causes of noninfectious diseases can help you understand their prevention and treatment.

Review Vocabulary
gene: a section of DNA on a chromosome that carries instructions for making a specific protein

New Vocabulary
- noninfectious disease
- allergy
- allergen
- chemotherapy

Figure 12 Allergic reactions are caused by many things.

Hives are one kind of allergic reaction.

Some common substances stimulate allergic responses in people.

Chronic Disease

It's a beautiful, late-summer day. Flowers are blooming everywhere. You and your cousin hurry to get to the ballpark before the first pitch of the game. "Achoo!" Your cousin sneezes. Her eyes are watery and red. "Oh no! I sure don't want to catch that cold," you mutter. "I don't have a cold," she responds, "it's my allergies." Not all diseases are caused by pathogens. Diseases and disorders such as diabetes, allergies, asthma, cancer, and heart disease are **noninfectious diseases.** They are not spread from one person to another. Many are chronic (KRAH nihk). This means that they can last for a long time. Although some chronic diseases can be cured, others cannot.

Some infectious diseases can be chronic too. For example, deer ticks carry a bacterium that causes Lyme disease. This bacterium can affect the nervous system, heart, and joints for weeks to years. It can become chronic if not treated. Antibiotics will kill the bacteria, but some damage cannot be reversed.

Allergies

If you've had an itchy rash after eating a certain food, you probably have an allergy to that food. An **allergy** is an overly strong reaction of the immune system to a foreign substance. Many people have allergic reactions, such as the one shown in **Figure 12,** to cosmetics, shellfish, strawberries, peanuts, and insect stings. Most allergic reactions are minor. However, severe allergic reactions can occur, causing shock and even death if they aren't treated promptly.

190 ◆ D CHAPTER 7 Immunity and Disease

Allergens Substances that cause an allergic response are called **allergens.** Some chemicals, certain foods, pollen, molds, some antibiotics, and dust are allergens for some people. Some foods cause hives or stomach cramps and diarrhea. Pollen can cause a stuffy nose, breathing difficulties, watery eyes, and a tired feeling in some people. Dust can contain cat and dog dander and dust mites, as shown in **Figure 13.** Asthma (AZ muh) is a lung disorder that is associated with reactions to allergens. A person with asthma can have shortness of breath, wheezing, and coughing when he or she comes into contact with something they are allergic to.

When you come in contact with an allergen, your immune system usually forms antibodies. Your body reacts by releasing chemicals called histamines (HIHS tuh meenz) that promote red, swollen tissues. Antihistamines are medications that can be used to treat allergic reactions and asthma. Some severe allergies are treated with repeated injections of small doses of the allergen. This allows your body to become less sensitive to the allergen.

 Reading Check *What does your body release in response to an allergen?*

Diabetes

A chronic disease associated with the levels of insulin produced by the pancreas is diabetes. Insulin is a hormone that enables glucose to pass from the bloodstream into your cells. Doctors recognize two types of diabetes—Type 1 and Type 2. Type 1 diabetes is the result of too little or no insulin production. In Type 2 diabetes, your body cannot properly process the insulin. Symptoms of diabetes include fatigue, excessive thirst, frequent urination, and tingling sensations in the hands and feet.

If glucose levels in the blood remain high for a long time, health problems can develop. These problems can include blurred vision, kidney failure, heart attack, stroke, loss of feeling in the feet, and the loss of consciousness (diabetic coma). Patients with Type 1 diabetes, as shown in **Figure 14,** must monitor their intake of sugars and usually require daily injections of insulin to control their glucose levels. Careful monitoring of diet and weight usually are enough to control Type 2 diabetes. Since 1980, there has been an increase in the number of people with diabetes. Although the cause of diabetes is unknown, scientists have discovered that Type 2 diabetes is more common in people who are overweight and that it might be inherited.

Color-enhanced SEM Magnification: 245×

Figure 13 Dust mites are smaller than a period at the end of a sentence. They can live in pillows, mattresses, carpets, furniture, and other places.

Figure 14 Type 1 diabetes requires daily monitoring by either checking the amount of glucose in blood or the amount excreted in urine.

Teacher FYI

Anaphylactic Shock Sometimes the body may experience an intense reaction to an allergen, causing blood vessels to dilate and bronchiole tubes to constrict. This condition is known as anaphylactic shock and can lead to death if not treated. A single beesting to a hypersensitive person can trigger anaphylactic shock.

Reading Check

Answer histamines

Fun Fact

Dander—human or animal skin flakes—is a favorite food of dust mites. Humans shed about six grams of dead skin each week, so dust mites rarely go hungry.

Use an Analogy

Antihistamine Action The neutralizing action of antihistamines to the histamines produced in allergic reactions can be compared to acids neutralizing bases in chemical reactions.

Teacher FYI

Diabetes Numbers An estimated 17 million people in the United States have diabetes, but only two-thirds of them are aware of it. Only about 10 percent of people with diabetes have Type 1; about 90 percent have Type 2.

Differentiated Instruction

Challenge Have a team of students prepare a joint report and a poster on first-aid procedures for individuals who are experiencing a severe allergic reaction. Have them present their material to the class. L3 ELL COOP LEARN IS **Interpersonal**

Chemicals and Disease

 INTEGRATE Chemistry

Chemicals are everywhere—in your body, the foods you eat, cosmetics, cleaning products, pesticides, fertilizers, and building materials. Of the thousands of chemical substances used by consumers, less than two percent are harmful. Those chemicals that are harmful to living things are called toxins, as shown in **Figure 15.** Toxins can cause birth defects, cell mutations, cancers, tissue damage, chronic diseases, and death.

The Effects The amount of a chemical that is taken into your body and how long your body is in contact with it determine how it affects you. For example, low levels of a toxin might cause cardiac or respiratory problems. However, higher levels of the same toxin might cause death. Some chemicals, such as the asbestos shown in **Figure 15,** can be inhaled over a long period of time. Eventually, the asbestos can cause chronic diseases of the lungs. Lead-based paints, if ingested, can accumulate in your body and eventually cause damage to the central nervous system. Another toxin, ethyl (EH thul) alcohol, is found in beer, wine, and liquor. It can cause birth defects in the children of mothers who drink alcohol during pregnancy.

Manufacturing, mining, transportation, and farming produce chemical wastes. These chemical substances interfere with the ability of soil, water, and air to support life. Pollution, caused by harmful chemicals, sometimes produces chronic diseases in humans. For example, long-term exposure to carbon monoxide, sulfur oxides, and nitrogen oxides in the air might cause a number of diseases, including bronchitis, emphysema (em fuh ZEE muh), and lung cancer.

Figure 15 Toxins can be in the environment.

Chemical spills can be dangerous and might end up in groundwater.

These scientists are testing the contents of barrels found in a dump.

Asbestos, if inhaled into the lungs over a long period of time, can cause chronic diseases of the lungs. Protective clothing must be worn when removing asbestos.

Table 3 Characteristics of Cancer Cells

Cell growth is uncontrolled.
These cells do not function as part of your body.
The cells take up space and interfere with normal bodily functions.
The cells travel throughout your body.
The cells produce tumors and abnormal growths anywhere in your body.

Cancer

Cancer has been a disease of humans since ancient times. Egyptian mummies show evidence of bone cancer. Ancient Greek scientists described several different kinds of cancers. Even medieval manuscripts report details about the disease.

Cancer is the name given to a group of closely related diseases that result from uncontrolled cell growth. It is a complicated disease, and no one fully understands how cancers form. Characteristics of cancer cells are shown in **Table 3.** Certain regulatory molecules in the body control the beginning and ending of cell division. If this control is lost, a mass of cells called a tumor (TEW mur) results from this abnormal growth. Tumors can occur anywhere in your body. Cancerous cells can leave a tumor, spread throughout the body via blood and lymph vessels, and then invade other tissues.

Reading Check *How do cancers spread?*

Types of Cancers Cancers can develop in any body tissue or organ. Leukemia (lew KEE mee uh) is a cancer of white blood cells. The cancerous white blood cells are immature and are no longer effective in fighting disease. The cancer cells multiply in the bone marrow and crowd out red blood cells, normal white blood cells, and platelets. Cancer of the lungs often starts in the bronchi and then spreads into the lungs. The surface area for air exchange in the lungs is reduced and breathing becomes difficult. Colorectal cancer, or cancer of the large intestine, is one of the leading causes of death among men and women. Changes in bowel movements and blood in the feces may be indications of the disease. In breast cancer, tumors grow in the breast. The second most common cancer in males is cancer of the prostate gland, which is an organ that surrounds the urethra.

INTEGRATE Environment

Dioxin Danger Dioxin is a dangerous chemical found in small amounts in certain herbicides. It can cause miscarriages, cancers, and liver disorders. Research to find out about the dioxin contamination in Times Beach, Missouri. Write a brief report in your Science Journal.

Activity

Top Ten Have students research the top ten causes of death in the United States and identify which are infectious and which are noninfectious. [L2] [IS] **Logical-Mathematical**

INTEGRATE Environment

Dioxin Danger Dioxin was found as a contaminant in the oil that was spread on the roads in Times Beach. The entire town was abandoned in 1983 and much of the surface soil was incinerated.

Career Investigate the qualifications and training of environmental protection specialists. Have students work in small groups to write an advertisement for a job opportunity in this field. [L2]

Reading Check

Answer Cancer cells may leave a tumor and move throughout the body via the blood and lymph vessels.

IDENTIFYING Misconceptions

Reducing Cancer Risk People are often heard to say, "Everything causes cancer, so why bother to do anything?" The fact is that there are a number of specific actions a person can take to reduce the risk of cancer. Students should take these seriously.

Differentiated Instruction

Hearing Impaired Have students request pamphlets from health organizations such as the American Heart Association, the American Cancer Society, the American Diabetes Association, and the Arthritis Foundation, to learn about new treatment methods for some chronic diseases and arrange a bulletin board display for the classroom. [L1] [IS] **Linguistic**

Use Science Words

Word Origin The Latin word for the crab, a crustacean, is *cancer*. Ask students to relate the activities of this animal to the spread of cancer cells. Possible answer: Crabs are known for their tenacious hold on prey with their claws. Cancer cells are tenacious in their invasion of tissues.

Caption Answer

Figure 16 Cleaning product labels note safety precautions and list harmful substances.

Inquiry Lab

Controlling Cancer Growth

Purpose To explore and observe controlling cancer growth, have students design simulations using molds and antibiotics.

Possible Materials white bread, oranges, strawberries, melons, cheese, small glass jars, penicillium, eye dropper

Estimated Time 1 class session for set-up; 5 minutes per week for several weeks

Teaching Strategies

• Students can design an experiment with controls (untreated food) and variables (foods treated with antibiotics).

• Students can predict and then observe how an antibiotic controls the growth of molds on various foods. (Foods should be left exposed to the air.)

• What effect does an antibiotic have on mold growth? slows or stops growth How does this experiment compare to how scientists try and control cancer growth? Scientists note the effects of different medicines on cancer growths.

For additional inquiry activities, see *Science Inquiry Labs.*

Figure 16 Tobacco products have been linked directly to lung cancer. Some chemicals around the home are carcinogenic.
Explain *why labels should not be removed from cleaning products.*

Causes In the latter part of the eighteenth century, a British physician recognized the association of soot to cancer in chimney sweeps. Since that time, scientists have learned more about causes of cancer. Research done in the 1940s and 1950s related genes to cancer.

Although not all the causes of cancer are known, many causes have been identified. Smoking has been linked to lung cancer. Lung cancer is the leading cause of cancer deaths for males in the United States. Exposure to certain chemicals also can increase your chances of developing cancer. These substances, called carcinogens (kar SIH nuh junz), include asbestos, various solvents, heavy metals, alcohol, and home and garden chemicals, as shown in **Figure 16.**

Exposure to X rays, nuclear radiation, and ultraviolet radiation of the Sun also increases your risk of getting cancer. Exposure to ultraviolet radiation might lead to skin cancer. Certain foods that are cured, or smoked, including barbecued meats, can give rise to cancers. Some food additives and certain viruses are suspected of causing cancers. Some people have a genetic predisposition for cancer, meaning that they have genes that make them more susceptible to the disease. This does not mean that they definitely will have cancer, but if it is triggered by certain factors they have a greater chance of developing cancer.

Treatment Surgery to remove cancerous tissue, radiation with X rays to kill cancer cells, and chemotherapy are some treatments for cancer. **Chemotherapy** (kee moh THER uh pee) is the use of chemicals to destroy cancer cells. However, early detection of cancer is the key to any successful treatment.

Research in the science of immune processes, called immunology, has led to some new approaches for treating cancer. For example, specialized antibodies produced in the laboratory are being tested as anticancer agents. These antibodies are used as carriers to deliver medicines and radioactive substances directly to cancer cells. In another test, killer T cells are removed from a cancer patient and treated with chemicals that stimulate T cell production. The treated cells are then reinjected into the patient. Trial tests have shown some success in destroying certain types of cancer cells with this technique.

Curriculum Connection

Health People who smoke pipes or cigars generally do not inhale. This reduces their chances for developing lung cancer and emphysema. However, since the burning tobacco is in close contact with the mouth and these products have a higher content of nicotine and tars than cigarettes, the smoker has a high risk of developing cancers of the lips and mouth. Have students make a poster to illustrate these facts. L2 LS **Kinesthetic**

Teacher FYI

Cancer History Examination of bones from Neolithic people, Egyptian mummies, and pre-Columbian Native Americans has revealed cancerous tumors. Ancient writings from Egypt, Babylon, and India give descriptions of malignant tumors. Hippocrates described the differences between benign and malignant tumors.

Prevention Knowing some causes of cancer might help you prevent it. The first step is to know the early warning signs, shown in **Table 4.** Medical attention and treatments such as chemotherapy or surgery in the early stages of some cancers can cure or keep them inactive.

A second step in cancer prevention concerns lifestyle choices. Choosing not to use tobacco and alcohol products can help prevent mouth and lung cancers and the other associated respiratory and circulatory system diseases. Selecting a healthy diet without many foods that are high in fats, salt, and sugar also might reduce your chances of developing cancer. Using sunscreen lotions and limiting the amount of time that you expose your skin to direct sunlight are good preventive measures against skin cancer. Before using harmful home or garden chemicals, carefully read the entire label and precisely follow precautions and directions for use.

Inhaling certain air pollutants such as carbon monoxide, sulfur dioxide, and asbestos fibers is dangerous to your health. To keep the air cleaner, the U.S. Government has regulations such as the Clean Air Act. These laws are intended to reduce the amount of these substances that are released into the air.

Table 4 Early Warning Signs of Cancer
Changes in bowel or bladder habits
A sore that does not heal
Unusual bleeding or discharge
Thickening or lump in the breast or elsewhere
Indigestion or difficulty swallowing
Obvious change in a wart or mole
Nagging cough or hoarseness

Provided by the National Cancer Institute

---

section 3 review

Summary

Chronic Disease
- Chronic diseases last for a long time.
- Allergies are strong reactions to foreign substances.
- Diabetes is a chronic disease associated with your body's insulin levels.

Chemicals and Disease
- Harmful chemicals can cause birth defects, cancers, chronic diseases, and death.

Cancer
- Cancer results from uncontrolled cell growth.
- Early detection and healthy lifestyle choices can help in the treatment or prevention of some cancers.

Self Check

1. **Infer** why diabetes is classified as a noninfectious disease.
2. **Describe** how toxins in the environment can be harmful to your body.
3. **Explain** how cancer cells affect body organ functions.
4. **Identify** some ways your body can respond to allergens.
5. **Think Critically** Joel has an ear infection. The doctor prescribes an antibiotic. After taking the antibiotic, Joel breaks out in a rash. What is happening to him?

Applying Math

6. **Make and Use Tables** Make a table that relates several causes of cancer and their effects on your body.

 Science Online bookd.msscience.com/self_check_quiz

SECTION 3 Noninfectious Diseases **D ◆ 195**

---

section 3 review

1. Diabetes is not caused by a pathogen.
2. Exposure to environmental toxins can increase your chances of developing cancer.
3. crowd out blood cells in bone marrow; reduce surface area for gas exchange in lungs
4. Your immune system forms antibodies; your body reacts by releasing chemicals called histamines.
5. Joel's immune system formed antibodies and he seems to be having an allergic reaction to the antibiotic.
6. cause: smoking, effect: impaired lung functioning; cause: ultraviolet light, effect: abnormal skin growths; cause: asbestos, effect: impaired lung functioning

SECTION 3 Noninfectious Diseases **D ◆ 195**

Design Your Own

Real-World Question

Purpose Students determine how bicarbonates in saliva protect their mouths from bacteria and chemical substances. L2

COOP LEARN **Kinesthetic**

Process Skills prepare a data table, observe, compare, identify and manipulate controls and variables, explain, predict

Time Required two 45-minute periods

Possible Materials

- The red cabbage juice should be prepared by chopping the cabbage into small pieces and boiling the pieces for 20 to 30 minutes. The juice must be filtered before it is used as an indicator.

- Dilute HCl can be used in place of vinegar or lemon juice. Prepare dilute acid by dissolving 80 mL of concentrated Wheal in 1 L of water.

Safety Precautions Students should wear safety goggles. Caution students not to eat or drink anything in science class.

Form a Hypothesis

Possible Hypothesis Many students will hypothesize that bicarbonates will neutralize acids to some degree.

Goals
- **Design** an experiment to test the reaction of a bicarbonate to acids and bases.
- **Test** the reaction of a bicarbonate to acids and bases.

Possible Materials
head of red cabbage
cooking pot
coffee filter
drinking glasses
clear household ammonia
baking soda
water
spoon
white vinegar
lemon juice
orange juice

Safety Precautions

WARNING: *Never eat or drink anything used in an investigation.*

Defensive Saliva

Real-World Question

What happens when you think about a juicy cheeseburger or smell freshly baked bread? Your mouth starts making saliva. Saliva is the first line of defense for fighting harmful bacteria, acids, and bases entering your body. Saliva contains salts, including bicarbonates. An example of a bicarbonate found in your kitchen is baking soda. Bicarbonates help to maintain normal pH levels in your mouth. When surfaces in your mouth have normal pH levels, the growth of bacteria is slowed and the effects of acids and bases are reduced. In this activity, you will design your own experiment to show the importance of saliva bicarbonates. How do the bicarbonates in saliva work to protect your mouth from harmful bacteria, acids, and bases?

Form a Hypothesis

Based on your reading in the text, form a hypothesis to explain how the bicarbonates in saliva react to acids and bases.

Alternative Inquiry Lab

The Effect of Bicarbonates As an alternate lab, have students design an experiment to test the effect of bicarbonates on acids and bases using red and blue litmus paper instead of cabbage juice. Acids will turn blue litmus paper red; bases will turn red litmus paper blue.

Students can extend the lab by testing bicarbonates used in over-the-counter medicines to neutralize acids and bases. Common bicarbonates include: magnesium carbonate ($MgCO_3$), calcium carbonate ($CaCO_3$), and sodium bicarbonate ($NaHCO$).

▶ Test Your Hypothesis

Make a Plan

1. **List** the materials you will need for your experiment. Red cabbage juice can be used as an indicator to test for acids and bases. Vinegar and citrus juices are acids, ammonia is a base, and baking soda (bicarbonate of soda) is a bicarbonate.

2. **Describe** how you will prepare the red cabbage juice and how you will use it to test for the presence of acids and bases.

3. **Describe** how you will test the effect of bicarbonate on acids and bases.

4. **List** the steps you will take to set up and complete your experiment. Describe exactly what you will do in each step.

5. Prepare a data table in your Science Journal to record your observations.

6. **Examine** the steps of your experiment to make certain they are in logical order.

Follow Your Plan

1. Ask your teacher to examine the steps of your experiment and data table before you start.

2. Conduct your experiment according to the approved plan.

3. **Record** your observations in your data table.

▶ Analyze Your Data

1. **Compare** the color change of the acids and bases in the cabbage juice.

2. **Describe** how well the bicarbonate neutralized the acids and bases.

3. **Identify** any problems you had while setting up and conducting your experiment.

▶ Conclude and Apply

1. **Conclude** whether or not your results support your hypothesis.

2. **Explain** why your saliva contains a bicarbonate based on your experiment.

3. **Predict** how quickly bacteria would grow in your glass containing acid compared to another glass containing acid and the bicarbonate.

4. **Describe** how saliva protects your mouth from bacteria.

5. **Predict** what would happen if your saliva were made of only water.

Communicating Your Data

Using what you learned in this experiment, create a poster about the importance of good dental hygiene. Invite a dental hygienist to speak to your class.

LAB D ◆ 197

▶ Test Your Hypothesis

Possible Procedure Add four parts acid or base to one part red cabbage juice indicator. Add a spoonful of bicarbonate a little at a time until a color change is observed. Proportions of the ingredients may have to be adjusted depending on their strength.

Teaching Strategies Most students will be familiar with the terms *acid* and *base* and understand that a base is the opposite of an acid.

Expected Outcomes The bicarbonate should neutralize both acids and bases as indicated by the appropriate color change.

▶ Analyze Your Data

Answers to Questions

1. Acids turn pink; bases turn green.
2. All the solutions will turn blue, signifying both acids and bases are neutralized.
3. Common problems include the preparation of cabbage juice and determining the proportions of the substances.

Error Analysis Have students compare the color changes that occurred during their experiments and explain why differences were observed.

▶ Conclude and Apply

1. Answers will vary.
2. Bicarbonates in saliva neutralize harmful acids and bases.
3. Bacteria would grow more rapidly in acid without bicarbonate added.
4. Bicarbonates maintain neutral pH levels to slow bacterial growth.
5. Acids and bases from foods would easily damage tooth enamel.

✔ Assessment

Oral Have students explain how the strength of acids, bases, and neutral substances are compared. pH values of 1 to 6 indicate acids with 1 being the strongest. pH values of 8 to 14 are bases with 14 being the strongest base. Neutral substances have a value of 7.

Communicating Your Data

Encourage students to illustrate their posters with drawings. They may wish to make the poster a cartoon in which the main character is a tooth that explains the steps in good oral hygiene.

Content Background

The development of antibiotics has significantly changed medicine. Injuries and illnesses that were once fatal are now easily treated. How do antibiotics kill bacteria without harming the cells of the person being treated? The key is the differences between bacterial cells and animal cells. For example, some antibiotics work by inhibiting cell wall formation. Because human cells do not have a cell wall, the drug does not affect them. Other antibiotics are less specific to bacterial characteristics, and therefore more toxic to humans.

Discussion

New Developments Why is there always a need for newly developed or discovered antibiotics? Bacteria develop resistance to antibiotics over time. A newly developed or discovered antibiotic may allow treatment of bacteria that have developed resistance to other drugs.

Activity

Interview Have student pairs interview their grandparents or older family friends. Have students ask about treatments for disease and infection that were used in the past. If interview subjects are not available, have students use reference materials to find their information. Students should present their findings to the class. **IS Interpersonal**

Applying Math

Answer about 7.2 million

SCIENCE Stats

Battling Bacteria

Did you know...

... **The term** *antibiotic* was first coined by an American microbiologist. The scientist received a Nobel prize in 1952 for the discovery of streptomycin (strep toh MY suhn), an antibiotic used against tuberculosis.

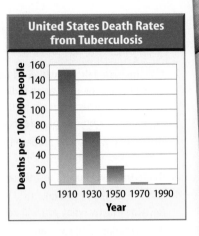

United States Death Rates from Tuberculosis

...**In recent decades many bacteria have become resistant** to antibiotics. For example, one group of bacteria that cause illnesses of the stomach and intestines—*Shigella* (shih GEL uh)—became harder to control. In 1985, less than one third of *Shigella* were resistant to the antibiotic ampicillin (am puh SI luhn). By 1991, however, more than two thirds of *Shigella* were resistant to the drug.

> **Applying Math** It is believed that 30 percent of the antibiotics prescribed for ear infections are unnecessary. Using the graph, calculate the number of unnecessary prescriptions.

Antibiotics Prescribed Each Year in the United States

...**People have long used natural remedies** to treat infections. These remedies include garlic, *Echinacea* (purple coneflower), and an antibiotic called squalamine, found in sharks' stomachs.

Find Out About It

Visit bookd.msscience.com/science_stats **to research the production of four antibiotics. Create a graph comparing the number of kilograms of each antibiotic produced in one year.**

Find Out About It

Have interested students research ethnobotany, the scientific study of plants used by particular cultural groups. Researchers in this field have explored many substances used as medicine in different areas of the world. Students should report their findings to the class. **L2 IS Linguistic**

Visual Learning

The Term *Antibiotic* Have students use the data in the graph to determine the effectiveness of antibiotics on decreasing the number of deaths due to tuberculosis. Deaths decreased from 25 per 100,000 in 1950 (before antibiotics) to 3 per 100,000 in 1970 (after antibiotics).

Reviewing Main Ideas

Section 1 The Immune System

1. Your body is protected against most pathogens by the immune system.

2. Active immunity is long lasting, but passive immunity is not.

3. Antigens are foreign molecules in your body. Your body makes an antibody that attaches to an antigen, making it harmless.

Section 2 Infectious Diseases

1. Pasteur and Koch discovered that microorganisms cause diseases. Lister learned that cleanliness helps control microorganisms.

2. Pathogens can be spread by air, water, food, and animal contact. Bacteria, viruses, fungi, and protists can cause infectious diseases.

3. Sexually transmitted diseases can be passed between persons during sexual contact.

4. HIV damages your body's immune system.

Section 3 Noninfectious Diseases

1. Causes of noninfectious diseases, such as diabetes and cancer, include genetics, chemicals, poor diet, and uncontrolled cell growth.

2. An allergy is a reaction of the immune system to a foreign substance.

3. Cancer results from uncontrolled cell growth, causing cells to multiply, spread through the body, and invade normal tissue.

4. Cancer is treated with surgery, chemotherapy, and radiation. Early detection can help cure or slow some cancers.

Visualizing Main Ideas

Copy and complete the following concept map on infectious diseases.

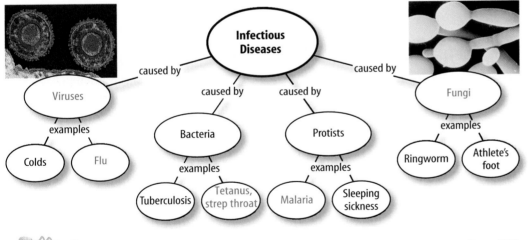

Infectious Diseases

caused by — Viruses — examples — Colds, Flu

caused by — Bacteria — examples — Tuberculosis, Tetanus, strep throat

caused by — Protists — examples — Malaria, Sleeping sickness

caused by — Fungi — examples — Ringworm, Athlete's foot

Reviewing Main Ideas

Summary statements can be used by students to review the major concepts of the chapter.

Visualizing Main Ideas

See student page.

Science⬤nline

Visit bookd.msscience.com
/self_check_quiz
/interactive_tutor
/vocabulary_puzzlemaker
/chapter_review
/standardized_test
/field_guide

Assessment Transparency

For additional assessment questions, use the *Assessment Transparency* located in the transparency book.

Assessment

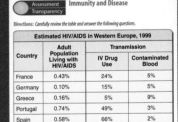

Assessment Transparency — Immunity and Disease

Directions: Carefully review the table and answer the following questions.

Estimated HIV/AIDS in Western Europe, 1999

Country	Adult Population Living with HIV/AIDS	Transmission	
		IV Drug Use	Contaminated Blood
France	0.43%	24%	5%
Germany	0.10%	15%	5%
Greece	0.16%	5%	9%
Portugal	0.74%	49%	3%
Spain	0.58%	66%	2%

1. According to the table, which country has the highest percentage of people with HIV/AIDS?
A France   C Portugal
B Germany   D Spain

2. According to the table, which country has the highest percentage of infection by blood transfusions?
F France
G Germany
H Greece
J Portugal

3. According to the table, which country has the highest percentage of people infected by drug use?
A France
B Germany
C Spain
D Greece

chapter **7** **Review**

Using Vocabulary

1. antigen
2. biological vector
3. infectious disease
4. vaccination
5. Active immunity
6. allergen
7. pasteurization
8. noninfectious disease

Checking Concepts

9. A
10. D
11. A
12. D
13. A
14. C
15. A
16. C
17. A
18. A

Using Vocabulary

active immunity p. 179	infectious disease p. 185
allergen p. 191	noninfectious disease p. 190
allergy p. 190	passive immunity p. 179
antibody p. 178	pasteurization p. 182
antigen p. 178	sexually transmitted
biological vector p. 185	disease (STD) p. 186
chemotherapy p. 194	vaccination p. 179
immune system p. 176	virus p. 182

Fill in the blanks with the correct vocabulary words.

1. A(n) _____ can cause infectious diseases.

2. A disease-carrying organism is called a(n) _____.

3. Measles is an example of _____.

4. Injection of weakened viruses is called _____.

5. _____ occurs when your body makes its own antibodies.

6. A(n) _____ stimulates histamine release.

7. Heating a liquid to kill harmful bacteria is called _____.

8. Diabetes is an example of a(n) _____ disease.

Checking Concepts

Choose the word or phrase that best answers the question.

9. Which of the following has not been found to be a biological vector?

   A)   **B)**   **C)**   **D)**

10. How can infectious diseases be caused?
    A) heredity   **C)** chemicals
    B) allergies   **D)** organisms

11. How do scientists know that a pathogen causes a specific disease?
    A) It is present in all cases of the disease.
    B) It does not infect other animals.
    C) It causes other diseases.
    D) It is treated with heat.

12. What is formed in the blood to fight invading antigens?
    A) hormones   **C)** pathogens
    B) allergens   **D)** antibodies

13. Which of the following is one of your body's general defenses against some pathogens?
    A) stomach enzymes
    B) HIV
    C) some vaccines
    D) hormones

14. Which of the following is known as an infectious disease?
    A) allergies   **C)** syphilis
    B) asthma   **D)** diabetes

15. Which disease is caused by a virus that attacks white blood cells?
    A) AIDS   **C)** flu
    B) measles   **D)** polio

16. Which of the following is a characteristic of cancer cells?
    A) controlled cell growth
    B) help your body stay healthy
    C) interfere with normal body functions
    D) do not multiply or spread

17. Which of the following is caused by a virus?
    A) AIDS   **C)** ringworm
    B) gonorrhea   **D)** syphilis

18. How can cancer cells be destroyed?
    A) chemotherapy   **C)** vaccines
    B) antigens   **D)** viruses

Science Online   bookd.msscience.com/vocabulary_puzzlemaker

Use the ExamView® Pro Testmaker CD-ROM to:
- create multiple versions of tests
- create modified tests with one mouse click for inclusion students
- edit existing questions and add your own questions
- build tests aligned with state standards using built-in State Curriculum Tags
- change English tests to Spanish with one mouse click and vice versa

Thinking Critically

19. **Explain** if it is better to vaccinate people or to wait until they build up their own immunity.

20. **Infer** what advantage a breast-fed baby might have compared to a formula-fed baby.

21. **Describe** how your body protects itself from antigens.

22. **Explain** how helper T cells and B cells work to eliminate antigens.

23. **Compare and contrast** antibodies, antigens, and antibiotics.

Use the graph below to answer question 24.

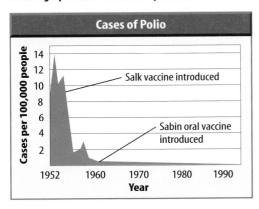

24. **Interpret Data** Using the graph above, explain the rate of polio cases between 1952 and 1965. What conclusions can you draw about the effectiveness of the polio vaccines?

25. **Concept Map** Make a network-tree concept map that compares the various defenses your body has against diseases. Compare general defenses, active immunity, and passive immunity.

  bookd.msscience.com/chapter_review

Performance Activities

26. **Poster** Design and construct a poster to illustrate how a person with the flu could spread the disease to family members, classmates, and others.

Applying Math

27. **Antibiotic Tablets** You have an earache and your doctor prescribes an antibiotic to treat the infection. The antibiotic can be taken as a tablet at dosages of 400 mg or 1,000 mg. How many 400 mg tablets are needed to equal one 1,000 mg tablet?

Use the graph below to answer questions 28 and 29.

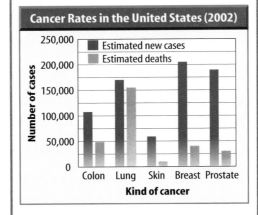

28. **Cancer Cases** The graph above shows the estimated number of new cases and estimated number of deaths for various cancers in the year 2002. Which cancer occurs most frequently? Most infrequently? Estimate the difference between new cases of colon cancer and new cases of skin cancer.

29. **Cancer Deaths** Estimate the difference between deaths from lung cancer and deaths from prostate cancer.

Thinking Critically

19. In many cases, it is better to vaccinate, as the antigens introduced by vaccinations are usually weakened or killed, and will therefore not cause the person to get the disease.

20. Breast-fed babies receive passive immunity from antibodies in their mother's milk.

21. Your skin prevents pathogens from entering the body, white blood cells destroy pathogens, cilia and mucus trap pathogens, and digestive juices kill pathogens that enter the stomach.

22. Helper T cells activate the immune system. B cells form antibodies and remain in the blood to defend against future attacks by the same antigen.

23. Antigens—foreign proteins and chemicals that invade your body; antibodies—formed by your immune system to destroy antigens; antibiotics—medicines that destroy or neutralize pathogens in the body

24. rate dropped after the vaccine was introduced; the dramatic decline was a result of the vaccine

25. General—fever, white blood cells; active immunity—production of antibodies, long-term; passive immunity—antibodies given to body, short-term

Performance Activities

26. Poster could show a person sneezing without covering the mouth and nose, coughing over food, and handling objects without washing hands. Use **Performance Assessment in the Science Classroom**, p. 145.

Applying Math

National Math Standards

1, 5, 6

27. $1{,}000 \div 400 = 2.5$ tablets

28. breast; skin; $107{,}000 - 58{,}000 = 49{,}000$

29. $155{,}000 - 30{,}000 = 125{,}000$

☑ Assessment   Resources

📁 Reproducible Masters
Chapter *Fast File* Resources
Chapter Review, pp. 35–36
Chapter Tests, pp. 37–40
Assessment Transparency Activity, p. 42
Glencoe Science Web site
Chapter Review Test
Standardized Test Practice

Glencoe Technology
🖱 Assessment Transparency
🌐 Exam*View*® Pro Testmaker
📼 MindJogger Videoquiz
🌐 Interactive Chalkboard

FAST FILE

Answer Sheet A practice answer sheet can be found at bookd.msscience.com/answer_sheet.

Part 1 Multiple Choice

1. D
2. B
3. C
4. A
5. C
6. D

Part 2 Short Response

7. washing small wounds with soap and water; washing the body, especially the hands; brushing teeth and using dental floss

8. in the respiratory system, weakens the cell walls of some pathogens; in the digestive tract, coats bacteria and prevents them from binding to the digestive organs

9. Second-line defenses work against only specific pathogens.

10. "Chewing tobacco and snuff cause cancer"

11. "It's safe to smoke for only a year or two," and "Smoking can help you when you're bored"; second pair: "Seeing someone smoke turns me off," and "I strongly dislike being around smokers."

12. overall negative opinions about smoking

Part 1 Multiple Choice

Record your answers on the answer sheet provided by your teacher or on a sheet of paper.

Use the graph below to answer questions 1 and 2.

Life Expectancy by Race and Sex, 1970–1997

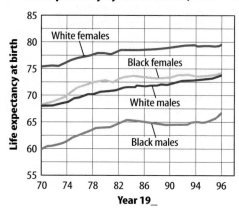

1. According to the information in the graph, which group had the lowest life expectancy in both 1975 and 1994?
   A. white males
   B. black females
   C. white females
   D. black males

2. A reasonable hypothesis based on the information in the graph is that life expectancy
   A. decreased for black males between 1970 and 1984.
   B. is longer for females than for males.
   C. decreased for white males between 1970 and 1980.
   D. is longer for males than for females.

3. Which of the following is NOT a sign of inflammation?
   A. redness   C. bleeding
   B. pain   D. swelling

Use the table below to answer questions 4–6.

Causes of Disease Before and After Vaccine Availability in the U.S.		
Disease	**Average Number of Cases per Year Before Vaccine Available**	**Cases in 1998 After Vaccine Available**
Measles	503,282	89
Diphtheria	175,885	1
Tetanus	1,314	34
Mumps	152,209	606
Rubella	47,745	345
Pertussis (whooping cough)	147,271	6,279

Data from the National Immunization Program, CDC

4. Which of the following diseases had the highest number of cases before vaccine?
   A. diphtheria   C. rubella
   B. mumps   D. pertussis

5. Which of the following diseases had the highest number of cases after vaccine?
   A. measles   C. mumps
   B. tetanus   D. rubella

6. Which of the diseases in the table are caused by bacteria?
   A. measles, rubella, mumps
   B. measles, tetanus, mumps
   C. mumps, pertussis, rubella
   D. tetanus, pertussis, diphtheria

Test-Taking Tip

Missing Information Questions will often ask about missing information. Notice what is missing as well as what is given.

Question 6 Base your answer on choices that can be found in the text, such as *measles* and *tetanus*.

Part 3 Open Ended

13. Active immunity is longer lasting because the body makes its own antibodies in response to an antigen. Some antibodies stay on duty in the blood, and more are rapidly produced if the pathogen enters the body again.

14. Dr. Cavazos can use Koch's Rules: identify the bacteria in every case of the disease, grow the organism with no other organisms present, inoculate the organism into a healthy host which then gets the disease, and remove the organism from the host then grow an organism identical to the original one.

15. Infectious diseases are caused by a pathogen, are spread from an infected organism to other organisms, and may be chronic. Noninfectious diseases are not spread from one person to another, are not caused by a pathogen, and many are chronic.

16. No, the person already has active immunity against measles because the person already had the disease

Part 2 | Short Response/Grid In

Record your answers on the answer sheet provided by your teacher or on a sheet of paper.

7. What are some health practices that can help fight infectious disease?

8. How does mucus help defend your body?

9. Why are the body's second-line defenses called specific immunity?

Use the table below to answer questions 10–12.

Teen Opinions on Smoking			
All numbers are percentages	Agree	Disagree	No opinion or don't know
Seeing someone smoke turns me off	67	22	10
I'd rather date people who don't smoke	86	8	6
It's safe to smoke for only a year or two	7	92	1
Smoking can help you when you're bored	7	92	1
Smoking helps reduce stress	21	78	3
Smoking helps keep your weight down	18	80	2
Chewing tobacco and snuff cause cancer	95	2	3
I strongly dislike being around smokers	65	22	13

Data from CDC

10. According to the table, which statement had the highest percentage of teen agreement?

11. According to the table, which pairs of statements had the same percentages of teen disagreement?

12. According to the information in the table, do teens generally have positive or negative opinions about smoking? Explain.

 Science Online bookd.msscience.com/standardized_test

Part 3 | Open Ended

Record your answers on a sheet of paper.

13. Which is longer lasting—active immunity or passive immunity? Why?

14. Dr. Cavazos has isolated a bacterium that she thinks causes a recently discovered disease. How can she prove it? What steps should she follow?

15. Compare and contrast infectious and noninfectious diseases.

16. Would a vaccination against measles be helpful if a person already had the disease a year ago? Explain.

17. Compare and contrast Type 1 and Type 2 diabetes.

Use the illustration below to answer questions 18 and 19.

18. Explain the four steps of the immune system response.

19. Sometimes a person is born without the cells labeled *2* in the illustration above. If this person was given a vaccination for tetanus, what results would be expected? Explain.

STANDARDIZED TEST PRACTICE D ◆ 203

Rubrics

The following rubrics are sample scoring devices for short response and open-ended questions.

Short Response

Points	Description
2	The student demonstrates a thorough understanding of the science of the task. The response may contain minor flaws that do not detract from the demonstration of a thorough understanding.
1	The student has provided a response that is only partially correct.
0	The student has provided a completely incorrect solution or no response at all.

Open Ended

Points	Description
4	The student demonstrates a thorough understanding of the science of the task. The response may contain minor flaws that do not detract from the demonstration of a thorough understanding.
3	The student demonstrates an understanding of the science of the task. The response is essentially correct and demonstrates an essential but less than thorough understanding of the science.
2	The student demonstrates only a partial understanding of the science of the task. Although the student may have used the correct approach to a solution or may have provided a correct solution, the work lacks an essential understanding of the underlying science concepts.
1	The student demonstrates a very limited understanding of the science of the task. The response is incomplete and exhibits many flaws.
0	The student provides a completely incorrect solution or no response at all.

---

and produced antibodies against it.

17. Both types result in high glucose levels in the blood. Type 1 diabetes is the result of too little or no insulin production. In type 2 diabetes, the body cannot properly process the insulin.

18. Four stages: 1. Recognition; white blood cells surround pathogens

and signal T cells. More T cells are produced. Helper T cells signal B cells. 2. Mobilization: B cells produce antibodies. 3. Disposal: Antibodies destroy pathogens. 4. Immunity: Some antibodies remain for future use.

19. The cell is a B cell which makes antibodies. If these cells are

absent, no antibodies could be made. If the person were given a vaccination against tetanus, no antibodies against tetanus would be made and the person could get tetanus.

Student
Resources

CONTENTS

Scientific Methods

Scientists use an orderly approach called the scientific method to solve problems. This includes organizing and recording data so others can understand them. Scientists use many variations in this method when they solve problems.

Identify a Question

The first step in a scientific investigation or experiment is to identify a question to be answered or a problem to be solved. For example, you might ask which gasoline is the most efficient.

Gather and Organize Information

After you have identified your question, begin gathering and organizing information. There are many ways to gather information, such as researching in a library, interviewing those knowledgeable about the subject, testing and working in the laboratory and field. Fieldwork is investigations and observations done outside of a laboratory.

Researching Information Before moving in a new direction, it is important to gather the information that already is known about the subject. Start by asking yourself questions to determine exactly what you need to know. Then you will look for the information in various reference sources, like the student is doing in **Figure 1.** Some sources may include textbooks, encyclopedias, government documents, professional journals, science magazines, and the Internet. Always list the sources of your information.

Figure 1 The Internet can be a valuable research tool.

Evaluate Sources of Information Not all sources of information are reliable. You should evaluate all of your sources of information, and use only those you know to be dependable. For example, if you are researching ways to make homes more energy efficient, a site written by the U.S. Department of Energy would be more reliable than a site written by a company that is trying to sell a new type of weatherproofing material. Also, remember that research always is changing. Consult the most current resources available to you. For example, a 1985 resource about saving energy would not reflect the most recent findings.

Sometimes scientists use data that they did not collect themselves, or conclusions drawn by other researchers. This data must be evaluated carefully. Ask questions about how the data were obtained, if the investigation was carried out properly, and if it has been duplicated exactly with the same results. Would you reach the same conclusion from the data? Only when you have confidence in the data can you believe it is true and feel comfortable using it.

Interpret Scientific Illustrations As you research a topic in science, you will see drawings, diagrams, and photographs to help you understand what you read. Some illustrations are included to help you understand an idea that you can't see easily by yourself, like the tiny particles in an atom in **Figure 2.** A drawing helps many people to remember details more easily and provides examples that clarify difficult concepts or give additional information about the topic you are studying. Most illustrations have labels or a caption to identify or to provide more information.

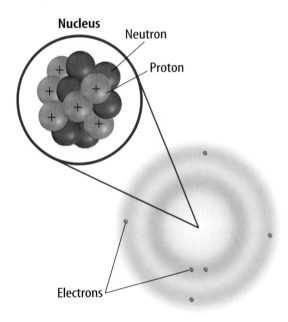

Figure 2 This drawing shows an atom of carbon with its six protons, six neutrons, and six electrons.

Concept Maps One way to organize data is to draw a diagram that shows relationships among ideas (or concepts). A concept map can help make the meanings of ideas and terms more clear, and help you understand and remember what you are studying. Concept maps are useful for breaking large concepts down into smaller parts, making learning easier.

Network Tree A type of concept map that not only shows a relationship, but how the concepts are related is a network tree, shown in **Figure 3.** In a network tree, the words are written in the ovals, while the description of the type of relationship is written across the connecting lines.

When constructing a network tree, write down the topic and all major topics on separate pieces of paper or notecards. Then arrange them in order from general to specific. Branch the related concepts from the major concept and describe the relationship on the connecting line. Continue to more specific concepts until finished.

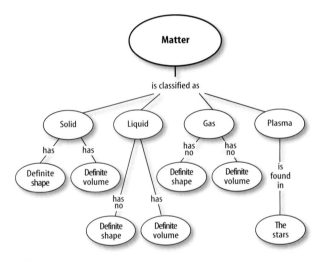

Figure 3 A network tree shows how concepts or objects are related.

Events Chain Another type of concept map is an events chain. Sometimes called a flow chart, it models the order or sequence of items. An events chain can be used to describe a sequence of events, the steps in a procedure, or the stages of a process.

When making an events chain, first find the one event that starts the chain. This event is called the initiating event. Then, find the next event and continue until the outcome is reached, as shown in **Figure 4.**

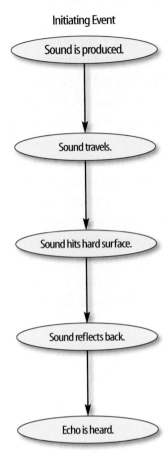

Initiating Event

Sound is produced.

↓

Sound travels.

↓

Sound hits hard surface.

↓

Sound reflects back.

↓

Echo is heard.

Figure 4 Events-chain concept maps show the order of steps in a process or event. This concept map shows how a sound makes an echo.

Cycle Map A specific type of events chain is a cycle map. It is used when the series of events do not produce a final outcome, but instead relate back to the beginning event, such as in **Figure 5.** Therefore, the cycle repeats itself.

To make a cycle map, first decide what event is the beginning event. This is also called the initiating event. Then list the next events in the order that they occur, with the last event relating back to the initiating event. Words can be written between the events that describe what happens from one event to the next. The number of events in a cycle map can vary, but usually contain three or more events.

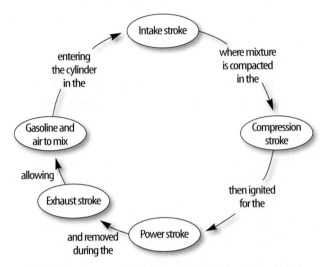

Figure 5 A cycle map shows events that occur in a cycle.

Spider Map A type of concept map that you can use for brainstorming is the spider map. When you have a central idea, you might find that you have a jumble of ideas that relate to it but are not necessarily clearly related to each other. The spider map on sound in **Figure 6** shows that if you write these ideas outside the main concept, then you can begin to separate and group unrelated terms so they become more useful.

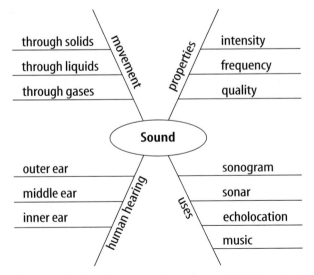

Figure 6 A spider map allows you to list ideas that relate to a central topic but not necessarily to one another.

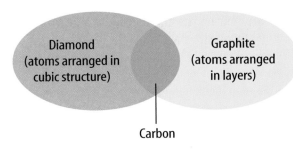

Carbon

Figure 7 This Venn diagram compares and contrasts two substances made from carbon.

Venn Diagram To illustrate how two subjects compare and contrast you can use a Venn diagram. You can see the characteristics that the subjects have in common and those that they do not, shown in **Figure 7.**

To create a Venn diagram, draw two overlapping ovals that that are big enough to write in. List the characteristics unique to one subject in one oval, and the characteristics of the other subject in the other oval. The characteristics in common are listed in the overlapping section.

Make and Use Tables One way to organize information so it is easier to understand is to use a table. Tables can contain numbers, words, or both.

To make a table, list the items to be compared in the first column and the characteristics to be compared in the first row. The title should clearly indicate the content of the table, and the column or row heads should be clear. Notice that in **Table 1** the units are included.

Table 1 Recyclables Collected During Week			
Day of Week	Paper (kg)	Aluminum (kg)	Glass (kg)
Monday	5.0	4.0	12.0
Wednesday	4.0	1.0	10.0
Friday	2.5	2.0	10.0

Make a Model One way to help you better understand the parts of a structure, the way a process works, or to show things too large or small for viewing is to make a model. For example, an atomic model made of a plastic-ball nucleus and pipe-cleaner electron shells can help you visualize how the parts of an atom relate to each other. Other types of models can by devised on a computer or represented by equations.

Form a Hypothesis

A possible explanation based on previous knowledge and observations is called a hypothesis. After researching gasoline types and recalling previous experiences in your family's car you form a hypothesis—our car runs more efficiently because we use premium gasoline. To be valid, a hypothesis has to be something you can test by using an investigation.

Predict When you apply a hypothesis to a specific situation, you predict something about that situation. A prediction makes a statement in advance, based on prior observation, experience, or scientific reasoning. People use predictions to make everyday decisions. Scientists test predictions by performing investigations. Based on previous observations and experiences, you might form a prediction that cars are more efficient with premium gasoline. The prediction can be tested in an investigation.

Design an Experiment A scientist needs to make many decisions before beginning an investigation. Some of these include: how to carry out the investigation, what steps to follow, how to record the data, and how the investigation will answer the question. It also is important to address any safety concerns.

Test the Hypothesis

Now that you have formed your hypothesis, you need to test it. Using an investigation, you will make observations and collect data, or information. This data might either support or not support your hypothesis. Scientists collect and organize data as numbers and descriptions.

Follow a Procedure In order to know what materials to use, as well as how and in what order to use them, you must follow a procedure. **Figure 8** shows a procedure you might follow to test your hypothesis.

Procedure

1. Use regular gasoline for two weeks.
2. Record the number of kilometers between fill-ups and the amount of gasoline used.
3. Switch to premium gasoline for two weeks.
4. Record the number of kilometers between fill-ups and the amount of gasoline used.

Figure 8 A procedure tells you what to do step by step.

Identify and Manipulate Variables and Controls In any experiment, it is important to keep everything the same except for the item you are testing. The one factor you change is called the independent variable. The change that results is the dependent variable. Make sure you have only one independent variable, to assure yourself of the cause of the changes you observe in the dependent variable. For example, in your gasoline experiment the type of fuel is the independent variable. The dependent variable is the efficiency.

Many experiments also have a control—an individual instance or experimental subject for which the independent variable is not changed. You can then compare the test results to the control results. To design a control you can have two cars of the same type. The control car uses regular gasoline for four weeks. After you are done with the test, you can compare the experimental results to the control results.

Collect Data

Whether you are carrying out an investigation or a short observational experiment, you will collect data, as shown in **Figure 9.** Scientists collect data as numbers and descriptions and organize it in specific ways.

Observe Scientists observe items and events, then record what they see. When they use only words to describe an observation, it is called qualitative data. Scientists' observations also can describe how much there is of something. These observations use numbers, as well as words, in the description and are called quantitative data. For example, if a sample of the element gold is described as being "shiny and very dense" the data are qualitative. Quantitative data on this sample of gold might include "a mass of 30 g and a density of 19.3 g/cm^3."

Figure 9 Collecting data is one way to gather information directly.

Figure 10 Record data neatly and clearly so it is easy to understand.

When you make observations you should examine the entire object or situation first, and then look carefully for details. It is important to record observations accurately and completely. Always record your notes immediately as you make them, so you do not miss details or make a mistake when recording results from memory. Never put unidentified observations on scraps of paper. Instead they should be recorded in a notebook, like the one in **Figure 10.** Write your data neatly so you can easily read it later. At each point in the experiment, record your observations and label them. That way, you will not have to determine what the figures mean when you look at your notes later. Set up any tables that you will need to use ahead of time, so you can record any observations right away. Remember to avoid bias when collecting data by not including personal thoughts when you record observations. Record only what you observe.

Estimate Scientific work also involves estimating. To estimate is to make a judgment about the size or the number of something without measuring or counting. This is important when the number or size of an object or population is too large or too difficult to accurately count or measure.

Sample Scientists may use a sample or a portion of the total number as a type of estimation. To sample is to take a small, representative portion of the objects or organisms of a population for research. By making careful observations or manipulating variables within that portion of the group, information is discovered and conclusions are drawn that might apply to the whole population. A poorly chosen sample can be unrepresentative of the whole. If you were trying to determine the rainfall in an area, it would not be best to take a rainfall sample from under a tree.

Measure You use measurements everyday. Scientists also take measurements when collecting data. When taking measurements, it is important to know how to use measuring tools properly. Accuracy also is important.

Length To measure length, the distance between two points, scientists use meters. Smaller measurements might be measured in centimeters or millimeters.

Length is measured using a metric ruler or meter stick. When using a metric ruler, line up the 0-cm mark with the end of the object being measured and read the number of the unit where the object ends. Look at the metric ruler shown in **Figure 11.** The centimeter lines are the long, numbered lines, and the shorter lines are millimeter lines. In this instance, the length would be 4.50 cm.

Figure 11 This metric ruler has centimeter and millimeter divisions.

Mass The SI unit for mass is the kilogram (kg). Scientists can measure mass using units formed by adding metric prefixes to the unit gram (g), such as milligram (mg). To measure mass, you might use a triple-beam balance similar to the one shown in **Figure 12.** The balance has a pan on one side and a set of beams on the other side. Each beam has a rider that slides on the beam.

When using a triple-beam balance, place an object on the pan. Slide the largest rider along its beam until the pointer drops below zero. Then move it back one notch. Repeat the process for each rider proceeding from the larger to smaller until the pointer swings an equal distance above and below the zero point. Sum the masses on each beam to find the mass of the object. Move all riders back to zero when finished.

Instead of putting materials directly on the balance, scientists often take a tare of a container. A tare is the mass of a container into which objects or substances are placed for measuring their masses. To mass objects or substances, find the mass of a clean container. Remove the container from the pan, and place the object or substances in the container. Find the mass of the container with the materials in it. Subtract the mass of the empty container from the mass of the filled container to find the mass of the materials you are using.

Figure 12 A triple-beam balance is used to determine the mass of an object.

Figure 13 Graduated cylinders measure liquid volume.

Liquid Volume To measure liquids, the unit used is the liter. When a smaller unit is needed, scientists might use a milliliter. Because a milliliter takes up the volume of a cube measuring 1 cm on each side it also can be called a cubic centimeter ($cm^3 = cm \times cm \times cm$).

You can use beakers and graduated cylinders to measure liquid volume. A graduated cylinder, shown in **Figure 13,** is marked from bottom to top in milliliters. In lab, you might use a 10-mL graduated cylinder or a 100-mL graduated cylinder. When measuring liquids, notice that the liquid has a curved surface. Look at the surface at eye level, and measure the bottom of the curve. This is called the meniscus. The graduated cylinder in **Figure 13** contains 79.0 mL, or 79.0 cm^3, of a liquid.

Temperature Scientists often measure temperature using the Celsius scale. Pure water has a freezing point of 0°C and boiling point of 100°C. The unit of measurement is degrees Celsius. Two other scales often used are the Fahrenheit and Kelvin scales.

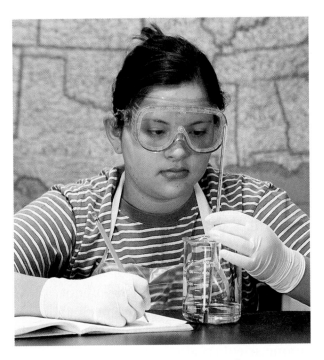

Figure 14 A thermometer measures the temperature of an object.

Scientists use a thermometer to measure temperature. Most thermometers in a laboratory are glass tubes with a bulb at the bottom end containing a liquid such as colored alcohol. The liquid rises or falls with a change in temperature. To read a glass thermometer like the thermometer in **Figure 14,** rotate it slowly until a red line appears. Read the temperature where the red line ends.

Form Operational Definitions An operational definition defines an object by how it functions, works, or behaves. For example, when you are playing hide and seek and a tree is home base, you have created an operational definition for a tree.

Objects can have more than one operational definition. For example, a ruler can be defined as a tool that measures the length of an object (how it is used). It can also be a tool with a series of marks used as a standard when measuring (how it works).

Analyze the Data

To determine the meaning of your observations and investigation results, you will need to look for patterns in the data. Then you must think critically to determine what the data mean. Scientists use several approaches when they analyze the data they have collected and recorded. Each approach is useful for identifying specific patterns.

Interpret Data The word *interpret* means "to explain the meaning of something." When analyzing data from an experiment, try to find out what the data show. Identify the control group and the test group to see whether or not changes in the independent variable have had an effect. Look for differences in the dependent variable between the control and test groups.

Classify Sorting objects or events into groups based on common features is called classifying. When classifying, first observe the objects or events to be classified. Then select one feature that is shared by some members in the group, but not by all. Place those members that share that feature in a subgroup. You can classify members into smaller and smaller subgroups based on characteristics. Remember that when you classify, you are grouping objects or events for a purpose. Keep your purpose in mind as you select the features to form groups and subgroups.

Compare and Contrast Observations can be analyzed by noting the similarities and differences between two more objects or events that you observe. When you look at objects or events to see how they are similar, you are comparing them. Contrasting is looking for differences in objects or events.

Recognize Cause and Effect A cause is a reason for an action or condition. The effect is that action or condition. When two events happen together, it is not necessarily true that one event caused the other. Scientists must design a controlled investigation to recognize the exact cause and effect.

Draw Conclusions

When scientists have analyzed the data they collected, they proceed to draw conclusions about the data. These conclusions are sometimes stated in words similar to the hypothesis that you formed earlier. They may confirm a hypothesis, or lead you to a new hypothesis.

Infer Scientists often make inferences based on their observations. An inference is an attempt to explain observations or to indicate a cause. An inference is not a fact, but a logical conclusion that needs further investigation. For example, you may infer that a fire has caused smoke. Until you investigate, however, you do not know for sure.

Apply When you draw a conclusion, you must apply those conclusions to determine whether the data supports the hypothesis. If your data do not support your hypothesis, it does not mean that the hypothesis is wrong. It means only that the result of the investigation did not support the hypothesis. Maybe the experiment needs to be redesigned, or some of the initial observations on which the hypothesis was based were incomplete or biased. Perhaps more observation or research is needed to refine your hypothesis. A successful investigation does not always come out the way you originally predicted.

Avoid Bias Sometimes a scientific investigation involves making judgments. When you make a judgment, you form an opinion. It is important to be honest and not to allow any expectations of results to bias your judgments. This is important throughout the entire investigation, from researching to collecting data to drawing conclusions.

Communicate

The communication of ideas is an important part of the work of scientists. A discovery that is not reported will not advance the scientific community's understanding or knowledge. Communication among scientists also is important as a way of improving their investigations.

Scientists communicate in many ways, from writing articles in journals and magazines that explain their investigations and experiments, to announcing important discoveries on television and radio. Scientists also share ideas with colleagues on the Internet or present them as lectures, like the student is doing in **Figure 15.**

Figure 15 A student communicates to his peers about his investigation.

SAFETY SYMBOLS

SAFETY SYMBOLS	HAZARD	EXAMPLES	PRECAUTION	REMEDY
DISPOSAL	Special disposal procedures need to be followed.	certain chemicals, living organisms	Do not dispose of these materials in the sink or trash can.	Dispose of wastes as directed by your teacher.
BIOLOGICAL	Organisms or other biological materials that might be harmful to humans	bacteria, fungi, blood, unpreserved tissues, plant materials	Avoid skin contact with these materials. Wear mask or gloves.	Notify your teacher if you suspect contact with material. Wash hands thoroughly.
EXTREME TEMPERATURE	Objects that can burn skin by being too cold or too hot	boiling liquids, hot plates, dry ice, liquid nitrogen	Use proper protection when handling.	Go to your teacher for first aid.
SHARP OBJECT	Use of tools or glassware that can easily puncture or slice skin	razor blades, pins, scalpels, pointed tools, dissecting probes, broken glass	Practice common-sense behavior and follow guidelines for use of the tool.	Go to your teacher for first aid.
FUME	Possible danger to respiratory tract from fumes	ammonia, acetone, nail polish remover, heated sulfur, moth balls	Make sure there is good ventilation. Never smell fumes directly. Wear a mask.	Leave foul area and notify your teacher immediately.
ELECTRICAL	Possible danger from electrical shock or burn	improper grounding, liquid spills, short circuits, exposed wires	Double-check setup with teacher. Check condition of wires and apparatus.	Do not attempt to fix electrical problems. Notify your teacher immediately.
IRRITANT	Substances that can irritate the skin or mucous membranes of the respiratory tract	pollen, moth balls, steel wool, fiberglass, potassium permanganate	Wear dust mask and gloves. Practice extra care when handling these materials.	Go to your teacher for first aid.
CHEMICAL	Chemicals can react with and destroy tissue and other materials	bleaches such as hydrogen peroxide; acids such as sulfuric acid, hydrochloric acid; bases such as ammonia, sodium hydroxide	Wear goggles, gloves, and an apron.	Immediately flush the affected area with water and notify your teacher.
TOXIC	Substance may be poisonous if touched, inhaled, or swallowed.	mercury, many metal compounds, iodine, poinsettia plant parts	Follow your teacher's instructions.	Always wash hands thoroughly after use. Go to your teacher for first aid.
FLAMMABLE	Flammable chemicals may be ignited by open flame, spark, or exposed heat.	alcohol, kerosene, potassium permanganate	Avoid open flames and heat when using flammable chemicals.	Notify your teacher immediately. Use fire safety equipment if applicable.
OPEN FLAME	Open flame in use, may cause fire.	hair, clothing, paper, synthetic materials	Tie back hair and loose clothing. Follow teacher's instruction on lighting and extinguishing flames.	Notify your teacher immediately. Use fire safety equipment if applicable.

 Eye Safety Proper eye protection should be worn at all times by anyone performing or observing science activities.

 Clothing Protection This symbol appears when substances could stain or burn clothing.

 Animal Safety This symbol appears when safety of animals and students must be ensured.

 Handwashing After the lab, wash hands with soap and water before removing goggles.

Safety in the Science Laboratory

The science laboratory is a safe place to work if you follow standard safety procedures. Being responsible for your own safety helps to make the entire laboratory a safer place for everyone. When performing any lab, read and apply the caution statements and safety symbol listed at the beginning of the lab.

General Safety Rules

1. Obtain your teacher's permission to begin all investigations and use laboratory equipment.

2. Study the procedure. Ask your teacher any questions. Be sure you understand safety symbols shown on the page.

3. Notify your teacher about allergies or other health conditions which can affect your participation in a lab.

4. Learn and follow use and safety procedures for your equipment. If unsure, ask your teacher.

5. Never eat, drink, chew gum, apply cosmetics, or do any personal grooming in the lab. Never use lab glassware as food or drink containers. Keep your hands away from your face and mouth.

6. Know the location and proper use of the safety shower, eye wash, fire blanket, and fire alarm.

Prevent Accidents

1. Use the safety equipment provided to you. Goggles and a safety apron should be worn during investigations.

2. Do NOT use hair spray, mousse, or other flammable hair products. Tie back long hair and tie down loose clothing.

3. Do NOT wear sandals or other open-toed shoes in the lab.

4. Remove jewelry on hands and wrists. Loose jewelry, such as chains and long necklaces, should be removed to prevent them from getting caught in equipment.

5. Do not taste any substances or draw any material into a tube with your mouth.

6. Proper behavior is expected in the lab. Practical jokes and fooling around can lead to accidents and injury.

7. Keep your work area uncluttered.

Laboratory Work

1. Collect and carry all equipment and materials to your work area before beginning a lab.

2. Remain in your own work area unless given permission by your teacher to leave it.

3. Always slant test tubes away from yourself and others when heating them, adding substances to them, or rinsing them.

4. If instructed to smell a substance in a container, hold the container a short distance away and fan vapors towards your nose.

5. Do NOT substitute other chemicals/substances for those in the materials list unless instructed to do so by your teacher.

6. Do NOT take any materials or chemicals outside of the laboratory.

7. Stay out of storage areas unless instructed to be there and supervised by your teacher.

Laboratory Cleanup

1. Turn off all burners, water, and gas, and disconnect all electrical devices.

2. Clean all pieces of equipment and return all materials to their proper places.

3. Dispose of chemicals and other materials as directed by your teacher. Place broken glass and solid substances in the proper containers. Never discard materials in the sink.

4. Clean your work area.

5. Wash your hands with soap and water thoroughly BEFORE removing your goggles.

Emergencies

1. Report any fire, electrical shock, glassware breakage, spill, or injury, no matter how small, to your teacher immediately. Follow his or her instructions.

2. If your clothing should catch fire, STOP, DROP, and ROLL. If possible, smother it with the fire blanket or get under a safety shower. NEVER RUN.

3. If a fire should occur, turn off all gas and leave the room according to established procedures.

4. In most instances, your teacher will clean up spills. Do NOT attempt to clean up spills unless you are given permission and instructions to do so.

5. If chemicals come into contact with your eyes or skin, notify your teacher immediately. Use the eyewash or flush your skin or eyes with large quantities of water.

6. The fire extinguisher and first-aid kit should only be used by your teacher unless it is an extreme emergency and you have been given permission.

7. If someone is injured or becomes ill, only a professional medical provider or someone certified in first aid should perform first-aid procedures.

1 Spinning Like a Top

Time Required ten minutes

Materials Complete this lab outside in an area with thick grass.

Safety Precaution Students should have one or two partners spot them to make certain they do not fall.

Teaching Strategy Explain to students that they continue to see the room spinning even after they are standing still because the hairs inside their inner ears sense the movement of fluids, but their eyes are seeing everything still. These mixed messages are sent to the brain, and the brain becomes confused.

Conclude and Apply

1. Answers will vary. Depending on the person, the room can seem to spin for more than a minute.
2. The fluid in the inner ears continues to spin, and the hairs inside the inner ear continue to sense movement.

Extra Try at Home Labs

EXTRA Labs

From Your Kitchen, Junk Drawer, or Yard

1 Spinning Like a Top

Real-World Question
How can you observe your inner ear restoring your body's balance?

Possible Materials 🔊
- large pillows
- stopwatch or watch

Procedure
1. Choose a carpeted location several meters away from any furniture.
2. Lay large pillows on the floor around you.
3. Spin around in a circle once, stare straight ahead, and observe what the room looks like. Have a friend spot you to prevent you from falling.
4. Spin around in circles continuously for 5 s, stare straight ahead, and observe what the room looks like. Have a friend spot you.
5. After you stop, use a stopwatch to time how long it takes for the room to stop spinning.
6. With a friend spotting you, spin for 10 s and time how long it takes for the room to stop spinning.

Conclude and Apply
1. How long did it take for the room to stop spinning after you spun in circles for 5 s and for 10 s?
2. Infer why the room appeared to spin even after you stopped spinning.

2 Vitamin Search

Real-World Question
How many vitamins and minerals are in the foods you eat?

Possible Materials
- labels from packaged foods and drinks
- nutrition guidebook or cookbook

Procedure
1. Create a data table to record the "% Daily Value" of important vitamins and minerals for a variety of foods.
2. Collect packages from a variety of packaged foods and check the Nutrition Facts chart for the "% Daily Value" of all the vitamins and minerals it contains. These values are listed at the bottom of the chart.
3. Use cookbooks or nutrition guidebooks to research the "% Daily Value" of vitamins and minerals found in several fresh fruits and vegetables such as strawberries, spinach, oranges, and lentils.

Conclude and Apply
1. Infer why a healthy diet includes fresh fruits and vegetables.
2. Infer why a healthy diet includes a wide variety of nutritious foods.

Nutrition Facts
Serving Size 1 Meal

Amount Per Serving

Calories 330   Calories from Fat 60

	% Daily Value*
Total Fat 7g	**10%**
Saturated Fat 3.5g	**17%**
Polyunsaturated Fat 1g	
Monounsaturated Fat 2.5g	
Cholesterol 35mg	**12%**
Sodium 460mg	**19%**
Total Carbohydrate 52g	**18%**
Dietary Fiber 6g	**24%**
Sugars 17g	
Protein 15g	

Vitamin A 15%		Vitamin C 70%	
Calcium 4%		Iron 10%	

* Percent Daily Values are based on a 2,000 calorie diet. Your daily values may be higher or lower depending on your calorie needs.

		Calories	2,000	2,500
Total Fat	Less than		65g	80g
Sat Fat	Less than		20g	25g
Cholesterol	Less than		300mg	300mg
Sodium	Less than		2,400mg	2,400mg
Total Carbohydrate			300g	375g
Dietary Fiber			25g	30g

Adult supervision required for all labs.

These labs are available at bookd.mssscience.com.

2 Vitamin Search

Time Required 40 minutes

Materials
- Purchase inexpensive nutrition guidebooks at a local grocery store.
- Many cookbooks contain nutritional information about fresh foods.

Safety Precaution Caution students never to eat or drink anything in science class.

Teaching Strategy Encourage students to evaluate the percentages of vitamins and minerals in their favorite foods and in the foods they eat most frequently.

Conclude and Apply

1. Packaged foods have few vitamins and minerals compared to fresh fruits and vegetables.
2. A single fruit or vegetable will have a high content of one vitamin or mineral but not others. A varied diet will ensure enough of all essential vitamins and minerals are consumed.

3 What's in blood?

Real-World Question
What are the proportions of the components of your blood?

Possible Materials
- bag of brown rice
- white rice
- small bag of wild rice
- measuring cup
- large bowl or large cooking tray

Procedure
1. Measure 1.25 L of brown rice and pour the rice into a large bowl or on a cooking tray.
2. Measure 100 mL of wild rice and pour it into the bowl or on the tray.
3. Count out 50 grains of white rice and place them in the bowl or on the tray.
4. Mix the three types of rice thoroughly and observe the proportions of the three major components of your blood.

Conclude and Apply
1. Infer what type of rice represents red blood cells.
2. Infer what type of rice represents white blood cells.
3. Infer what type of rice represents platelets.

4 Modeling Glucose

Real-World Question
What does a molecule of glucose used in respiration look like?

Possible Materials
- red polystyrene balls or gumdrops (6)
- green polystyrene balls or gumdrops (6)
- yellow polystyrene balls or gumdrops (12)
- box of toothpicks

Procedure
1. Use toothpicks to connect the six red polystyrene balls together in a line. These balls represent carbon atoms.
2. Attach a green ball and a yellow ball to the first carbon atom. The green ball goes to the left and the yellow ball to the right. The green ball represents an oxygen atom, and the yellow ball represents a hydrogen atom.
3. Attach an oxygen atom and a hydrogen atom in a line to the right of the second, fourth and fifth carbon atoms. Attach a hydrogen atom to the left of each of these carbon atoms.
4. Attach a hydrogen atom and oxygen atom in a line to the left of the third carbon atom and a hydrogen atom to the right.
5. Attach two hydrogen atoms and one oxygen atom to the sixth carbon atom. Attach a hydrogen atom to the oxygen atom.

Conclude and Apply
1. Construct models of the other molecules used during respiration.
2. Infer why oxygen is needed during respiration.

Extra Try at Home Labs

3 What's in blood?

Time Required 15 minutes

Materials
- Purchase a wild rice variety with a black color.
- There are approximately 400 grains of rice in 10 mL.

Safety Precaution Caution students not to eat or drink in science class.

Teaching Strategy
Consider having the class replicate the number of red blood cells, white blood cells, and platelets in 0.1 mL of blood by placing 12.5 L of brown rice, 1 L of wild rice, and 12.5 mL (500 grains) of white rice into a small aquarium or large jar.

Conclude and Apply
1. brown rice
2. wild (black) rice
3. white rice

4 Modeling Glucose

Time required 40 minutes

Materials Polystyrene balls of any three different colors can be substituted.

Safety Precaution Caution students to use the toothpicks with care.

Teaching Strategy Have students draw a large arrow on a sheet of paper and use their models to construct the chemical reaction for respiration. Students can also combine their models to show a balanced chemical reaction.

Conclude and Apply
1. Students should connect two blue balls together to represent an oxygen molecule, a red and two blue to represent carbon dioxide, and two yellow connected to a blue to represent a molecule of water.
2. Oxygen burns and breaks down glucose molecules into energy.

5 Pupil Power

Time Required ten minutes

Materials
- Students can work in pairs using handheld mirrors.
- Pocket flashlights work best for this lab.

Safety Precautions
- Students should never shine a light directly into their eyes.
- Caution students not to shine the light into the mirror. Reflected light could shine into their eyes.

Teaching Strategy Students may have to try this lab several times to position the flashlight correctly so that they can clearly see the pupils of their eyes.

Conclude and Apply
1. The eye pupils will abruptly diminish in size.
2. The eye's pupil controls the amount of light entering the eye. In darkness, the pupil opens up wide to gather more light, but it quickly shrinks in size when exposed to light.

5 Pupil Power

Real-World Question
Why do your eyes have pupils?

Possible Materials
- mirror
- flashlight

Procedure
1. Examine your eyes in a mirror in a brightly lit room. Observe the size of the pupil and iris of each eye.
2. Darken the room so that there is no light.
3. Turn on a flashlight and cover its light with the palm of your hand.
4. Hold the flashlight about 10–15 cm in front of your mouth with the beam facing straight up.
5. Quickly remove your hand and immediately observe the pupils of your eyes.

Conclude and Apply
1. Describe what happened to the pupils of your eyes.
2. Infer why your pupils responded to the light in this way.

6 Identifying Iodine

Real-World Question
How many iodine-rich foods are in your home?

Possible Materials
- Science Journal
- pen or pencil

Procedure
1. The element iodine is needed in a person's diet for the thyroid gland to work properly. Search your kitchen for the foods richest in iodine including fish, shellfish (clams, oysters, mussels, scallops), seaweed, and kelp.
2. Record all the iodine-rich foods you find in your Science Journal.
3. Search your kitchen for foods that may contain iodine if they are grown in rich soil such as onions, mushrooms, lettuce, spinach, green peppers, pineapple, peanuts, and whole wheat bread.
4. Record all of these foods that you find in your Science Journal.

Conclude and Apply
1. Infer whether or not your family eats a diet rich in iodine.
2. Infer why iodine is often added to table salt.
3. Research two diseases caused by a lack of iodine in the diet.

Adult supervision required for all labs.

These labs are available at bookd.msscience.com.

6 Identifying Iodine

Time Required 20 minutes

Materials Consider bringing several examples of iodine-rich foods to school.

Safety Precautions
- Caution students that consuming too much seafood can lead to toxic levels of heavy metals due to high ocean pollution levels.
- Students should not eat in the lab.

Teaching Strategy Explain that tuna, salmon, and other common canned fish are good sources of iodine, but cod, haddock, and perch are the best sources.

Conclude and Apply
1. Answers will vary.
2. Iodine is added to salt to prevent iodine deficiency in people's diets.
3. goiter and cretinism

7 Acid Defense

⏵ *Real-World Question*
How is stomach acid your internal first line of defense?

Possible Materials
- drinking glasses (2)
- milk
- cola or lemon juice
- masking tape
- marker
- measuring cup

⏵ *Procedure*
1. Pour 100 mL of milk into each glass.
2. Pour 20 mL of cola into the second glass.
3. Using the masking tape and marker, label the first glass *No Acid* and the second glass *Acid*.
4. Place the glasses in direct sunlight and observe the mixture each day for several days.

⏵ *Conclude and Apply*
1. Compare the odor of the mixture in both glasses after one or two days.
2. Infer how this experiment modeled one of your internal defenses against disease.

---

7 Acid Defense

Time Required ten minutes for set-up; two-minute observation periods for several days

Materials Clear away space on your window sills for the experiments.

Safety Precautions
- If acid splashes into the eyes, flush the eyes with water immediately and seek medical attention.
- Cloth aprons and rubber gloves should be worn when handling the acid.
- Caution students never to eat or drink anything in science class.

Teaching Strategy Explain that the pH of stomach acid is around 1, which is similar to the pH of concentrated hydrochloric acid. Have students research the pH of the acid they used.

Conclude and Apply
1. After one day, the milk without the added acid will become thick with white lumps floating in it, and it will smell sour. The milk with the acid in it will not sour until two or three days later.
2. Stomach acid kills many disease-causing bacteria that enter the digestive system in foods or drinks.

Adult supervision required for all labs.

Computer Skills

People who study science rely on computers, like the one in **Figure 16,** to record and store data and to analyze results from investigations. Whether you work in a laboratory or just need to write a lab report with tables, good computer skills are a necessity.

Using the computer comes with responsibility. Issues of ownership, security, and privacy can arise. Remember, if you did not author the information you are using, you must provide a source for your information. Also, anything on a computer can be accessed by others. Do not put anything on the computer that you would not want everyone to know. To add more security to your work, use a password.

Use a Word Processing Program

A computer program that allows you to type your information, change it as many times as you need to, and then print it out is called a word processing program. Word processing programs also can be used to make tables.

Figure 16 A computer will make reports neater and more professional looking.

Learn the Skill To start your word processing program, a blank document, sometimes called "Document 1," appears on the screen. To begin, start typing. To create a new document, click the *New* button on the standard tool bar. These tips will help you format the document.

- The program will automatically move to the next line; press *Enter* if you wish to start a new paragraph.
- Symbols, called non-printing characters, can be hidden by clicking the *Show/Hide* button on your toolbar.
- To insert text, move the cursor to the point where you want the insertion to go, click on the mouse once, and type the text.
- To move several lines of text, select the text and click the *Cut* button on your toolbar. Then position your cursor in the location that you want to move the cut text and click *Paste.* If you move to the wrong place, click *Undo.*
- The spell check feature does not catch words that are misspelled to look like other words, like "cold" instead of "gold." Always reread your document to catch all spelling mistakes.
- To learn about other word processing methods, read the user's manual or click on the *Help* button.
- You can integrate databases, graphics, and spreadsheets into documents by copying from another program and pasting it into your document, or by using desktop publishing (DTP). DTP software allows you to put text and graphics together to finish your document with a professional look. This software varies in how it is used and its capabilities.

Use a Database

A collection of facts stored in a computer and sorted into different fields is called a database. A database can be reorganized in any way that suits your needs.

Learn the Skill A computer program that allows you to create your own database is a database management system (DBMS). It allows you to add, delete, or change information. Take time to get to know the features of your database software.

- Determine what facts you would like to include and research to collect your information.
- Determine how you want to organize the information.
- Follow the instructions for your particular DBMS to set up fields. Then enter each item of data in the appropriate field.
- Follow the instructions to sort the information in order of importance.
- Evaluate the information in your database, and add, delete, or change as necessary.

Use the Internet

The Internet is a global network of computers where information is stored and shared. To use the Internet, like the students in **Figure 17,** you need a modem to connect your computer to a phone line and an Internet Service Provider account.

Learn the Skill To access internet sites and information, use a "Web browser," which lets you view and explore pages on the World Wide Web. Each page is its own site, and each site has its own address, called a URL. Once you have found a Web browser, follow these steps for a search (this also is how you search a database).

Figure 17 The Internet allows you to search a global network for a variety of information.

- Be as specific as possible. If you know you want to research "gold," don't type in "elements." Keep narrowing your search until you find what you want.
- Web sites that end in *.com* are commercial Web sites; *.org, .edu,* and *.gov* are nonprofit, educational, or government Web sites.
- Electronic encyclopedias, almanacs, indexes, and catalogs will help locate and select relevant information.
- Develop a "home page" with relative ease. When developing a Web site, NEVER post pictures or disclose personal information such as location, names, or phone numbers. Your school or community usually can host your Web site. A basic understanding of HTML (hypertext mark-up language), the language of Web sites, is necessary. Software that creates HTML code is called authoring software, and can be downloaded free from many Web sites. This software allows text and pictures to be arranged as the software is writing the HTML code.

Use a Spreadsheet

A spreadsheet, shown in **Figure 18,** can perform mathematical functions with any data arranged in columns and rows. By entering a simple equation into a cell, the program can perform operations in specific cells, rows, or columns.

Learn the Skill Each column (vertical) is assigned a letter, and each row (horizontal) is assigned a number. Each point where a row and column intersect is called a cell, and is labeled according to where it is located—Column A, Row 1 (A1).

- Decide how to organize the data, and enter it in the correct row or column.
- Spreadsheets can use standard formulas or formulas can be customized to calculate cells.
- To make a change, click on a cell to make it activate, and enter the edited data or formula.
- Spreadsheets also can display your results in graphs. Choose the style of graph that best represents the data.

	A	B	C	D	E
	Test Runs	Time	Distance	Speed	
1	Car 1	5 mins	5 miles	60 mph	
2	Car 2	10 mins	4 miles	24 mph	
3	Car 3	6 mins	3 miles	30 mph	

Figure 18 A spreadsheet allows you to perform mathematical operations on your data.

Use Graphics Software

Adding pictures, called graphics, to your documents is one way to make your documents more meaningful and exciting. This software adds, edits, and even constructs graphics. There is a variety of graphics software programs. The tools used for drawing can be a mouse, keyboard, or other specialized devices. Some graphics programs are simple. Others are complicated, called computer-aided design (CAD) software.

Learn the Skill It is important to have an understanding of the graphics software being used before starting. The better the software is understood, the better the results. The graphics can be placed in a word-processing document.

- Clip art can be found on a variety of internet sites, and on CDs. These images can be copied and pasted into your document.
- When beginning, try editing existing drawings, then work up to creating drawings.
- The images are made of tiny rectangles of color called pixels. Each pixel can be altered.
- Digital photography is another way to add images. The photographs in the memory of a digital camera can be downloaded into a computer, then edited and added to the document.
- Graphics software also can allow animation. The software allows drawings to have the appearance of movement by connecting basic drawings automatically. This is called in-betweening, or tweening.
- Remember to save often.

Presentation Skills

Develop Multimedia Presentations

Most presentations are more dynamic if they include diagrams, photographs, videos, or sound recordings, like the one shown in **Figure 19.** A multimedia presentation involves using stereos, overhead projectors, televisions, computers, and more.

Learn the Skill Decide the main points of your presentation, and what types of media would best illustrate those points.

- Make sure you know how to use the equipment you are working with.
- Practice the presentation using the equipment several times.
- Enlist the help of a classmate to push play or turn lights out for you. Be sure to practice your presentation with him or her.
- If possible, set up all of the equipment ahead of time, and make sure everything is working properly.

Figure 19 These students are engaging the audience using a variety of tools.

Computer Presentations

There are many different interactive computer programs that you can use to enhance your presentation. Most computers have a compact disc (CD) drive that can play both CDs and digital video discs (DVDs). Also, there is hardware to connect a regular CD, DVD, or VCR. These tools will enhance your presentation.

Another method of using the computer to aid in your presentation is to develop a slide show using a computer program. This can allow movement of visuals at the presenter's pace, and can allow for visuals to build on one another.

Learn the Skill In order to create multimedia presentations on a computer, you need to have certain tools. These may include traditional graphic tools and drawing programs, animation programs, and authoring systems that tie everything together. Your computer will tell you which tools it supports. The most important step is to learn about the tools that you will be using.

- Often, color and strong images will convey a point better than words alone. Use the best methods available to convey your point.
- As with other presentations, practice many times.
- Practice your presentation with the tools you and any assistants will be using.
- Maintain eye contact with the audience. The purpose of using the computer is not to prompt the presenter, but to help the audience understand the points of the presentation.

Reduce Fractions

$$\frac{66 \div 6}{90 \div 6} = \frac{11}{15}$$

Add and Subtract Fractions

$$\frac{4}{9} + \frac{2}{9} = \frac{6}{9}$$

$$\frac{6 \div 3}{9 \div 3} = \frac{2}{3}$$

Math Review

Use Fractions

A fraction compares a part to a whole. In the fraction $\frac{2}{3}$, the 2 represents the part and is the numerator. The 3 represents the whole and is the denominator.

Reduce Fractions To reduce a fraction, you must find the largest factor that is common to both the numerator and the denominator, the greatest common factor (GCF). Divide both numbers by the GCF. The fraction has then been reduced, or it is in its simplest form.

Example Twelve of the 20 chemicals in the science lab are in powder form. What fraction of the chemicals used in the lab are in powder form?

Step 1 Write the fraction.

$$\frac{part}{whole} = \frac{12}{20}$$

Step 2 To find the GCF of the numerator and denominator, list all of the factors of each number.

Factors of 12: 1, 2, 3, 4, 6, 12 (the numbers that divide evenly into 12)

Factors of 20: 1, 2, 4, 5, 10, 20 (the numbers that divide evenly into 20)

Step 3 List the common factors.

1, 2, 4.

Step 4 Choose the greatest factor in the list.

The GCF of 12 and 20 is 4.

Step 5 Divide the numerator and denominator by the GCF.

$$\frac{12 \div 4}{20 \div 4} = \frac{3}{5}$$

In the lab, $\frac{3}{5}$ of the chemicals are in powder form.

Practice Problem At an amusement park, 66 of 90 rides have a height restriction. What fraction of the rides, in its simplest form, has a height restriction?

Add and Subtract Fractions To add or subtract fractions with the same denominator, add or subtract the numerators and write the sum or difference over the denominator. After finding the sum or difference, find the simplest form for your fraction.

Example 1 In the forest outside your house, $\frac{1}{8}$ of the animals are rabbits, $\frac{3}{8}$ are squirrels, and the remainder are birds and insects. How many are mammals?

Step 1 Add the numerators.

$$\frac{1}{8} + \frac{3}{8} = \frac{(1 + 3)}{8} = \frac{4}{8}$$

Step 2 Find the GCF.

$$\frac{4}{8} \quad (GCF, 4)$$

Step 3 Divide the numerator and denominator by the GCF.

$$\frac{4}{4} = 1, \ \frac{8}{4} = 2$$

$\frac{1}{2}$ of the animals are mammals.

Example 2 If $\frac{7}{16}$ of the Earth is covered by freshwater, and $\frac{1}{16}$ of that is in glaciers, how much freshwater is not frozen?

Step 1 Subtract the numerators.

$$\frac{7}{16} - \frac{1}{16} = \frac{(7 - 1)}{16} = \frac{6}{16}$$

Step 2 Find the GCF.

$$\frac{6}{16} \quad (GCF, 2)$$

Step 3 Divide the numerator and denominator by the GCF.

$$\frac{6}{2} = 3, \ \frac{16}{2} = 8$$

$\frac{3}{8}$ of the freshwater is not frozen.

Practice Problem A bicycle rider is going 15 km/h for $\frac{4}{9}$ of his ride, 10 km/h for $\frac{2}{9}$ of his ride, and 8 km/h for the remainder of the ride. How much of his ride is he going over 8 km/h?

Unlike Denominators To add or subtract fractions with unlike denominators, first find the least common denominator (LCD). This is the smallest number that is a common multiple of both denominators. Rename each fraction with the LCD, and then add or subtract. Find the simplest form if necessary.

Example 1 A chemist makes a paste that is $\frac{1}{2}$ table salt (NaCl), $\frac{1}{3}$ sugar ($C_6H_{12}O_6$), and the rest water (H_2O). How much of the paste is a solid?

Step 1 Find the LCD of the fractions.

$\frac{1}{2} + \frac{1}{3}$ (LCD, 6)

Step 2 Rename each numerator and each denominator with the LCD.

$1 \times 3 = 3, \ 2 \times 3 = 6$
$1 \times 2 = 2, \ 3 \times 2 = 6$

Step 3 Add the numerators.

$\frac{3}{6} + \frac{2}{6} = \frac{(3 + 2)}{6} = \frac{5}{6}$

$\frac{5}{6}$ of the paste is a solid.

Example 2 The average precipitation in Grand Junction, CO, is $\frac{7}{10}$ inch in November, and $\frac{3}{5}$ inch in December. What is the total average precipitation?

Step 1 Find the LCD of the fractions.

$\frac{7}{10} + \frac{3}{5}$ (LCD, 10)

Step 2 Rename each numerator and each denominator with the LCD.

$7 \times 1 = 7, \ 10 \times 1 = 10$
$3 \times 2 = 6, \ 5 \times 2 = 10$

Step 3 Add the numerators.

$\frac{7}{10} + \frac{6}{10} = \frac{(7 + 6)}{10} = \frac{13}{10}$

$\frac{13}{10}$ inches total precipitation, or $1\frac{3}{10}$ inches.

Practice Problem On an electric bill, about $\frac{1}{8}$ of the energy is from solar energy and about $\frac{1}{10}$ is from wind power. How much of the total bill is from solar energy and wind power combined?

Example 3 In your body, $\frac{7}{10}$ of your muscle contractions are involuntary (cardiac and smooth muscle tissue). Smooth muscle makes $\frac{3}{15}$ of your muscle contractions. How many of your muscle contractions are made by cardiac muscle?

Step 1 Find the LCD of the fractions.

$\frac{7}{10} - \frac{3}{15}$ (LCD, 30)

Step 2 Rename each numerator and each denominator with the LCD.

$7 \times 3 = 21, \ 10 \times 3 = 30$
$3 \times 2 = 6, \ 15 \times 2 = 30$

Step 3 Subtract the numerators.

$\frac{21}{30} - \frac{6}{30} = \frac{(21 - 6)}{30} = \frac{15}{30}$

Step 4 Find the GCF.

$\frac{15}{30}$ (GCF, 15)

$\frac{1}{2}$

$\frac{1}{2}$ of all muscle contractions are cardiac muscle.

Example 4 Tony wants to make cookies that call for $\frac{3}{4}$ of a cup of flour, but he only has $\frac{1}{3}$ of a cup. How much more flour does he need?

Step 1 Find the LCD of the fractions.

$\frac{3}{4} - \frac{1}{3}$ (LCD, 12)

Step 2 Rename each numerator and each denominator with the LCD.

$3 \times 3 = 9, \ 4 \times 3 = 12$
$1 \times 4 = 4, \ 3 \times 4 = 12$

Step 3 Subtract the numerators.

$\frac{9}{12} - \frac{4}{12} = \frac{(9 - 4)}{12} = \frac{5}{12}$

$\frac{5}{12}$ of a cup of flour.

Practice Problem Using the information provided to you in Example 3 above, determine how many muscle contractions are voluntary (skeletal muscle).

Unlike Denominators

Problem 1

$1 \times 5 = 5, 8 \times 5 = 40$
$1 \times 4 = 4, 10 \times 4 = 40$
$\frac{5}{40} + \frac{4}{40} = \frac{9}{40}$

Problem 2

If $\frac{7}{10}$ are involuntary, the remainder are voluntary.

$\frac{10}{10} - \frac{7}{10} = \frac{3}{10}$

Multiply Fractions

$$\frac{3}{14} \times \frac{5}{16} = \frac{(3 \times 5)}{(14 \times 16)} = \frac{15}{224}$$

Find a Reciprocal

$$\frac{9}{4}$$

Divide Fractions

The reciprocal of $\frac{7}{10}$ is $\frac{10}{7}$.

$$\frac{3}{11} \times \frac{10}{7} = \frac{(3 \times 10)}{(11 \times 7)} = \frac{30}{77}$$

Multiply Fractions To multiply with fractions, multiply the numerators and multiply the denominators. Find the simplest form if necessary.

Example Multiply $\frac{3}{5}$ by $\frac{1}{3}$.

Step 1 Multiply the numerators and denominators.

$$\frac{3}{5} \times \frac{1}{3} = \frac{(3 \times 1)}{(5 \times 3)} = \frac{3}{15}$$

Step 2 Find the GCF.

$$\frac{3}{15} \quad (\text{GCF, 3})$$

Step 3 Divide the numerator and denominator by the GCF.

$$\frac{3}{3} = 1, \quad \frac{15}{3} = 5$$

$$\frac{1}{5}$$

$\frac{3}{5}$ multiplied by $\frac{1}{3}$ is $\frac{1}{5}$.

Practice Problem Multiply $\frac{3}{14}$ by $\frac{5}{16}$.

Find a Reciprocal Two numbers whose product is 1 are called multiplicative inverses, or reciprocals.

Example Find the reciprocal of $\frac{3}{8}$.

Step 1 Inverse the fraction by putting the denominator on top and the numerator on the bottom.

$$\frac{8}{3}$$

The reciprocal of $\frac{3}{8}$ is $\frac{8}{3}$.

Practice Problem Find the reciprocal of $\frac{4}{9}$.

Divide Fractions To divide one fraction by another fraction, multiply the dividend by the reciprocal of the divisor. Find the simplest form if necessary.

Example 1 Divide $\frac{1}{9}$ by $\frac{1}{3}$.

Step 1 Find the reciprocal of the divisor.

The reciprocal of $\frac{1}{3}$ is $\frac{3}{1}$.

Step 2 Multiply the dividend by the reciprocal of the divisor.

$$\frac{\frac{1}{9}}{\frac{1}{3}} = \frac{1}{9} \times \frac{3}{1} = \frac{(1 \times 3)}{(9 \times 1)} = \frac{3}{9}$$

Step 3 Find the GCF.

$$\frac{3}{9} \quad (\text{GCF, 3})$$

Step 4 Divide the numerator and denominator by the GCF.

$$\frac{3}{3} = 1, \quad \frac{9}{3} = 3$$

$$\frac{1}{3}$$

$\frac{1}{9}$ divided by $\frac{1}{3}$ is $\frac{1}{3}$.

Example 2 Divide $\frac{3}{5}$ by $\frac{1}{4}$.

Step 1 Find the reciprocal of the divisor.

The reciprocal of $\frac{1}{4}$ is $\frac{4}{1}$.

Step 2 Multiply the dividend by the reciprocal of the divisor.

$$\frac{\frac{3}{5}}{\frac{1}{4}} = \frac{3}{5} \times \frac{4}{1} = \frac{(3 \times 4)}{(5 \times 1)} = \frac{12}{5}$$

$\frac{3}{5}$ divided by $\frac{1}{4}$ is $\frac{12}{5}$ or $2\frac{2}{5}$.

Practice Problem Divide $\frac{3}{11}$ by $\frac{7}{10}$.

Math Skill Handbook

Math Skill Handbook

Use Ratios

When you compare two numbers by division, you are using a ratio. Ratios can be written 3 to 5, 3:5, or $\frac{3}{5}$. Ratios, like fractions, also can be written in simplest form.

Ratios can represent probabilities, also called odds. This is a ratio that compares the number of ways a certain outcome occurs to the number of outcomes. For example, if you flip a coin 100 times, what are the odds that it will come up heads? There are two possible outcomes, heads or tails, so the odds of coming up heads are 50:100. Another way to say this is that 50 out of 100 times the coin will come up heads. In its simplest form, the ratio is 1:2.

Example 1 A chemical solution contains 40 g of salt and 64 g of baking soda. What is the ratio of salt to baking soda as a fraction in simplest form?

Step 1 Write the ratio as a fraction.

$$\frac{salt}{baking\ soda} = \frac{40}{64}$$

Step 2 Express the fraction in simplest form. The GCF of 40 and 64 is 8.

$$\frac{40}{64} = \frac{40 \div 8}{64 \div 8} = \frac{5}{8}$$

The ratio of salt to baking soda in the sample is 5:8.

Example 2 Sean rolls a 6-sided die 6 times. What are the odds that the side with a 3 will show?

Step 1 Write the ratio as a fraction.

$$\frac{number\ of\ sides\ with\ a\ 3}{number\ of\ sides} = \frac{1}{6}$$

Step 2 Multiply by the number of attempts.

$$\frac{1}{6} \times 6\ attempts = \frac{6}{6}\ attempts = 1\ attempt$$

1 attempt out of 6 will show a 3.

Practice Problem Two metal rods measure 100 cm and 144 cm in length. What is the ratio of their lengths in simplest form?

Use Decimals

A fraction with a denominator that is a power of ten can be written as a decimal. For example, 0.27 means $\frac{27}{100}$. The decimal point separates the ones place from the tenths place.

Any fraction can be written as a decimal using division. For example, the fraction $\frac{5}{8}$ can be written as a decimal by dividing 5 by 8. Written as a decimal, it is 0.625.

Add or Subtract Decimals When adding and subtracting decimals, line up the decimal points before carrying out the operation.

Example 1 Find the sum of 47.68 and 7.80.

Step 1 Line up the decimal places when you write the numbers.

$$\begin{array}{r} 47.68 \\ + \ 7.80 \end{array}$$

Step 2 Add the decimals.

$$\begin{array}{r} 47.68 \\ + \ 7.80 \\ \hline 55.48 \end{array}$$

The sum of 47.68 and 7.80 is 55.48.

Example 2 Find the difference of 42.17 and 15.85.

Step 1 Line up the decimal places when you write the number.

$$\begin{array}{r} 42.17 \\ - 15.85 \end{array}$$

Step 2 Subtract the decimals.

$$\begin{array}{r} 42.17 \\ - 15.85 \\ \hline 26.32 \end{array}$$

The difference of 42.17 and 15.85 is 26.32.

Practice Problem Find the sum of 1.245 and 3.842.

Use Ratios

$$\frac{100\ cm}{144\ cm} = \frac{100 \div 4}{144 \div 4} = \frac{25}{36}$$

25:36

Add or Subtract Decimals

$$\begin{array}{r} 1 \\ 1.245 \\ + \ 3.842 \\ \hline 5.087 \end{array}$$

Math Skill Handbook

Math Skill Handbook

Multiply Decimals

Multiply 4.6 and 2.2 by 10.

$46 \times 22 = 1012$

Each factor had one decimal place.

10.12

Divide Decimals

Multiply both factors by 10.

Divide 756 by 36.

$$
\begin{array}{r}
21 \\
36\overline{)756} \\
72 \\
\overline{36} \\
36 \\
\overline{0}
\end{array}
$$

Use Proportions

$\dfrac{3}{18} = \dfrac{5}{w}$

$w \times 3 = 5 \times 18$

$\dfrac{3w}{3} = \dfrac{90}{3}$

$w = 30$

Multiply Decimals To multiply decimals, multiply the numbers like any other number, ignoring the decimal point. Count the decimal places in each factor. The product will have the same number of decimal places as the sum of the decimal places in the factors.

Example Multiply 2.4 by 5.9.

Step 1 Multiply the factors like two whole numbers.
$24 \times 59 = 1416$

Step 2 Find the sum of the number of decimal places in the factors. Each factor has one decimal place, for a sum of two decimal places.

Step 3 The product will have two decimal places.
14.16

The product of 2.4 and 5.9 is 14.16.

Practice Problem Multiply 4.6 by 2.2.

Divide Decimals When dividing decimals, change the divisor to a whole number. To do this, multiply both the divisor and the dividend by the same power of ten. Then place the decimal point in the quotient directly above the decimal point in the dividend. Then divide as you do with whole numbers.

Example Divide 8.84 by 3.4.

Step 1 Multiply both factors by 10.
$3.4 \times 10 = 34$, $8.84 \times 10 = 88.4$

Step 2 Divide 88.4 by 34.

$$
\begin{array}{r}
2.6 \\
34\overline{)88.4} \\
-68 \\
\overline{204} \\
-204 \\
\overline{0}
\end{array}
$$

8.84 divided by 3.4 is 2.6.

Practice Problem Divide 75.6 by 3.6.

Use Proportions

An equation that shows that two ratios are equivalent is a proportion. The ratios $\dfrac{2}{4}$ and $\dfrac{5}{10}$ are equivalent, so they can be written as $\dfrac{2}{4} = \dfrac{5}{10}$. This equation is a proportion.

When two ratios form a proportion, the cross products are equal. To find the cross products in the proportion $\dfrac{2}{4} = \dfrac{5}{10}$, multiply the 2 and the 10, and the 4 and the 5. Therefore $2 \times 10 = 4 \times 5$, or $20 = 20$.

Because you know that both proportions are equal, you can use cross products to find a missing term in a proportion. This is known as solving the proportion.

Example The heights of a tree and a pole are proportional to the lengths of their shadows. The tree casts a shadow of 24 m when a 6-m pole casts a shadow of 4 m. What is the height of the tree?

Step 1 Write a proportion.
$$\frac{\text{height of tree}}{\text{height of pole}} = \frac{\text{length of tree's shadow}}{\text{length of pole's shadow}}$$

Step 2 Substitute the known values into the proportion. Let h represent the unknown value, the height of the tree.
$\dfrac{h}{6} = \dfrac{24}{4}$

Step 3 Find the cross products.
$h \times 4 = 6 \times 24$

Step 4 Simplify the equation.
$4h = 144$

Step 5 Divide each side by 4.
$\dfrac{4h}{4} = \dfrac{144}{4}$
$h = 36$

The height of the tree is 36 m.

Practice Problem The ratios of the weights of two objects on the Moon and on Earth are in proportion. A rock weighing 3 N on the Moon weighs 18 N on Earth. How much would a rock that weighs 5 N on the Moon weigh on Earth?

Use Percentages

The word *percent* means "out of one hundred." It is a ratio that compares a number to 100. Suppose you read that 77 percent of the Earth's surface is covered by water. That is the same as reading that the fraction of the Earth's surface covered by water is $\frac{77}{100}$. To express a fraction as a percent, first find the equivalent decimal for the fraction. Then, multiply the decimal by 100 and add the percent symbol.

Example Express $\frac{13}{20}$ as a percent.

Step 1 Find the equivalent decimal for the fraction.

$$
\begin{array}{r}
0.65 \\
20\overline{)13.00} \\
\underline{12\,0} \\
1\,00 \\
\underline{1\,00} \\
0
\end{array}
$$

Step 2 Rewrite the fraction $\frac{13}{20}$ as 0.65.

Step 3 Multiply 0.65 by 100 and add the % sign.
$0.65 \times 100 = 65 = 65\%$

So, $\frac{13}{20} = 65\%$.

This also can be solved as a proportion.

Example Express $\frac{13}{20}$ as a percent.

Step 1 Write a proportion.
$$\frac{13}{20} = \frac{x}{100}$$

Step 2 Find the cross products.
$1300 = 20x$

Step 3 Divide each side by 20.
$$\frac{1300}{20} = \frac{20x}{20}$$
$65\% = x$

Practice Problem In one year, 73 of 365 days were rainy in one city. What percent of the days in that city were rainy?

Solve One-Step Equations

A statement that two things are equal is an equation. For example, $A = B$ is an equation that states that A is equal to B.

An equation is solved when a variable is replaced with a value that makes both sides of the equation equal. To make both sides equal the inverse operation is used. Addition and subtraction are inverses, and multiplication and division are inverses.

Example 1 Solve the equation $x - 10 = 35$.

Step 1 Find the solution by adding 10 to each side of the equation.
$x - 10 = 35$
$x - 10 + 10 = 35 + 10$
$x = 45$

Step 2 Check the solution.
$x - 10 = 35$
$45 - 10 = 35$
$35 = 35$

Both sides of the equation are equal, so $x = 45$.

Example 2 In the formula $a = bc$, find the value of c if $a = 20$ and $b = 2$.

Step 1 Rearrange the formula so the unknown value is by itself on one side of the equation by dividing both sides by b.
$a = bc$
$\frac{a}{b} = \frac{bc}{b}$
$\frac{a}{b} = c$

Step 2 Replace the variables a and b with the values that are given.
$\frac{a}{b} = c$
$\frac{20}{2} = c$
$10 = c$

Step 3 Check the solution.
$a = bc$
$20 = 2 \times 10$
$20 = 20$

Both sides of the equation are equal, so $c = 10$ is the solution when $a = 20$ and $b = 2$.

Practice Problem In the formula $h = gd$, find the value of d if $g = 12.3$ and $h = 17.4$.

Use Percentages

$$\frac{73}{365} = \frac{x}{100}$$
$$\frac{7300}{365} = \frac{365x}{365}$$
$20\% = x$

Solve One-Step Equations

$h = gd$
$$\frac{17.4}{12.3} = \frac{12.3d}{12.3}$$
$1.41 = d$

Use Statistics

mean

$8 + 4 + 12 + 8 + 11 + 14 + 16 = 73$

$73 \div 7 = 10.4$

median

4, 8, 8, <u>11</u>, 12, 14, 16

mode

4, <u>8</u>, <u>8</u>, 11, 12, 14, 16

range

<u>4</u>, 8, 8, 11, 12, 14, <u>16</u>

$16 - 4 = 12$

Use Statistics

The branch of mathematics that deals with collecting, analyzing, and presenting data is statistics. In statistics, there are three common ways to summarize data with a single number—the mean, the median, and the mode.

The **mean** of a set of data is the arithmetic average. It is found by adding the numbers in the data set and dividing by the number of items in the set.

The **median** is the middle number in a set of data when the data are arranged in numerical order. If there were an even number of data points, the median would be the mean of the two middle numbers.

The **mode** of a set of data is the number or item that appears most often.

Another number that often is used to describe a set of data is the range. The **range** is the difference between the largest number and the smallest number in a set of data.

A **frequency table** shows how many times each piece of data occurs, usually in a survey. **Table 2** below shows the results of a student survey on favorite color.

Table 2 Student Color Choice		
Color	**Tally**	**Frequency**
red	||||	4
blue	卌	5
black	||	2
green	|||	3
purple	卌 ||	7
yellow	卌 |	6

Based on the frequency table data, which color is the favorite?

Example The speeds (in m/s) for a race car during five different time trials are 39, 37, 44, 36, and 44.

To find the mean:

Step 1 Find the sum of the numbers.

$39 + 37 + 44 + 36 + 44 = 200$

Step 2 Divide the sum by the number of items, which is 5.

$200 \div 5 = 40$

The mean is 40 m/s.

To find the median:

Step 1 Arrange the measures from least to greatest.

36, 37, 39, 44, 44

Step 2 Determine the middle measure.

36, 37, <u>39</u>, 44, 44

The median is 39 m/s.

To find the mode:

Step 1 Group the numbers that are the same together.

44, 44, 36, 37, 39

Step 2 Determine the number that occurs most in the set.

<u>44, 44</u>, 36, 37, 39

The mode is 44 m/s.

To find the range:

Step 1 Arrange the measures from largest to smallest.

44, 44, 39, 37, 36

Step 2 Determine the largest and smallest measures in the set.

<u>44</u>, 44, 39, 37, <u>36</u>

Step 3 Find the difference between the largest and smallest measures.

$44 - 36 = 8$

The range is 8 m/s.

Practice Problem Find the mean, median, mode, and range for the data set 8, 4, 12, 8, 11, 14, 16.

Math Skill Handbook

Math Skill Handbook

Use Geometry

The branch of mathematics that deals with the measurement, properties, and relationships of points, lines, angles, surfaces, and solids is called geometry.

Perimeter The **perimeter** (P) is the distance around a geometric figure. To find the perimeter of a rectangle, add the length and width and multiply that sum by two, or $2(l + w)$. To find perimeters of irregular figures, add the length of the sides.

Example 1 Find the perimeter of a rectangle that is 3 m long and 5 m wide.

Step 1 You know that the perimeter is 2 times the sum of the width and length.
$P = 2(3\text{ m} + 5\text{ m})$

Step 2 Find the sum of the width and length.
$P = 2(8\text{ m})$

Step 3 Multiply by 2.
$P = 16\text{ m}$

The perimeter is 16 m.

Example 2 Find the perimeter of a shape with sides measuring 2 cm, 5 cm, 6 cm, 3 cm.

Step 1 You know that the perimeter is the sum of all the sides.
$P = 2 + 5 + 6 + 3$

Step 2 Find the sum of the sides.
$P = 2 + 5 + 6 + 3$
$P = 16$

The perimeter is 16 cm.

Practice Problem Find the perimeter of a rectangle with a length of 18 m and a width of 7 m.

Practice Problem Find the perimeter of a triangle measuring 1.6 cm by 2.4 cm by 2.4 cm.

Area of a Rectangle The **area** (A) is the number of square units needed to cover a surface. To find the area of a rectangle, multiply the length times the width, or $l \times w$. When finding area, the units also are multiplied. Area is given in square units.

Example Find the area of a rectangle with a length of 1 cm and a width of 10 cm.

Step 1 You know that the area is the length multiplied by the width.
$A = (1\text{ cm} \times 10\text{ cm})$

Step 2 Multiply the length by the width. Also multiply the units.
$A = 10\text{ cm}^2$

The area is 10 cm².

Practice Problem Find the area of a square whose sides measure 4 m.

Area of a Triangle To find the area of a triangle, use the formula:

$$A = \frac{1}{2}(\text{base} \times \text{height})$$

The base of a triangle can be any of its sides. The height is the perpendicular distance from a base to the opposite endpoint, or vertex.

Example Find the area of a triangle with a base of 18 m and a height of 7 m.

Step 1 You know that the area is $\frac{1}{2}$ the base times the height.
$A = \frac{1}{2}(18\text{ m} \times 7\text{ m})$

Step 2 Multiply $\frac{1}{2}$ by the product of 18×7. Multiply the units.
$A = \frac{1}{2}(126\text{ m}^2)$
$A = 63\text{ m}^2$

The area is 63 m².

Practice Problem Find the area of a triangle with a base of 27 cm and a height of 17 cm.

Perimeter

Problem 1
$P = 2(18\text{ m} + 7\text{ m})$
$P = 2(25\text{ m})$
$P = 50\text{ m}$

Problem 2
$P = 1.6\text{ cm} + 2.4\text{ cm} + 2.4\text{ cm}$
$P = 6.4\text{ cm}$

Area of a Rectangle
$A = (4\text{ m} \times 4\text{ m})$
$A = 16\text{ m}^2$

Area of a Triangle
$A = \frac{1}{2}(27\text{ cm} \times 17\text{ cm})$
$A = \frac{1}{2}(459\text{ cm}^2)$
$A = 229.5\text{ cm}^2$

Circumference of a Circle

$C = 2\pi r$

$C = 2\pi(19)$

$C = 38\pi$

$C = 119.3$

Area of a Circle

$A = \pi r^2$

$A = \pi(16\text{ m})^2$

$A = \pi\,256\text{ m}^2$

$A = 803.8\text{ m}^2$

Circumference of a Circle The **diameter** (*d*) of a circle is the distance across the circle through its center, and the **radius** (*r*) is the distance from the center to any point on the circle. The radius is half of the diameter. The distance around the circle is called the **circumference** (C). The formula for finding the circumference is:

$$C = 2\pi r \ \ or \ \ C = \pi d$$

The circumference divided by the diameter is always equal to 3.1415926... This nonterminating and nonrepeating number is represented by the Greek letter π (pi). An approximation often used for π is 3.14.

Example 1 Find the circumference of a circle with a radius of 3 m.

Step 1 You know the formula for the circumference is 2 times the radius times π.
$$C = 2\pi(3)$$

Step 2 Multiply 2 times the radius.
$$C = 6\pi$$

Step 3 Multiply by π.
$$C = 19\text{ m}$$

The circumference is 19 m.

Example 2 Find the circumference of a circle with a diameter of 24.0 cm.

Step 1 You know the formula for the circumference is the diameter times π.
$$C = \pi(24.0)$$

Step 2 Multiply the diameter by π.
$$C = 75.4\text{ cm}$$

The circumference is 75.4 cm.

Practice Problem Find the circumference of a circle with a radius of 19 cm.

Area of a Circle The formula for the area of a circle is:
$$A = \pi r^2$$

Example 1 Find the area of a circle with a radius of 4.0 cm.

Step 1 $A = \pi(4.0)^2$

Step 2 Find the square of the radius.
$$A = 16\pi$$

Step 3 Multiply the square of the radius by π.
$$A = 50\text{ cm}^2$$

The area of the circle is 50 cm^2.

Example 2 Find the area of a circle with a radius of 225 m.

Step 1 $A = \pi(225)^2$

Step 2 Find the square of the radius.
$$A = 50625\pi$$

Step 3 Multiply the square of the radius by π.
$$A = 158962.5$$

The area of the circle is 158,962 m^2.

Example 3 Find the area of a circle whose diameter is 20.0 mm.

Step 1 You know the formula for the area of a circle is the square of the radius times π, and that the radius is half of the diameter.
$$A = \pi\left(\frac{20.0}{2}\right)^2$$

Step 2 Find the radius.
$$A = \pi(10.0)^2$$

Step 3 Find the square of the radius.
$$A = 100\pi$$

Step 4 Multiply the square of the radius by π.
$$A = 314\text{ mm}^2$$

The area is 314 mm^2.

Practice Problem Find the area of a circle with a radius of 16 m.

Volume The measure of space occupied by a solid is the **volume** (V). To find the volume of a rectangular solid multiply the length times width times height, or $V = l \times w \times h$. It is measured in cubic units, such as cubic centimeters (cm^3).

Example Find the volume of a rectangular solid with a length of 2.0 m, a width of 4.0 m, and a height of 3.0 m.

Step 1 You know the formula for volume is the length times the width times the height.
$$V = 2.0 \text{ m} \times 4.0 \text{ m} \times 3.0 \text{ m}$$

Step 2 Multiply the length times the width times the height.
$$V = 24 \text{ m}^3$$

The volume is 24 m^3.

Practice Problem Find the volume of a rectangular solid that is 8 m long, 4 m wide, and 4 m high.

To find the volume of other solids, multiply the area of the base times the height.

Example 1 Find the volume of a solid that has a triangular base with a length of 8.0 m and a height of 7.0 m. The height of the entire solid is 15.0 m.

Step 1 You know that the base is a triangle, and the area of a triangle is $\frac{1}{2}$ the base times the height, and the volume is the area of the base times the height.
$$V = \left[\frac{1}{2}(b \times h)\right] \times 15$$

Step 2 Find the area of the base.
$$V = \left[\frac{1}{2}(8 \times 7)\right] \times 15$$
$$V = \left(\frac{1}{2} \times 56\right) \times 15$$

Step 3 Multiply the area of the base by the height of the solid.
$$V = 28 \times 15$$
$$V = 420 \text{ m}^3$$

The volume is 420 m^3.

Example 2 Find the volume of a cylinder that has a base with a radius of 12.0 cm, and a height of 21.0 cm.

Step 1 You know that the base is a circle, and the area of a circle is the square of the radius times π, and the volume is the area of the base times the height.
$$V = (\pi r^2) \times 21$$
$$V = (\pi 12^2) \times 21$$

Step 2 Find the area of the base.
$$V = 144\pi \times 21$$
$$V = 452 \times 21$$

Step 3 Multiply the area of the base by the height of the solid.
$$V = 9490 \text{ cm}^3$$

The volume is 9490 cm^3.

Example 3 Find the volume of a cylinder that has a diameter of 15 mm and a height of 4.8 mm.

Step 1 You know that the base is a circle with an area equal to the square of the radius times π. The radius is one-half the diameter. The volume is the area of the base times the height.
$$V = (\pi r^2) \times 4.8$$
$$V = \left[\pi\left(\frac{1}{2} \times 15\right)^2\right] \times 4.8$$
$$V = (\pi 7.5^2) \times 4.8$$

Step 2 Find the area of the base.
$$V = 56.25\pi \times 4.8$$
$$V = 176.63 \times 4.8$$

Step 3 Multiply the area of the base by the height of the solid.
$$V = 847.8$$

The volume is 847.8 mm^3.

Practice Problem Find the volume of a cylinder with a diameter of 7 cm in the base and a height of 16 cm.

Volume

Problem 1
$$V = 8 \text{ m} \times 4 \text{ m} \times 4 \text{ m}$$
$$V = 128 \text{ m}^3$$

Problem 2
$$V = \pi r^2 \times \text{height}$$
$$V = \left[\pi\left(\frac{1}{2} \times 7\right)^2\right] \times 16$$
$$V = [\pi(3.5)^2] \times 16$$
$$V = [\pi(12.25)] \times 16$$
$$V = 38.46 \times 16$$
$$V = 615.36$$

Math Skill Handbook

Dimensional Analysis

$$x \, mg = 1 \, \cancel{kg} \times \frac{1000 \, \cancel{g}}{1 \, \cancel{kg}} \times \frac{1000 \, mg}{1 \, \cancel{g}} =$$

1,000,000 mg

1,000,000 mg = 1 kg

Math Skill Handbook

Science Applications

Measure in SI

The metric system of measurement was developed in 1795. A modern form of the metric system, called the International System (SI), was adopted in 1960 and provides the standard measurements that all scientists around the world can understand.

The SI system is convenient because unit sizes vary by powers of 10. Prefixes are used to name units. Look at **Table 3** for some common SI prefixes and their meanings.

Table 3 Some SI Prefixes			
Prefix	**Symbol**	**Meaning**	
kilo-	k	1,000	thousand
hecto-	h	100	hundred
deka-	da	10	ten
deci-	d	0.1	tenth
centi-	c	0.01	hundredth
milli-	m	0.001	thousandth

Example How many grams equal one kilogram?

Step 1 Find the prefix *kilo* in **Table 3.**

Step 2 Using **Table 3,** determine the meaning of *kilo.* According to the table, it means 1,000. When the prefix *kilo* is added to a unit, it means that there are 1,000 of the units in a "*kilo*unit."

Step 3 Apply the prefix to the units in the question. The units in the question are grams. There are 1,000 grams in a kilogram.

Practice Problem Is a milligram larger or smaller than a gram? How many of the smaller units equal one larger unit? What fraction of the larger unit does one smaller unit represent?

Dimensional Analysis

Convert SI Units In science, quantities such as length, mass, and time sometimes are measured using different units. A process called dimensional analysis can be used to change one unit of measure to another. This process involves multiplying your starting quantity and units by one or more conversion factors. A conversion factor is a ratio equal to one and can be made from any two equal quantities with different units. If 1,000 mL equal 1 L then two ratios can be made.

$$\frac{1,000 \text{ mL}}{1 \text{ L}} = \frac{1 \text{ L}}{1,000 \text{ mL}} = 1$$

One can covert between units in the SI system by using the equivalents in **Table 3** to make conversion factors.

Example 1 How many cm are in 4 m?

Step 1 Write conversion factors for the units given. From **Table 3,** you know that 100 cm = 1 m. The conversion factors are

$$\frac{100 \text{ cm}}{1 \text{ m}} \quad and \quad \frac{1 \text{ m}}{100 \text{ cm}}$$

Step 2 Decide which conversion factor to use. Select the factor that has the units you are converting from (m) in the denominator and the units you are converting to (cm) in the numerator.

$$\frac{100 \text{ cm}}{1 \text{ m}}$$

Step 3 Multiply the starting quantity and units by the conversion factor. Cancel the starting units with the units in the denominator. There are 400 cm in 4 m.

$$4 \, \cancel{m} \times \frac{100 \text{ cm}}{1 \, \cancel{m}} = 400 \text{ cm}$$

Practice Problem How many milligrams are in one kilogram? (Hint: You will need to use two conversion factors from **Table 3.**)

Table 4 Unit System Equivalents

Type of Measurement	Equivalent
Length	1 in = 2.54 cm
	1 yd = 0.91 m
	1 mi = 1.61 km
Mass and Weight*	1 oz = 28.35 g
	1 lb = 0.45 kg
	1 ton (short) = 0.91 tonnes (metric tons)
	1 lb = 4.45 N
Volume	$1\ in^3 = 16.39\ cm^3$
	1 qt = 0.95 L
	1 gal = 3.78 L
Area	$1\ in^2 = 6.45\ cm^2$
	$1\ yd^2 = 0.83\ m^2$
	$1\ mi^2 = 2.59\ km^2$
	1 acre = 0.40 hectares
Temperature	$°C = \dfrac{(°F - 32)}{1.8}$
	$K = °C + 273$

*Weight is measured in standard Earth gravity.

Convert Between Unit Systems Table 4 gives a list of equivalents that can be used to convert between English and SI units.

Example If a meterstick has a length of 100 cm, how long is the meterstick in inches?

Step 1 Write the conversion factors for the units given. From **Table 4,** 1 in = 2.54 cm.

$$\frac{1\ in}{2.54\ cm} \quad and \quad \frac{2.54\ cm}{1\ in}$$

Step 2 Determine which conversion factor to use. You are converting from cm to in. Use the conversion factor with cm on the bottom.

$$\frac{1\ in}{2.54\ cm}$$

Step 3 Multiply the starting quantity and units by the conversion factor. Cancel the starting units with the units in the denominator. Round your answer based on the number of significant figures in the conversion factor.

$$100\ \cancel{cm} \times \frac{1\ in}{2.54\ \cancel{cm}} = 39.37\ in$$

The meterstick is 39.4 in long.

Practice Problem A book has a mass of 5 lbs. What is the mass of the book in kg?

Practice Problem Use the equivalent for in and cm (1 in = 2.54 cm) to show how $1\ in^3 = 16.39\ cm^3$.

Convert Between Unit Systems

$$\frac{(1\ in)^3}{(2.54\ cm)^3}$$

$$= \frac{1\ in \times 1\ in \times 1\ in}{2.54\ cm \times 2.54\ cm \times 2.54\ cm}$$

$$= \frac{1\ in^3}{16.39\ cm^3}$$

Precision and Significant Digits

When you make a measurement, the value you record depends on the precision of the measuring instrument. This precision is represented by the number of significant digits recorded in the measurement. When counting the number of significant digits, all digits are counted except zeros at the end of a number with no decimal point such as 2,050, and zeros at the beginning of a decimal such as 0.03020. When adding or subtracting numbers with different precision, round the answer to the smallest number of decimal places of any number in the sum or difference. When multiplying or dividing, the answer is rounded to the smallest number of significant digits of any number being multiplied or divided.

Example The lengths 5.28 and 5.2 are measured in meters. Find the sum of these lengths and record your answer using the correct number of significant digits.

Step 1 Find the sum.

5.28 m	2 digits after the decimal
+ 5.2 m	1 digit after the decimal
10.48 m	

Step 2 Round to one digit after the decimal because the least number of digits after the decimal of the numbers being added is 1.

The sum is 10.5 m.

Practice Problem How many significant digits are in the measurement 7,071,301 m? How many significant digits are in the measurement 0.003010 g?

Practice Problem Multiply 5.28 and 5.2 using the rule for multiplying and dividing. Record the answer using the correct number of significant digits.

Scientific Notation

Many times numbers used in science are very small or very large. Because these numbers are difficult to work with scientists use scientific notation. To write numbers in scientific notation, move the decimal point until only one non-zero digit remains on the left. Then count the number of places you moved the decimal point and use that number as a power of ten. For example, the average distance from the Sun to Mars is 227,800,000,000 m. In scientific notation, this distance is 2.278×10^{11} m. Because you moved the decimal point to the left, the number is a positive power of ten.

The mass of an electron is about 0.000 000 000 000 000 000 000 000 000 000 911 kg. Expressed in scientific notation, this mass is 9.11×10^{-31} kg. Because the decimal point was moved to the right, the number is a negative power of ten.

Example Earth is 149,600,000 km from the Sun. Express this in scientific notation.

Step 1 Move the decimal point until one non-zero digit remains on the left.
1.496 000 00

Step 2 Count the number of decimal places you have moved. In this case, eight.

Step 3 Show that number as a power of ten, 10^8.

The Earth is 1.496×10^8 km from the Sun.

Practice Problem How many significant digits are in 149,600,000 km? How many significant digits are in 1.496×10^8 km?

Practice Problem Parts used in a high performance car must be measured to 7×10^{-6} m. Express this number as a decimal.

Practice Problem A CD is spinning at 539 revolutions per minute. Express this number in scientific notation.

Make and Use Graphs

Data in tables can be displayed in a graph—a visual representation of data. Common graph types include line graphs, bar graphs, and circle graphs.

Line Graph A line graph shows a relationship between two variables that change continuously. The independent variable is changed and is plotted on the *x*-axis. The dependent variable is observed, and is plotted on the *y*-axis.

Example Draw a line graph of the data below from a cyclist in a long-distance race.

Table 5 Bicycle Race Data	
Time (h)	Distance (km)
0	0
1	8
2	16
3	24
4	32
5	40

Step 1 Determine the *x*-axis and *y*-axis variables. Time varies independently of distance and is plotted on the *x*-axis. Distance is dependent on time and is plotted on the *y*-axis.

Step 2 Determine the scale of each axis. The *x*-axis data ranges from 0 to 5. The *y*-axis data ranges from 0 to 40.

Step 3 Using graph paper, draw and label the axes. Include units in the labels.

Step 4 Draw a point at the intersection of the time value on the *x*-axis and corresponding distance value on the *y*-axis. Connect the points and label the graph with a title, as shown in **Figure 20.**

Distance v. Time

Figure 20 This line graph shows the relationship between distance and time during a bicycle ride.

Practice Problem A puppy's shoulder height is measured during the first year of her life. The following measurements were collected: (3 mo, 52 cm), (6 mo, 72 cm), (9 mo, 83 cm), (12 mo, 86 cm). Graph this data.

Find a Slope The slope of a straight line is the ratio of the vertical change, rise, to the horizontal change, run.

$$\text{Slope} = \frac{\text{vertical change (rise)}}{\text{horizontal change (run)}} = \frac{\text{change in } y}{\text{change in } x}$$

Example Find the slope of the graph in **Figure 20.**

Step 1 You know that the slope is the change in *y* divided by the change in *x*.
$$\text{Slope} = \frac{\text{change in } y}{\text{change in } x}$$

Step 2 Determine the data points you will be using. For a straight line, choose the two sets of points that are the farthest apart.
$$\text{Slope} = \frac{(40-0) \text{ km}}{(5-0) \text{ hr}}$$

Step 3 Find the change in *y* and *x*.
$$\text{Slope} = \frac{40 \text{ km}}{5 \text{h}}$$

Step 4 Divide the change in *y* by the change in *x*.
$$\text{Slope} = \frac{8 \text{ km}}{\text{h}}$$

The slope of the graph is 8 km/h.

Line Graph

x	y
3	52
6	72
9	83
12	86

Puppy Growth

Composition of Air

Bar Graph To compare data that does not change continuously you might choose a bar graph. A bar graph uses bars to show the relationships between variables. The *x*-axis variable is divided into parts. The parts can be numbers such as years, or a category such as a type of animal. The *y*-axis is a number and increases continuously along the axis.

Example A recycling center collects 4.0 kg of aluminum on Monday, 1.0 kg on Wednesday, and 2.0 kg on Friday. Create a bar graph of this data.

Step 1 Select the *x*-axis and *y*-axis variables. The measured numbers (the masses of aluminum) should be placed on the *y*-axis. The variable divided into parts (collection days) is placed on the *x*-axis.

Step 2 Create a graph grid like you would for a line graph. Include labels and units.

Step 3 For each measured number, draw a vertical bar above the *x*-axis value up to the *y*-axis value. For the first data point, draw a vertical bar above Monday up to 4.0 kg.

Practice Problem Draw a bar graph of the gases in air: 78% nitrogen, 21% oxygen, 1% other gases.

Circle Graph

The total amount of aluminum collected is:

$4.0 \text{ kg} + 1.0 \text{ kg} + 2.0 \text{ kg} = 7.0 \text{ kg}$

$\frac{4.0 \text{ kg}}{7.0 \text{ kg}} = \frac{x}{360°}; \ x = 206°$

$\frac{1.0 \text{ kg}}{7.0 \text{ kg}} = \frac{x}{360°}; \ x = 51°$

$\frac{2.0 \text{ kg}}{7.0 \text{ kg}} = \frac{x}{360°}; \ x = 103°$

Circle Graph To display data as parts of a whole, you might use a circle graph. A circle graph is a circle divided into sections that represent the relative size of each piece of data. The entire circle represents 100%, half represents 50%, and so on.

Example Air is made up of 78% nitrogen, 21% oxygen, and 1% other gases. Display the composition of air in a circle graph.

Step 1 Multiply each percent by 360° and divide by 100 to find the angle of each section in the circle.

$78\% \times \frac{360°}{100} = 280.8°$

$21\% \times \frac{360°}{100} = 75.6°$

$1\% \times \frac{360°}{100} = 3.6°$

Step 2 Use a compass to draw a circle and to mark the center of the circle. Draw a straight line from the center to the edge of the circle.

Step 3 Use a protractor and the angles you calculated to divide the circle into parts. Place the center of the protractor over the center of the circle and line the base of the protractor over the straight line.

Practice Problem Draw a circle graph to represent the amount of aluminum collected during the week shown in the bar graph to the left.

Math Skill Handbook

Use and Care of a Microscope

Eyepiece Contains magnifying lenses you look through.

Arm Supports the body tube.

Low-power objective Contains the lens with the lowest power magnification.

Stage clips Hold the microscope slide in place.

Coarse adjustment Focuses the image under low power.

Fine adjustment Sharpens the image under high magnification.

Body tube Connects the eyepiece to the revolving nosepiece.

Revolving nosepiece Holds and turns the objectives into viewing position.

High-power objective Contains the lens with the highest magnification.

Stage Supports the microscope slide.

Light source Provides light that passes upward through the diaphragm, the specimen, and the lenses.

Base Provides support for the microscope.

Caring for a Microscope

1. Always carry the microscope holding the arm with one hand and supporting the base with the other hand.

2. Don't touch the lenses with your fingers.

3. The coarse adjustment knob is used only when looking through the lowest-power objective lens. The fine adjustment knob is used when the high-power objective is in place.

4. Cover the microscope when you store it.

Using a Microscope

1. Place the microscope on a flat surface that is clear of objects. The arm should be toward you.

2. Look through the eyepiece. Adjust the diaphragm so light comes through the opening in the stage.

3. Place a slide on the stage so the specimen is in the field of view. Hold it firmly in place by using the stage clips.

4. Always focus with the coarse adjustment and the low-power objective lens first. After the object is in focus on low power, turn the nosepiece until the high-power objective is in place. Use ONLY the fine adjustment to focus with the high-power objective lens.

Making a Wet-Mount Slide

1. Carefully place the item you want to look at in the center of a clean, glass slide. Make sure the sample is thin enough for light to pass through.

2. Use a dropper to place one or two drops of water on the sample.

3. Hold a clean coverslip by the edges and place it at one edge of the water. Slowly lower the coverslip onto the water until it lies flat.

4. If you have too much water or a lot of air bubbles, touch the edge of a paper towel to the edge of the coverslip to draw off extra water and draw out unwanted air.

Diversity of Life: Classification of Living Organisms

A six-kingdom system of classification of organisms is used today. Two kingdoms—Kingdom Archaebacteria and Kingdom Eubacteria—contain organisms that do not have a nucleus and that lack membrane-bound structures in the cytoplasm of their cells. The members of the other four kingdoms have a cell or cells that contain a nucleus and structures in the cytoplasm, some of which are surrounded by membranes. These kingdoms are Kingdom Protista, Kingdom Fungi, Kingdom Plantae, and Kingdom Animalia.

Kingdom Archaebacteria

one-celled; some absorb food from their surroundings; some are photosynthetic; some are chemosynthetic; many are found in extremely harsh environments including salt ponds, hot springs, swamps, and deep-sea hydrothermal vents

Kingdom Eubacteria

one-celled; most absorb food from their surroundings; some are photosynthetic; some are chemosynthetic; many are parasites; many are round, spiral, or rod-shaped; some form colonies

Kingdom Protista

Phylum Euglenophyta one-celled; photosynthetic or take in food; most have one flagellum; euglenoids

Phylum Bacillariophyta one-celled; photosynthetic; have unique double shells made of silica; diatoms

Phylum Dinoflagellata one-celled; photosynthetic; contain red pigments; have two flagella; dinoflagellates

Phylum Chlorophyta one-celled, many-celled, or colonies; photosynthetic; contain chlorophyll; live on land, in freshwater, or salt water; green algae

Phylum Rhodophyta most are many-celled; photosynthetic; contain red pigments; most live in deep, saltwater environments; red algae

Phylum Phaeophyta most are many-celled; photosynthetic; contain brown pigments; most live in saltwater environments; brown algae

Phylum Rhizopoda one-celled; take in food; are free-living or parasitic; move by means of pseudopods; amoebas

Kingdom Eubacteria
Bacillus anthracis

Phylum Chlorophyta
Desmids

Amoeba

Phylum Zoomastigina one-celled; take in food; free-living or parasitic; have one or more flagella; zoomastigotes

Phylum Ciliophora one-celled; take in food; have large numbers of cilia; ciliates

Phylum Sporozoa one-celled; take in food; have no means of movement; are parasites in animals; sporozoans

Phylum Myxomycota
Slime mold

Phyla Myxomycota and Acrasiomycota one- or many-celled; absorb food; change form during life cycle; cellular and plasmodial slime molds

Phylum Oomycota many-celled; are either parasites or decomposers; live in freshwater or salt water; water molds, rusts and downy mildews

Kingdom Fungi

Phylum Zygomycota many-celled; absorb food; spores are produced in sporangia; zygote fungi; bread mold

Phylum Ascomycota one- and many-celled; absorb food; spores produced in asci; sac fungi; yeast

Phylum Basidiomycota many-celled; absorb food; spores produced in basidia; club fungi; mushrooms

Phylum Deuteromycota members with unknown reproductive structures; imperfect fungi; *Penicillium*

Phylum Mycophycota organisms formed by symbiotic relationship between an ascomycote or a basidiomycote and green alga or cyanobacterium; lichens

Phylum Oomycota
Phytophthora infestans

Lichens

Kingdom Plantae

Divisions Bryophyta (mosses), **Anthocerophyta** (hornworts), **Hepaticophyta** (liverworts), **Psilophyta** (whisk ferns) many-celled nonvascular plants; reproduce by spores produced in capsules; green; grow in moist, land environments

Division Lycophyta many-celled vascular plants; spores are produced in conelike structures; live on land; are photosynthetic; club mosses

Division Arthrophyta vascular plants; ribbed and jointed stems; scalelike leaves; spores produced in conelike structures; horsetails

Division Pterophyta vascular plants; leaves called fronds; spores produced in clusters of sporangia called sori; live on land or in water; ferns

Division Ginkgophyta deciduous trees; only one living species; have fan-shaped leaves with branching veins and fleshy cones with seeds; ginkgoes

Division Cycadophyta palmlike plants; have large, featherlike leaves; produces seeds in cones; cycads

Division Coniferophyta deciduous or evergreen; trees or shrubs; have needlelike or scalelike leaves; seeds produced in cones; conifers

Division Gnetophyta shrubs or woody vines; seeds are produced in cones; division contains only three genera; gnetum

Division Anthophyta dominant group of plants; flowering plants; have fruits with seeds

Kingdom Animalia

Phylum Porifera aquatic organisms that lack true tissues and organs; are asymmetrical and sessile; sponges

Phylum Cnidaria radially symmetrical organisms; have a digestive cavity with one opening; most have tentacles armed with stinging cells; live in aquatic environments singly or in colonies; includes jellyfish, corals, hydra, and sea anemones

Phylum Platyhelminthes bilaterally symmetrical worms; have flattened bodies; digestive system has one opening; parasitic and free-living species; flatworms

Division Bryophyta
Liverwort

Division Anthophyta
Tomato plant

Phylum Platyhelminthes
Flatworm

Phylum Chordata

Phylum Nematoda round, bilaterally symmetrical body; have digestive system with two openings; free-living forms and parasitic forms; roundworms

Phylum Mollusca soft-bodied animals, many with a hard shell and soft foot or footlike appendage; a mantle covers the soft body; aquatic and terrestrial species; includes clams, snails, squid, and octopuses

Phylum Annelida bilaterally symmetrical worms; have round, segmented bodies; terrestrial and aquatic species; includes earthworms, leeches, and marine polychaetes

Phylum Arthropoda largest animal group; have hard exoskeletons, segmented bodies, and pairs of jointed appendages; land and aquatic species; includes insects, crustaceans, and spiders

Phylum Echinodermata marine organisms; have spiny or leathery skin and a water-vascular system with tube feet; are radially symmetrical; includes sea stars, sand dollars, and sea urchins

Phylum Chordata organisms with internal skeletons and specialized body systems; most have paired appendages; all at some time have a notochord, nerve cord, gill slits, and a post-anal tail; include fish, amphibians, reptiles, birds, and mammals

PERIODIC TABLE OF THE ELEMENTS

Columns of elements are called groups. Elements in the same group have similar chemical properties.

| | Element — Hydrogen |
| Atomic number — 1 |
| Symbol — H |
| Atomic mass — 1.008 |

Gas
Liquid
Solid
Synthetic

State of matter

The first three symbols tell you the state of matter of the element at room temperature. The fourth symbol identifies elements that are not present in significant amounts on Earth. Useful amounts are made synthetically.

Rows of elements are called periods. Atomic number increases across a period.

The arrow shows where these elements would fit into the periodic table. They are moved to the bottom of the table to save space.

The number in parentheses is the mass number of the longest-lived isotope for that element.

1								
1 Hydrogen 1 **H** 1.008	**2**							
2 Lithium 3 **Li** 6.941	Beryllium 4 **Be** 9.012							
3 Sodium 11 **Na** 22.990	Magnesium 12 **Mg** 24.305	**3**	**4**	**5**	**6**	**7**	**8**	**9**
4 Potassium 19 **K** 39.098	Calcium 20 **Ca** 40.078	Scandium 21 **Sc** 44.956	Titanium 22 **Ti** 47.867	Vanadium 23 **V** 50.942	Chromium 24 **Cr** 51.996	Manganese 25 **Mn** 54.938	Iron 26 **Fe** 55.845	Cobalt 27 **Co** 58.933
5 Rubidium 37 **Rb** 85.468	Strontium 38 **Sr** 87.62	Yttrium 39 **Y** 88.906	Zirconium 40 **Zr** 91.224	Niobium 41 **Nb** 92.906	Molybdenum 42 **Mo** 95.94	Technetium 43 **Tc** (98)	Ruthenium 44 **Ru** 101.07	Rhodium 45 **Rh** 102.906
6 Cesium 55 **Cs** 132.905	Barium 56 **Ba** 137.327	Lanthanum 57 **La** 138.906	Hafnium 72 **Hf** 178.49	Tantalum 73 **Ta** 180.948	Tungsten 74 **W** 183.84	Rhenium 75 **Re** 186.207	Osmium 76 **Os** 190.23	Iridium 77 **Ir** 192.217
7 Francium 87 **Fr** (223)	Radium 88 **Ra** (226)	Actinium 89 **Ac** (227)	Rutherfordium 104 **Rf** (261)	Dubnium 105 **Db** (262)	Seaborgium 106 **Sg** (266)	Bohrium 107 **Bh** (264)	Hassium 108 **Hs** (277)	Meitnerium 109 **Mt** (268)

Lanthanide series	Cerium 58 **Ce** 140.116	Praseodymium 59 **Pr** 140.908	Neodymium 60 **Nd** 144.24	Promethium 61 **Pm** (145)	Samarium 62 **Sm** 150.36
Actinide series	Thorium 90 **Th** 232.038	Protactinium 91 **Pa** 231.036	Uranium 92 **U** 238.029	Neptunium 93 **Np** (237)	Plutonium 94 **Pu** (244)

Science Online
Visit bookd.msscience.com for updates to the periodic table.

Metal
Metalloid
Nonmetal

The color of an element's block tells you if the element is a metal, nonmetal, or metalloid.

18

13 | **14** | **15** | **16** | **17**

Boron	Carbon	Nitrogen	Oxygen	Fluorine	Neon
5	6	7	8	9	10
B	**C**	**N**	**O**	**F**	**Ne**
10.811	12.011	14.007	15.999	18.998	20.180

Helium
2
He
4.003

10 | **11** | **12**

Aluminum	Silicon	Phosphorus	Sulfur	Chlorine	Argon
13	14	15	16	17	18
Al	**Si**	**P**	**S**	**Cl**	**Ar**
26.982	28.086	30.974	32.065	35.453	39.948

Nickel	Copper	Zinc	Gallium	Germanium	Arsenic	Selenium	Bromine	Krypton
28	29	30	31	32	33	34	35	36
Ni	**Cu**	**Zn**	**Ga**	**Ge**	**As**	**Se**	**Br**	**Kr**
58.693	63.546	65.409	69.723	72.64	74.922	78.96	79.904	83.798

Palladium	Silver	Cadmium	Indium	Tin	Antimony	Tellurium	Iodine	Xenon
46	47	48	49	50	51	52	53	54
Pd	**Ag**	**Cd**	**In**	**Sn**	**Sb**	**Te**	**I**	**Xe**
106.42	107.868	112.411	114.818	118.710	121.760	127.60	126.904	131.293

Platinum	Gold	Mercury	Thallium	Lead	Bismuth	Polonium	Astatine	Radon
78	79	80	81	82	83	84	85	86
Pt	**Au**	**Hg**	**Tl**	**Pb**	**Bi**	**Po**	**At**	**Rn**
195.078	196.967	200.59	204.383	207.2	208.980	(209)	(210)	(222)

Darmstadtium	Roentgenium	Ununbium		Ununquadium
110	111	* 112		* 114
Ds	**Rg**	**Uub**		**Uuq**
(281)	(272)	(285)		(289)

* The names and symbols for elements 112 and 114 are temporary. Final names will be selected when the elements' discoveries are verified.

Europium	Gadolinium	Terbium	Dysprosium	Holmium	Erbium	Thulium	Ytterbium	Lutetium
63	64	65	66	67	68	69	70	71
Eu	**Gd**	**Tb**	**Dy**	**Ho**	**Er**	**Tm**	**Yb**	**Lu**
151.964	157.25	158.925	162.500	164.930	167.259	168.934	173.04	174.967

Americium	Curium	Berkelium	Californium	Einsteinium	Fermium	Mendelevium	Nobelium	Lawrencium
95	96	97	98	99	100	101	102	103
Am	**Cm**	**Bk**	**Cf**	**Es**	**Fm**	**Md**	**No**	**Lr**
(243)	(247)	(247)	(251)	(252)	(257)	(258)	(259)	(262)

Glossary/Glosario

Cómo usar el glosario en español:
1. Busca el término en inglés que desees encontrar.
2. El término en español, junto con la definición, se encuentran en la columna de la derecha.

Pronunciation Key

Use the following key to help you sound out words in the glossary.

a	back (BAK)	ew	food (FEWD)
ay	day (DAY)	yoo	pure (PYOOR)
ah	father (FAH thur)	yew	few (FYEW)
ow	flower (FLOW ur)	uh	comma (CAH muh)
ar	car (CAR)	u (+ con)	rub (RUB)
e	less (LES)	sh	shelf (SHELF)
ee	leaf (LEEF)	ch	nature (NAY chur)
ih	trip (TRIHP)	g	gift (GIHFT)
i (i + con + e)	idea (i DEE uh)	j	gem (JEM)
oh	go (GOH)	ing	sing (SING)
aw	soft (SAWFT)	zh	vision (VIH zhun)
or	orbit (OR buht)	k	cake (KAYK)
oy	coin (COYN)	s	seed, cent (SEED, SENT)
oo	foot (FOOT)	z	zone, raise (ZOHN, RAYZ)

English — **A** — **Español**

active immunity: long-lasting immunity that results when the body makes its own antibodies in response to a specific antigen. (p. 179)

allergen: substance that causes an allergic reaction. (p. 191)

allergy: overly strong reaction of the immune system to a foreign substance. (p. 190)

alveoli (al VEE uh li): tiny, thin-walled, grapelike clusters at the end of each bronchiole that are surrounded by capillaries; carbon dioxide and oxygen exchange takes place. (p. 95)

amino acid: building block of protein. (p. 37)

amniotic (am nee AH tihk) sac: thin, liquid-filled, protective membrane that forms around the embryo. (p. 159)

antibody: a protein made in response to a specific antigen that can attach to the antigen and cause it to be useless. (p. 178)

antigen (AN tih jun): any complex molecule that is foreign to your body. (p. 178)

artery: blood vessel that carries blood away from the heart, and has thick, elastic walls made of connective tissue and smooth muscle tissue. (p. 68)

asthma: lung disorder in which the bronchial tubes contract quickly and cause shortness of breath, wheezing, or coughing; may occur as an allergic reaction. (p. 100)

inmunidad activa: inmunidad duradera que resulta cuando el cuerpo produce sus propios anticuerpos en respuesta a un antígeno específico. (p. 179)

alergeno: sustancia que causa una reacción alérgica. (p. 191)

alergia: reacción exagerada del sistema inmune a una sustancia extraña. (p. 190)

alvéolos: pequeños racimos de pared delgada que se encuentran al final de cada bronquíolo y que están rodeados por capilares; aquí tiene lugar el intercambio de oxígeno y dióxido de carbono. (p. 95)

aminoácido: bloque de construcción de las proteínas. (p. 37)

saco amniótico: membrana protectora delgada y llena de líquido que se forma alrededor del embrión. (p. 159)

anticuerpo: proteína formada en respuesta a un antígeno específico y que puede unirse al antígeno para provocar que éste sea inutilizado. (p. 178)

antígeno: molécula compleja que es extraña para el cuerpo. (p. 178)

arteria: vaso sanguíneo que transporta sangre desde el corazón y tiene paredes gruesas y elásticas hechas de tejido conectivo y tejido muscular liso. (p. 68)

asma: desorden pulmonar en el que los tubos bronquiales se contraen rápidamente y causan dificultad para respirar, silbido o tos; puede ocurrir como una reacción alérgica. (p. 100)

atrium (AY tree um): two upper chambers of the heart that contract at the same time during a heartbeat. (p. 65)

axon (AK sahn): neuron structure that carries messages away from the cell body. (p. 119)

aurícula: las dos cámaras superiores del corazón que se contraen al mismo tiempo durante el latido cardiaco. (p. 65)

axón: estructura de la neurona que transmite los mensajes desde el cuerpo de la célula. (p. 119)

B

biological vector: disease-carrying organism, such as a rat, mosquito, or fly, that spreads infectious disease. (p. 185)

bladder: elastic, muscular organ that holds urine until it leaves the body through the urethra. (p. 104)

brain stem: connects the brain to the spinal cord and is made up of the midbrain, the pons, and the medulla. (p. 122)

bronchi (BRAHN ki): two short tubes that branch off the lower end of the trachea and carry air into the lungs. (p. 95)

vector biológico: organismo portador de enfermedades, como las ratas, mosquitos y moscas, que propagan enfermedades infecciosas. (p. 185)

vejiga: órgano muscular elástico que retiene la orina hasta que ésta sale del cuerpo por la uretra. (p. 104)

tronco cerebral: conecta al cerebro con la médula espinal y está compuesto por el mesencéfalo, el puente de Varolio y la médula. (p. 122)

bronquios: dos tubos cortos que se ramifican en la parte inferior de la tráquea y llevan el aire a los pulmones. (p. 95)

C

capillary: microscopic blood vessel that connects arteries and veins; has walls one cell thick, through which nutrients and oxygen diffuse into body cells, and waste materials and carbon dioxide diffuse out of body cells. (p. 69)

carbohydrate (kar boh HI drayt): nutrient that usually is the body's main source of energy. (p. 38)

cardiac muscle: striated, involuntary muscle found only in the heart. (p. 17)

cartilage: in humans, thick, smooth, flexible and slippery tissue layer that covers the ends of bones, makes movement easier by reducing friction, and absorbs shocks. (p. 10)

central nervous system: division of the nervous system, made up of the brain and spinal cord. (p. 121)

cerebellum (sur uh BEL um): part of the brain that controls voluntary muscle movements, maintains muscle tone, and helps maintain balance. (p. 122)

cerebrum (suh REE brum): largest part of the brain, where memory is stored, movements are controlled, and impulses from the senses are interpreted. (p. 122)

chemical digestion: occurs when enzymes and other chemicals break down large food molecules into smaller ones. (p. 47)

capilar: vaso sanguíneo microscópico que conecta las arterias con las venas; su pared tiene el grosor de una célula y los nutrientes y el oxígeno se difunden a través de ella hacia las células del cuerpo y los materiales de desecho y el dióxido de carbono hacia afuera de éstas. (p. 69)

carbohidrato: nutriente que generalmente es la principal fuente de energía para el cuerpo. (p. 38)

músculo cardiaco: músculo estriado involuntario que sólo se encuentra en el corazón. (p. 17)

cartílago: en los humanos, capa gruesa y lisa de tejido resbaladizo y flexible que cubre los extremos de los huesos, facilita el movimiento reduciendo la fricción y absorbe los impactos. (p. 10)

sistema nervioso central: parte del sistema nervioso, compuesto por el cerebro y la médula espinal. (p. 121)

cerebelo: parte del cerebro que controla los movimientos de los músculos voluntarios, mantiene el tono muscular y ayuda a mantener el equilibrio. (p. 122)

cerebro: la parte más grande del encéfalo, donde se almacena la memoria, se controlan los movimientos y se interpretan los impulsos provenientes de los sentidos. (p. 122)

digestión química: ocurre cuando las enzimas y otros químicos desintegran las moléculas grandes de los alimentos en otras más pequeñas. (p. 47)

Glossary/Glosario

chemotherapy (kee moh THAYR uh pee): use of chemicals to destroy cancer cells. (p. 194)

chyme (KIME): liquid product of digestion. (p. 51)

cochlea (KOH klee uh): fluid-filled structure in the inner ear in which sound vibrations are converted into nerve impulses that are sent to the brain. (p. 132)

coronary (KOR uh ner ee) circulation: flow of blood to and from the tissues of the heart. (p. 65)

quimioterapia: uso de sustancias químicas para destruir las células cancerosas. (p. 194)

quimo: producto líquido de la digestión. (p. 51)

cóclea: estructura del oído interno llena de líquido en la que las vibraciones sonoras se convierten en impulsos nerviosos que son enviados al cerebro. (p. 132)

circulación coronaria: flujo sanguíneo desde y hacia los tejidos del corazón. (p. 65)

D

dendrite: neuron structure that receives messages and sends them to the cell body. (p. 119)

dermis: skin layer below the epidermis that contains blood vessels, nerves, oil and sweat glands, and other structures. (p. 21)

diaphragm (DI uh fram): muscle beneath the lungs that contracts and relaxes to move gases in and out of the body. (p. 96)

digestion: mechanical and chemical breakdown of food into small molecules that cells can absorb and use. (p. 47)

dendrita: estructura de la neurona que recibe mensajes y los envía al cuerpo de la célula. (p. 119)

dermis: capa de la piel debajo de la epidermis que contiene vasos sanguíneos, nervios, glándulas sudoríparas, glándulas sebáceas y otras estructuras. (p. 21)

diafragma: músculo que está debajo de los pulmones y que se contrae y relaja para mover gases hacia dentro y fuera del cuerpo. (p. 96)

digestión: desintegración mecánica y química de los alimentos en moléculas pequeñas que las células pueden absorber y utilizar. (p. 47)

E

embryo: fertilized egg that has attached to the wall of the uterus. (p. 159)

emphysema (em fuh SEE muh): lung disease in which the alveoli enlarge. (p. 99)

enzyme: a type of protein that speeds up chemical reactions in the body without being changed or used up itself. (p. 48)

epidermis: outer, thinnest skin layer that constantly produces new cells to replace the dead cells rubbed off its surface. (p. 20)

embrión: óvulo fertilizado que se ha adherido a la pared del útero. (p. 159)

enfisema: enfermedad pulmonar en la cual se dilatan los alvéolos. (p. 99)

enzima: tipo de proteína que acelera las reacciones químicas en el cuerpo sin ser utilizada o consumida. (p. 48)

epidermis: la capa más delgada y externa de la piel que produce constantemente células nuevas para reemplazar las células muertas que se pierden por fricción de su superficie. (p. 20)

F

fat: nutrient that stores energy, cushions organs, and helps the body absorb vitamins. (p. 39)

fetal stress: can occur during the birth process or after birth as an infant adjusts from a watery, dark, constant-temperature environment to its new environment. (p. 162)

grasa: nutriente que almacena energía, amortigua a los órganos y ayuda al cuerpo a absorber vitaminas. (p. 39)

estrés fetal: puede ocurrir durante el proceso del nacimiento o luego del mismo mientras un nuevo ser humano se adapta de un ambiente acuoso, oscuro y de temperatura constante a su nuevo ambiente. (p. 162)

fetus: in humans, a developing baby after the first two months of pregnancy until birth. (p. 160)

food group: group of foods—such as bread, cereal, rice, and pasta—containing the same type of nutrients. (p. 44)

feto: en los humanos, bebé en desarrollo desde los primeros dos meses de embarazo hasta el nacimiento. (p. 160)

grupo alimenticio: grupo de alimentos—como el pan, el cereal, el arroz y la pasta—que contiene el mismo tipo de nutrientes. (p. 44)

hemoglobin (HEE muh gloh bun): chemical in red blood cells that carries oxygen from the lungs to body cells, and carries some carbon dioxide from body cells back to the lungs. (p. 75)

homeostasis: regulation of an organism's internal, life-maintaining. (p. 119)

hormone (HOR mohn): in humans, chemical produced by the endocrine system, released directly into the bloodstream by ductless glands; affects specific target tissues, and can speed up or slow down cellular activities. (p. 146)

hemoglobina: sustancia química de los glóbulos rojos que transporta oxígeno de los pulmones a las células del cuerpo y parte del dióxido de carbono de las células del cuerpo a los pulmones. (p. 75)

homeostasis: control de las condiciones internas que mantienen la vida de un organismo. (p. 119)

hormona: en los humanos, sustancia química producida por el sistema endocrino, liberada directamente al torrente sanguíneo mediante glándulas sin conductos; afecta a tejidos que constituyen blancos específicos y puede acelerar o frenar actividades celulares. (p. 146)

immune system: complex group of defenses that protects the body against pathogens—includes the skin and respiratory, digestive, and circulatory systems. (p. 176)

infectious disease: disease caused by a virus, bacterium, fungus, or protist that is spread from an infected organism or the environment to another organism. (p. 185)

involuntary muscle: muscle, such as heart muscle, that cannot be consciously controlled. (p. 15)

sistema inmune: grupo complejo de defensas que protege al cuerpo contra agentes patógenos—incluye la piel y los sistemas respiratorio, digestivo y circulatorio. (p. 176)

enfermedad infecciosa: enfermedad causada por virus, bacterias, hongos o protistas, propagada por un organismo infectado o del medio ambiente hacia otro organismo. (p. 185)

músculo involuntario: músculo, como el músculo cardiaco, que no puede controlarse conscientemente. (p. 15)

joint: any place where two or more bones come together; can be movable or immovable. (p. 11)

articulación: cualquier lugar en donde se unen dos o más huesos, pudiendo ser fija o flexible. (p. 11)

kidney: bean-shaped urinary system organ that is made up of about 1 million nephrons and filters blood, producing urine. (p. 102)

riñón: órgano del sistema urinario en forma de fríjol, compuesto por cerca de un millón de nefronas; filtra la sangre y produce la orina. (p. 102)

Glossary/Glosario

Glossary/Glosario

L

larynx: airway to which the vocal cords are attached. (p. 95)

ligament: tough band of tissue that holds bones together at joints. (p. 11)

lymph (LIHMF): tissue fluid that has diffused into lymphatic capillaries. (p. 80)

lymph nodes: bean-shaped organs found throughout the body that filter out microorganisms and foreign materials taken up by the lymphocytes. (p. 80)

lymphatic system: carries lymph through a network of lymph capillaries and vessels, and drains it into large veins near the heart; helps fight infections and diseases. (p. 80)

lymphocyte (LIHM fuh site): a type of white blood cell that fights infection. (p. 80)

laringe: vía respiratoria que contiene las cuerdas vocales. (p. 95)

ligamento: banda de tejido resistente que mantiene unidos a los huesos de las articulaciones. (p. 11)

linfa: fluido tisular que se ha difundido hacia los capilares linfáticos. (p. 80)

ganglio linfático: órganos en forma de fríjol que se encuentran en todo el cuerpo; filtran y extraen microorganismos y materiales extraños captados por los linfocitos. (p. 80)

sistema linfático: sistema que transporta la linfa a través de una red de vasos y capilares linfáticos y la vierte en venas grandes cerca del corazón; ayuda a combatir enfermedades e infecciones. (p. 80)

linfocito: tipo de glóbulo blanco que combate las infecciones. (p. 80)

M

mechanical digestion: breakdown of food through chewing, mixing, and churning. (p. 47)

melanin: pigment produced by the epidermis that protects skin from sun damage and gives skin and eyes their color. (p. 21)

menstrual cycle: hormone-controlled monthly cycle of changes in the female reproductive system that includes the maturation of an egg and preparation of the uterus for possible pregnancy. (p. 154)

menstruation (men STRAY shun): monthly flow of blood and tissue cells that occurs when the lining of the uterus breaks down and is shed. (p. 154)

mineral: inorganic nutrient that regulates many chemical reactions in the body. (p. 42)

muscle: organ that can relax, contract, and provide the force to move bones and body parts. (p. 14)

digestión mecánica: desdoblamiento del alimento a través de la masticación, mezcla y agitación. (p. 47)

melanina: pigmento producido por la epidermis que protege a la piel del daño producido por la luz solar y le da a la piel y a los ojos su color. (p. 21)

ciclo menstrual: ciclo mensual de cambios en el sistema reproductor femenino, el cual es controlado por hormonas e incluye la maduración de un óvulo y la preparación del útero para un posible embarazo. (p. 154)

menstruación: flujo mensual de sangre y células tisulares que ocurre cuando el endometrio uterino se rompe y se desprende. (p. 154)

mineral: nutriente inorgánico que regula una gran cantidad de reacciones químicas en el cuerpo. (p. 42)

músculo: órgano que puede relajarse, contraerse y proporcionar la fuerza para mover los huesos y las partes del cuerpo. (p. 14)

N

nephron (NEF rahn): tiny filtering unit of the kidney. (p. 103)

neuron (NOO rahn): basic functioning unit of the nervous system, made up of a cell body, dendrites, and axons. (p. 119)

nefrona: pequeña unidad de filtrado del riñón. (p. 103)

neurona: unidad básica de funcionamiento del sistema nervioso, formada por un cuerpo celular, dendritas y axones. (p. 119)

noninfectious disease: disease, such as cancer, diabetes, or asthma, that is not spread from one person to another. (p. 190)

nutrients (NEW tree unts): substances in foods—proteins, carbohydrates, fats, vitamins, minerals, and water—that provide energy and materials for cell development, growth, and repair. (p. 36)

enfermedad no infecciosa: enfermedad que no se trasmite de una persona a otra, como el cáncer, la diabetes o el asma. (p. 190)

nutrientes: sustancias de los alimentos—proteínas, carbohidratos, grasas, vitaminas, minerales y agua—que proporcionan energía y materiales para el desarrollo, crecimiento y reparación de las células. (p. 36)

O

olfactory (ohl FAK tree) cell: nasal nerve cell that becomes stimulated by molecules in the air and sends impulses to the brain for interpretation of odors. (p. 133)

ovary: in humans, female reproductive organ that produces eggs and is located in the lower part of the body. (p. 153)

ovulation (ahv yuh LAY shun): monthly process in which an egg is released from an ovary and enters the oviduct, where it can become fertilized by sperm. (p. 153)

célula olfatoria: célula nerviosa nasal que al ser estimulada por moléculas del aire envía impulsos al cerebro para la interpretación de los olores. (p. 133)

ovario: en los humanos, órgano reproductor femenino que produce óvulos y está localizado en la parte inferior del cuerpo. (p. 153)

ovulación: proceso mensual en el que un óvulo es liberado de un ovario y entra al oviducto, donde puede ser fertilizado por los espermatozoides. (p. 153)

P

passive immunity: immunity that results when antibodies produced in one animal are introduced into another's body; does not last as long as active immunity. (p. 179)

pasteurization (pas chur ruh ZAY shun): process in which a liquid is heated to a temperature that kills most bacteria. (p. 182)

periosteum (pur ee AHS tee um): tough, tight-fitting membrane that covers a bone's surface and contains blood vessels that transport nutrients into the bone. (p. 9)

peripheral nervous system: division of the nervous system, made up of all the nerves outside the CNS; connects the brain and spinal cord to other body parts. (p. 121)

peristalsis (per uh STAHL sus): waves of muscular contractions that move food through the digestive tract. (p. 50)

pharynx (FER ingks): tubelike passageway for food, liquid, and air. (p. 94)

plasma: liquid part of blood, made mostly of water, in which oxygen, nutrients, and minerals are dissolved. (p. 74)

inmunidad pasiva: inmunidad que resulta cuando los anticuerpos producidos en un animal son introducidos en el cuerpo de otro; no es tan duradera como la inmunidad activa. (p. 179)

pasterización: proceso mediante el cual un líquido es calentado a una temperatura que mata a la mayoría de las bacterias. (p. 182)

periostio: membrana fuertemente adherida y resistente que cubre la superficie de los huesos, contiene vasos sanguíneos y transporta nutrientes al interior del hueso. (p. 9)

sistema nervioso periférico: parte del sistema nervioso, compuesto por todos los nervios fuera del sistema nervioso central; conecta al cerebro y a la médula espinal con las otras partes del cuerpo. (p. 121)

peristalsis: contracciones musculares ondulantes que mueven el alimento a través del tracto digestivo. (p. 50)

faringe: pasaje en forma de tubo por donde circulan alimentos, líquidos y aire. (p. 94)

plasma: parte líquida de la sangre compuesta principalmente por agua y en la que se encuentran disueltos oxígeno, nutrientes y minerales. (p. 74)

platelet: irregularly shaped cell fragment that helps clot blood and releases chemicals, that help form fibrin. (p. 75)

pregnancy: period of development—usually about 38 or 39 weeks in female humans—from fertilized egg until birth. (p. 158)

protein: large molecule that contains carbon, hydrogen, oxygen, nitrogen, and sometimes sulfur and is made up of amino acids; used by the body for growth and for replacement and repair of body cells. (p. 37)

pulmonary circulation: flow of blood through the heart to the lungs and back to the heart. (p. 66)

plaqueta: fragmento celular de forma irregular que ayuda a coagular la sangre y libera químicos que ayudan a formar fibrina. (p. 75)

embarazo: período del desarrollo—generalmente unas 38 o 39 semanas en las hembras humanas—que va desde el óvulo fertilizado hasta el nacimiento. (p. 158)

proteína: molécula grande que contiene carbono, hidrógeno, oxígeno, nitrógeno y algunas veces azufre, constituida por aminoácidos y usada por el cuerpo para el crecimiento y reemplazo o reparación de las células del cuerpo. (p. 37)

circulación pulmonar: flujo sanguíneo del corazón hacia los pulmones y de regreso al corazón. (p. 66)

R

reflex: automatic, involuntary response to a stimulus; controlled by the spinal cord. (p. 125)

retina: light-sensitive tissue at the back of the eye; contains rods and cones. (p. 129)

reflejo: respuesta automática e involuntaria a un estímulo controlada por la médula espinal. (p. 125)

retina: tejido sensible a la luz situado en la parte posterior del ojo; contiene conos y bastones. (p. 129)

S

semen (SEE mun): mixture of sperm and a fluid that helps sperm move and supplies them with an energy source. (p. 152)

sexually transmitted disease (STD): infectious disease, such as chlamydia, AIDS, or genital herpes, that is passed from one person to another during sexual contact. (p. 186)

skeletal muscle: voluntary, striated muscle that moves bones, works in pairs, and is attached to bones by tendons. (p. 17)

skeletal system: all the bones in the body; forms an internal, living framework that provides shape and support, protects internal organs, moves bones, forms blood cells, and stores calcium and phosphorus compounds for later use. (p. 8)

smooth muscle: involuntary, nonstriated muscle that controls movement of internal organs. (p. 17)

sperm: in humans, male reproductive cells produced in the testes. (p. 152)

synapse (SIHN aps): small space across which an impulse moves from an axon to the dendrites or cell body of another neuron. (p. 121)

semen: mezcla de espermatozoides y un fluido que ayuda a la movilización de los espermatozoides y les suministra una fuente de energía. (p. 152)

enfermedad de transmisión sexual (ETS): enfermedad infecciosa como la clamidiasis, SIDA y herpes genital, transmitida de una persona a otra mediante contacto sexual. (p. 186)

músculo esquelético: músculo estriado voluntario que mueve los huesos, trabaja en pares y se fija a los huesos por medio de los tendones. (p. 17)

sistema esquelético: todos los huesos en el cuerpo forman una estructura viva interna que proporciona forma y soporte, protege a los órganos internos, mueve a los huesos, forma células sanguíneas y almacena compuestos de calcio y fósforo para uso posterior. (p. 8)

músculo liso: músculo no estriado involuntario que controla el movimiento de los órganos internos. (p. 17)

espermatozoides: en los humanos, células reproductoras masculinas producidas por los testículos. (p. 152)

sinapsis: espacio pequeño a través del cual un impulso se mueve del axón a las dendritas o al cuerpo celular de otra neurona. (p. 121)

systemic circulation: largest part of the circulatory system, in which oxygen-rich blood flows to all the organs and body tissues, except the heart and lungs, and oxygen-poor blood is returned to the heart. (p. 67)

circulación sistémica: la parte más grande del sistema circulatorio en la que la sangre rica en oxígeno fluye hacia todos los órganos y tejidos corporales excepto el corazón y los pulmones, y la sangre pobre en oxígeno regresa al corazón. (p. 67)

taste bud: major sensory receptor on the tongue; contains taste hairs that send impulses to the brain for interpretation of tastes. (p. 134)

papila gustativa: receptor sensorial principal de la lengua que contiene cilios gustativos que envían impulsos al cerebro para interpretación de los sabores. (p. 134)

tendon: thick band of tissue that attaches bones to muscles. (p. 17)

tendón: banda gruesa de tejido que une los músculos a los huesos. (p. 17)

testis: male organ that produces sperm and testosterone. (p. 152)

testículos: órganos masculinos que producen espermatozoides y testosterona. (p. 152)

trachea (TRAY kee uh): air-conducting tube that connects the larynx with the bronchi, is lined with mucous membranes and cilia, and contains strong cartilage rings. (p. 95)

tráquea: tubo conductor de aire que conecta a la laringe con los bronquios y que está recubierta por una membrana mucosa y cilios; está formada por anillos cartilaginosos resistentes. (p. 95)

ureter: tube that carries urine from each kidney to the bladder. (p. 104)

uréter: tubo que conduce a la orina de cada riñón hacia la vejiga. (p. 104)

urethra (yoo REE thruh): tube that carries urine from the bladder to the outside of the body. (p. 104)

uretra: tubo que conduce a la orina de la vejiga al exterior del cuerpo. (p. 104)

urinary system: system of excretory organs that rids the blood of wastes, controls blood volume by removing excess water, and balances concentrations of salts and water. (p. 101)

sistema urinario: sistema de órganos excretores que elimina los desechos de la sangre, controla el volumen de sangre eliminando el exceso de agua y balancea las concentraciones de sales y agua. (p. 101)

urine: wastewater that contains excess water, salts, and other wastes that are not reabsorbed by the body. (p. 102)

orina: líquido de desecho que contiene el exceso de agua, sales y otros desechos que no son reabsorbidos por el cuerpo. (p. 102)

uterus: in humans, hollow, muscular, pear-shaped organ where a fertilized egg develops into a baby. (p. 153)

útero: en los humanos, órgano en forma de pera, hueco y musculoso, en el que un óvulo fertilizado se desarrolla en bebé. (p. 153)

vaccination: process of giving a vaccine by mouth or by injection to provide active immunity against a disease. (p. 179)

vacunación: proceso de aplicar una vacuna por vía oral o mediante una inyección para proporcionar inmunidad activa contra una enfermedad. (p. 179)

vagina (vuh JI nuh): muscular tube that connects the lower end of the uterus to the outside of the body; the birth canal through which a baby travels when being born. (p. 153)

vagina: tubo musculoso que conecta el extremo inferior del útero con el exterior del cuerpo; el canal del nacimiento a través del cual sale un bebé al nacer. (p. 153)

vein: blood vessel that carries blood back to the heart, and has one-way valves that keep blood moving toward the heart. (p. 68)

ventricles (VEN trih kulz): two lower chambers of the heart, that contract at the same time, during a heartbeat. (p. 66)

villi (VIH li): fingerlike projections covering the wall of the small intestine that increase the surface area for food absorption. (p. 52)

virus: strand of hereditary material surrounded by a protein coating that can infect and multiply in a host cell. (p. 182)

vitamin: water-soluble or fat-soluble organic nutrient needed in small quantities for growth, for preventing some diseases, and for regulating body functions. (p. 40)

voluntary muscle: muscle, such as a leg or arm muscle, that can be consciously controlled. (p. 15)

vena: vaso sanguíneo que lleva sangre de regreso al corazón y tiene válvulas unidireccionales que mantienen a la sangre en movimiento hacia el corazón. (p. 68)

ventrículos: las dos cámaras inferiores del corazón que se contraen al mismo tiempo durante el latido cardiaco. (p. 66)

vellosidades: proyecciones en forma de dedos que cubren la pared del intestino delgado y que incrementan la superficie de absorción de nutrientes. (p. 52)

virus: pieza de material hereditario rodeado de una capa de proteína que infecta y se multiplica en las células huéspedes. (p. 182)

vitamina: nutriente orgánico soluble al agua y al aceite, necesario en pequeñas cantidades para el crecimiento, prevención de algunas enfermedades y regulación de las funciones del cuerpo. (p. 40)

músculo voluntario: músculo, como el músculo de una pierna o un brazo, que puede controlarse conscientemente. (p. 15)

Italic numbers = illustration/photo   **Bold numbers = vocabulary term**
lab = a page on which the entry is used in a lab
act = a page on which the entry is used in an activity

Index

Magnification Key: Magnifications listed are the magnifications at which images were originally photographed.
LM–Light Microscope
SEM–Scanning Electron Microscope
TEM–Transmission Electron Microscope

Acknowledgments: Glencoe would like to acknowledge the artists and agencies who participated in illustrating this program: Absolute Science Illustration; Andrew Evansen; Argosy; Articulate Graphics; Craig Attebery, represented by Frank & Jeff Lavaty; CHK America; John Edwards and Associates; Gagliano Graphics; Pedro Julio Gonzalez, represented by Melissa Turk & The Artist Network; Robert Hynes, represented by Mendola Ltd.; Morgan Cain & Associates; JTH Illustration; Laurie O'Keefe; Matthew Pippin, represented by Beranbaum Artist's Representative; Precision Graphics; Publisher's Art; Rolin Graphics, Inc.; Wendy Smith, represented by Melissa Turk & The Artist Network; Kevin Torline, represented by Berendsen and Associates, Inc.; WILDlife ART; Phil Wilson, represented by Cliff Knecht Artist Representative; Zoo Botanica.

Photo Credits

Cover Dan McCoy/Rainbow; **i ii** Dan McCoy/Rainbow; **iv** (bkgd)John Evans, (inset)Dan McCoy/Rainbow; **v** (t)PhotoDisc, (b)John Evans; **vi** (l)John Evans, (r)Geoff Butler; **vii** (l)John Evans, (r)PhotoDisc; **viii** PhotoDisc; **ix** Aaron Haupt Photography; **x** National Cancer Institute/Science Photo Library/Photo Researchers; **xi** Science Pictures Ltd/Science Photo Library/Photo Researchers; **xii** Ruth Dixon; **1** Richard Hutchings; **2** Bettmann/CORBIS; **3** AFP/CORBIS; **4** (t)Rosenfeld Images LTD/Science Library/Photo Researchers, (b)Raphael Gaillarde/Liaison; **5** Jeff Greenberg/PhotoEdit; **6–7** Charles O'Rear/CORBIS; **7** Matt Meadows; **8** John Serro/Visuals Unlimited; **12** Geoff Butler; **13** Photo Researchers; **14** Digital Stock; **15** Aaron Haupt; **16** (t)PhotoDisc, (b)M. McCarron; **17** (l)Breck P. Kent, (c)Runk/Schoenberger from Grant Heilman, (r)PhotoTake, NYC/Carolina Biological Supply Company; **21** (tl)Clyde H. Smith/Peter Arnold, Inc., (tcl)Erik Sampers/Photo Researchers, (tcr)Dean Conger/CORBIS, (tr)Michael A. Keller/CORBIS, (bl)Ed Bock/The Stock Market/CORBIS, (bcl)Joe McDonald/Visuals Unlimited, (bcr)Art Stein/Photo Researchers, (br)Peter Turnley/CORBIS; **23** Jim Grace/Photo Researchers; **24** Photo Researchers; **25** Mark Burnett; **28** (t)Sara Davis/The Herald-Sun, (b)Sara Davis/The Herald-Sun; **30** Breck P. Kent; **33** (l)CORBIS, (r)Jim Grace/Photo Researchers; **34–35** Meckes/Ottawa/Photo Researchers; **36 37 38** KS Studios; **39** (l)KS Studios, (r)Visuals Unlimited; **41** (cabbages, avocado)Artville, (liver)DK Images, (doctor)Michael W. Thomas, (girls)Digital Vision/PictureQuest, (blood cells, clot)David M. Philips/Visuals Unlimited, (others)Digital Stock; **42** Gary Kreyer from Grant Heilman; **43** Larry Stepanowicz/Visuals Unlimited; **44 45** KS Studios; **47** (l)KS Studios, (r)Tom McHugh/Photo Researchers; **49** Geoff Butler; **51** (l)Benjamin/Custom Medical Stock Photo, (r)Dr. K.F.R. Schiller/Photo Researchers; **52** Biophoto Associates/Photo Researchers; **54** KS Studios; **55** Matt Meadows; **56** Goldwater/Network/Saba Press Photos; **57 59** KS Studios; **61** (l)Jose Luis Pelaez, Inc./CORBIS, (r)Dean Berry/Index Stock Imagery; **62–63** Steve Allen/Getty Images; **64 67** Aaron Haupt; **69** Matt Meadows; **70** Martin M. Rotker; **71** (t)StudiOhio, (b)Matt Meadows; **73** First Image; **75** National Cancer Institute/Science Photo Library/Photo Researchers; **79** Meckes/Ottawa/Photo Researchers; **81** Aaron Haupt; **82** (t)Matt Meadows/Peter Arnold, Inc., (b)Matt Meadows; **84** no credit; **85** (l)Manfred Kage/Peter Arnold, Inc., (r)K.G. Murti/Visuals Unlimited; **116–117** John Terrance Turner/FPG/Getty Images; **118 125** KS Studios; **126** Michael Newman/PhotoEdit, Inc.; **127** KS Studios; **131** Aaron Haupt; **135** Mark Burnett; **136** (t)Jeff Greenberg/PhotoEdit, Inc., (b)Amanita Pictures; **137** Amanita Pictures; **138** Toni Morrison; **139** (l)David R. Frazier/Photo Researchers, (r)Michael Brennan/CORBIS; **143** Eamonn McNulty/Science Photo Library/Photo Researchers; **144–145** Lawerence Manning/CORBIS; **145** John Evans; **146** David Young-Wolff/PhotoEdit, Inc.; **155** Ariel Skelley/The Stock Market/CORBIS; **157** David M. Phillips/Photo Researchers; **158** (l)Tim Davis/Photo Researchers, (r)Chris Sorensen/The Stock Market/CORBIS; **159** Science Pictures Ltd/Science Photo Library/Photo Researchers; **160** Petit Format/Nestle/Science Source/Photo Researchers; **162** (l)Jeffery W. Myers/Stock Boston, (r)Ruth Dixon; **163** (tl)Mark Haupt, (tr)Aaron Haupt, (b)Mark Burnett; **164** KS Studios; **165** (l)NASA/Roger Ressmeyer/CORBIS, (r)AFP/CORBIS; **166** (t)Chris Carroll/CORBIS, (b)Richard Hutchings; **167** Matt Meadows; **168** (l)Ron Kimball Photography, (r)SuperStock, (b)Martin B. Withers/Frank Lane Picture Agency/CORBIS; **169** (l)Bob Daemmrich, (r)Maria Taglienti/The Image Bank/Getty Images; **174–175** S. Lowry/University of Ulster/Stone/Getty Images; **176** Dr. P. Marazzi/Science Photo Library/Photo Researchers; **177** (l)Michael A. Keller/The Stock Market/CORBIS, (r)Runk/Schoenberger from Grant Heilman, (b)NIBSC/Science Photo Library/Photo Researchers; **180** CC Studio/Science Photo Library/Photo Researchers; **183** (tl)Visuals Unlimited, (tr)Jack Bostrack/Visuals Unlimited, (cl)Cytographics Inc./Visuals Unlimited, (cr)Cabisco/Visuals Unlimited; **184** MM/Michelle Del Guercio/Photo Researchers; **185** Holt Studios International/Nigel Cattlin/Photo Researchers; **186** (t)Oliver Meckes/Eye of Science/Photo Researchers, (b)Visuals Unlimited; **187** Oliver Meckes/Eye Of Science/Gelderblom/Photo Researchers; **188** Mark Burnett; **190** (l)Caliendo/Custom Medical Stock Photo, (r)Amanita Pictures; **191** (t)Andrew Syred/Science Photo Library/Photo Researchers, (b)Custom Medical Stock Photo; **192** (l)Jan Stromme/Bruce Coleman, Inc., (c)Mug Shots/The Stock Market/CORBIS, (r)J.Chiasson-Liats/Liaison Agency/Getty Images; **194** KS Studios; **196** (t)Tim Courlas, (b)Matt Meadows; **197** Matt Meadows; **198** Layne Kennedy/CORBIS; **199** (l)Gelderblom/Eye of Science/Photo Researchers, (r)Garry T. Cole/BPS/Stone/Getty Images; **204** PhotoDisc; **206** Tom Pantages; **210** Michell D. Bridwell/PhotoEdit, Inc.; **211** (t)Mark Burnett, (b)Dominic Oldershaw; **212** StudiOhio; **213** Timothy Fuller; **214** Aaron Haupt; **216** KS Studios; **217** Matt Meadows; **218** KS Studios; **220** David S. Addison/Visuals Unlimited; **222** Amanita Pictures; **223** Bob Daemmrich; **225** Davis Barber/PhotoEdit, Inc.; **241** Matt Meadows; **242** (l)Dr. Richard Kessel, (c)NIBSC/Science Photo Library/Photo Researchers, (r)David John/Visuals Unlimited; **243** (t)Runk/Schoenberger from Grant Heilman, (bl)Andrew Syred/Science Photo Library/Photo Researchers, (br)Rich Brommer; **244** (tr)G.R. Roberts, (l)Ralph Reinhold/Earth Scenes, (br)Scott Johnson/Animals Animals; **245** Martin Harvey/DRK Photo.

PERIODIC TABLE OF THE ELEMENTS

Columns of elements are called groups. Elements in the same group have similar chemical properties.

Gas

Liquid

Solid

Synthetic

	Element	Hydrogen
	Atomic number	1
	Symbol	H
	Atomic mass	1.008

State of matter

The first three symbols tell you the state of matter of the element at room temperature. The fourth symbol identifies elements that are not present in significant amounts on Earth. Useful amounts are made synthetically.

	1	2	3	4	5	6	7	8	9
1	Hydrogen 1 **H** 1.008								
2	Lithium 3 **Li** 6.941	Beryllium 4 **Be** 9.012							
3	Sodium 11 **Na** 22.990	Magnesium 12 **Mg** 24.305							
4	Potassium 19 **K** 39.098	Calcium 20 **Ca** 40.078	Scandium 21 **Sc** 44.956	Titanium 22 **Ti** 47.867	Vanadium 23 **V** 50.942	Chromium 24 **Cr** 51.996	Manganese 25 **Mn** 54.938	Iron 26 **Fe** 55.845	Cobalt 27 **Co** 58.933
5	Rubidium 37 **Rb** 85.468	Strontium 38 **Sr** 87.62	Yttrium 39 **Y** 88.906	Zirconium 40 **Zr** 91.224	Niobium 41 **Nb** 92.906	Molybdenum 42 **Mo** 95.94	Technetium 43 **Tc** (98)	Ruthenium 44 **Ru** 101.07	Rhodium 45 **Rh** 102.906
6	Cesium 55 **Cs** 132.905	Barium 56 **Ba** 137.327	Lanthanum 57 **La** 138.906	Hafnium 72 **Hf** 178.49	Tantalum 73 **Ta** 180.948	Tungsten 74 **W** 183.84	Rhenium 75 **Re** 186.207	Osmium 76 **Os** 190.23	Iridium 77 **Ir** 192.217
7	Francium 87 **Fr** (223)	Radium 88 **Ra** (226)	Actinium 89 **Ac** (227)	Rutherfordium 104 **Rf** (261)	Dubnium 105 **Db** (262)	Seaborgium 106 **Sg** (266)	Bohrium 107 **Bh** (264)	Hassium 108 **Hs** (277)	Meitnerium 109 **Mt** (268)

The number in parentheses is the mass number of the longest-lived isotope for that element.

Rows of elements are called periods. Atomic number increases across a period.

The arrow shows where these elements would fit into the periodic table. They are moved to the bottom of the table to save space.

Lanthanide series	Cerium 58 **Ce** 140.116	Praseodymium 59 **Pr** 140.908	Neodymium 60 **Nd** 144.24	Promethium 61 **Pm** (145)	Samarium 62 **Sm** 150.36
Actinide series	Thorium 90 **Th** 232.038	Protactinium 91 **Pa** 231.036	Uranium 92 **U** 238.029	Neptunium 93 **Np** (237)	Plutonium 94 **Pu** (244)